THE WORL[...]
ATRO[...]ITIES

ACKNOWLEDGEMENTS

Corbis UK Ltd 45, 110, 129, 134, 160, 166, 171, 177
Bettmann 86, 102, 146, 152
Hulton-Deutsch Collection 96
Hulton Getty Picture Collection 22, 42, 53, 58, 64, 74, 80

THE WORLD'S WORST
ATROCITIES

Nigel Cawthorne

CHANCELLOR
PRESS

This 1999 edition published by Chancellor Press an imprint of
Bounty Books, a division of the Octopus Publishing Group Limited,
2–4 Heron Quays, London E14 4JP.
An Hachette Livre UK Company

This edition published as part of the *True Crime Collection*

© Octopus Publishing Group Limited

Reprinted in 2002, 2003, 2005, 2007

ISBN: 978-0-753700-90-7

Printed and bound in Great Britain by Mackays of Chatham

Contents

Introduction

This book was written during the war in Kosovo. Every day new atrocities were appearing on television screens worldwide. Consequently, I have not included here any atrocity committed in the Balkans in the break-up of Yugoslavia. It seemed to me that if I included a Serb massacre of unarmed Kosovars or Nato's bombing of a bus in Serbia, claiming this as one of the world's worst atrocities, events would quickly surpass it. Simply to pick out one random act of barbarism or another would be tempting fate.

Moreover, it is not as if there is any shortage of material. The twentieth century has provided particularly rich pickings – not because it is any more barbarous than previous centuries, but because we expect people to behave better. Preceding centuries were a bit more roughshod: humanitarianism was not the universal code of civilisation and people were not expected to behave any better back then. Against a background where cruelty and barbarism are the norm, it is difficult to commit an atrocity. In ancient times, people apparently took massacres, sackings, burnings, infanticide, torture and other forms of random outrage for granted. The rape of the Sabine women, for example, seems quite a jolly affair; the rape of Nanking does not.

Even so, I have included a number of atrocities from preceding centuries. No book on atrocities could get by without a mention of Genghis Khan, who was easily the biggest killer of ancient times and who runs a close third after Stalin and Hitler in the list of the world's worst mass murderers.

The Gulags, the forced collectivisation of farming in the Soviet Union, the Holocaust, the Great Leap Forward and the Cultural Revolution in China – although atrocious – are simply too big to include as a single atrocity. Therefore, I have included highlights, so that one atrocious act can stand for all.

However, a real problem arises with Ireland. Again, one is in danger of being upstaged by events. Should I include Bloody Sunday in Derry in 1972, I wondered? As this book went to press, another official enquiry was just beginning, so the jury is still out. There are plenty of loyalists who, at the time at least, did not consider it an atrocity at all. Appalling though the 13 deaths were, they are small beer for the purposes of this book. The British Army had a much higher death toll in Amritsar in 1919. Besides, there have been other 'Bloody Sundays' with higher death tolls.

On Bloody Sunday, 21 November 1920, the IRA killed 11 Englishmen suspected of being spies. In reprisal, the Black and Tans – the British auxiliary police force in Ireland – shot at the spectators in a Dublin football ground that afternoon, killing 12 and wounding 60.

On Bloody Sunday, 22 January 1905, the police fired on demonstrators trying to take a petition to the Tsar in St Petersburg, killing 100 and wounding hundreds more. It marked the beginning of the violent phase of the Russian revolve.

Given my dilemma, I decided to include Cromwell and his long-celebrated atrocities in Ireland instead. History books in Irish schools say that unarmed civilians were massacred in Drogheda and Wexford. But by the time I got to writing that chapter, Tom Reilly, a local historian from Drogheda, had published a book claiming that it never happened. Cromwell was a perfect gentleman. His men acted according to the rules of war.

What of the potato famine, then? Maybe as many as one million Irish people died of starvation and over two million fled abroad. Although the death and deportation are usually ascribed to English oppression, there was no malice involved. It was more a case of bureaucratic bungling. The blight itself can hardly be blamed on the British. True, Parliament in London was slow to grasp the scale of the famine.

Nevertheless, it sent £8 million in aid. The potato blight also led to famine in the Isle of Wight and Lower Rhineland, places not usually associated with English oppression. God knows that Ireland has suffered more that its fair share of atrocities through the centuries, but long many it be preserved from being one of *The World's Worst Atrocities*.

1❖The Mongol Hordes

I have committed many acts of cruelty and had an incalculable number of men killed, never knowing whether what I did was right. But I am indifferent to what people think of me.' So said Genghis Khan in the thirteenth century.

In the career of Genghis Khan, one atrocity followed another. By the time he died in 1227, he had been responsible for the death of around 20 million peoples – around one-tenth of the population of the known world. He began his atrocious career by murdering his brother after a dispute over a fish; he was just 12 at the time.

At the age of 33, he became undisputed leader of the Mongol hordes – the Genghis Khan, meaning 'universal ruler'. In 1211, he began his conquest of imperial China, burning and pillaging every town and village on the way. Three years later he controlled the Middle Kingdom – China north of the Yellow River – and forced those outside his rule to deliver him 500 young men and women, plus 3,000 head of livestock, as the price of peace. In 1217, he left his champion Muqali there as viceroy to mop up any further resistance and went home to the steppes. It was then he looked to the west and started a campaign that would take him to the gates of Europe.

The King of Gulja, to the west of Mongolia, paid homage to Genghis Khan. He was assassinated by Guchulug, the Emperor of Qara-Khitai in what is now Kazahkstan, and his widow and son called on Genghis Khan for help. This he happily provided, sending his general, Jebe, who killed Guchulug and, within a year, had delivered the whole of the Qara-Khitai empire to the Khan. This brought Genghis Khan into direct contact with the world of Islam.

To the west of Qara-Khitai was Khwarezam, which covered what is now north-east Iran, Afghanistan, Turkmeniya, Uzbekistan and Tadzikistan. In 1212, following a *coup d'état*, Shah Mohammed had installed himself as ruler of the important trading city of Samarkand.

Khan had no desire to go to war against Khwarezam. As the nomads of the steppes did not weave, it was important for them to maintain good relations with Khwarezam as they bought cloth from Samarkand. Genghis

Khan sent a caravan to the Shah carrying exquisite jade, ivory, gold bars and felt made from perfectly white camel hair. The 300 caravanners were accompanied by a Mongolian noble who carried a message from the Khan. It read, 'I know your power and the vast extent of your empire. I have the greatest desire to live in peace with you. I shall regard you as my son. For your part, you must know that I have conquered the Middle Kingdom and subdued all the tribes of the north. You know that my country is a swarm of warriors, a mine of silver, and that I have no need to covet further domains. We have equal interest in encouraging trade between our subjects.'

The Shah was a little suspicious of this message; he accepted the Khan's gifts but sent his messenger back without a reply. Genghis Khan sent a second caravan, this time consisting of 500 camels, laden with the fur of beaver and sable. With it was Uquna, an official of the Mongolian court.

At the frontier town of Otrar, the local governor had 100 of the caravanners – including Uquna – butchered and their cargo confiscated. Genghis Khan had one more go at diplomacy, sending a new emissary, this time a Muslim. The Shah had him put to death and his entourage returned to the Khan with their heads shaven. As a final insult to the Khan, he confirmed the governor of Otrar in office.

There could be only one response. In the summer of 1219, Genghis Khan assembled between 150,000 and 200,000 horsemen, many of them battle-hardened veterans of the conquest of China. Together with his horseman, his best generals, his four sons and one of his wives – Qulan, which means 'she-ass' – Genghis Khan set off to make war.

Shah Mohammed's army easily outnumbered Genghis Khan's, but he did not know where the Mongols were going to attack so he deployed his men all along the border. This was an idiotic strategy – they were spread so thinly that wherever the Mongols attacked they were bound to win. If the Shah had thought about it for a moment, he would have known where Genghis Khan was going to attack: at Otrar, of course – the governor there had killed his emissary.

Otrar was a walled city, though this was no problem for the Mongols. During their campaign in China they had captured a great deal of siege machinery – along with Chinese soldiers who could use them. The Chinese had also perfected gunpowder and knew how to make bombs and mortars; they had rockets and bombards – primitive cannon – which fired metal balls.

The Mongolians also had siege engines of their own, dating back 1000 years. They were massive crossbows mounted on trestles that fired huge arrows over 200 yards, and catapults that could fling huge boulders with great force. Under covering fire, sappers tunnelled under the walls. Towers with retractable ladders were trundled up to the walls, while the gates were pummelled by huge battering rams.

The governor knew what fate awaited him if the city fell. He fought shoulder to shoulder with his men, who held off the Mongols for a month. Then, when the city fell, the governor retreated to the citadel with his men and fought on. When they ran out of arrows, he took to hurling bricks at the assailants. However, eventually he was overcome and taken. Trussed up with leather thongs and taken before the Khan, who ordered that he suffer an exemplary punishment, molten silver was poured into his ears and eye sockets.

A second Mongolian column, under the command of the general Jochi, lay siege to the citadel of Sighnaq and demanded unconditional surrender. When this was not forthcoming, he attacked. The citadel was taken after a week and Jochi had the throats and bodies of all the inhabitants of the town slashed open.

A third column, under Alaq-Noyan, attacked Banakat to the west of Tashkent. After three days, the Turkish mercenaries who were defending the city sued for peace. Once the Mongols entered the city, the inhabitants were enslaved. The city's craftsmen were assigned to combat units or sent back to Mongolia; the women were distributed among the clans; the rest of the citizens were taken as hostages, who could be used as a human screen in the next battle.

The next objective was Khojend. Its commander was Temur Malik, who had a reputation as a skilled tactician and a courageous leader. With 1,000 crack troops, he retreated to the citadel, a fortified castle that stood on the riverbank. It was so well fortified, it needed 20,000 Mongols and an army of 50,000 prisoners to take it.

The Mongols set their prisoners to work building a bridge of boats across the width of the river. Then they filled the boats with rocks and sunk them, damming the river. Temur Malik's men tried to harry them but they were hopelessly out-numbered. He knew that, once the river was dry and the foot of the walls exposed, the fort was done for, so he and his men jumped in boats of their own and escaped with enemy squadrons in hot pursuit. He made it back to the Shah's camp safe and sound.

The Mongols entered the city of Nur disguised as caravanners. Once they were inside the city walls, the authorities capitulated and paid a tribute of 1,500 dinars; yet that did not save the city – the people were driven out, the city looted and the booty sent back to Mongolia.

Next to fall was Bukhara, which was one of the finest cities in the west. For Muslims, it was a place of worship and was famed for its carpet weaving. When the Mongols attacked, the Turkish garrison tried to break out. They were hunted down and slaughtered. The Mongol prisoners were sent to break the gates down and catapults shattered the defences. Genghis Khan entered the city personally while fighting was still going on in the citadel. When it was captured, the last of the defenders were put to death. The inhabitants were lined up and told to leave; any found hiding in the city were stabbed to death on the spot.

Genghis Khan himself rode into the great mosque, believing it to be the Shah's palace. As sacred Koranic books were thrown in the dirt, hundreds of devoted Muslims killed themselves rather than submit to the barbaric invaders. Men slaughtered their wives rather than let the Mongols take them – the Mongols made a practice of making men watch while they raped their womenfolk. Among those who died by their own hand was the imam.

'It was an appalling day,' says a Muslim historian. 'Nothing was heard but the sobbing of men, women and children, separated forever as the Mongol troops parcelled the population among themselves.'

To Genghis Khan were attributed the words, 'I tell you I am the scourge of Allah, and if you had not been great sinners Allah would not have brought down my wrath upon your heads.'

The city was then burnt to the ground. For dozens of years afterwards Bukhara lay uninhabited. Thousands of corpses there, too many to be buried, exuded diseases which drove away the living. Those who lived in the surrounding region moved away. The irrigation ditches collapsed; the fields turned to desert and the animals, left to their own devices, perished. All that was left were the ruins.

Genghis Khan then turned on Samarkand. Behind him trudged a swelling army of prisoners, forced to work as slave labourers to destroy their own country. Samarkand was a city steeped in history. It had been ancient when Alexander the Great had conquered it in 329 BC, now it was one of the foremost trading centres in the world. It sent melons as far as Baghdad, packed in lead boxes lined with snow to keep them fresh. It boasted goldsmiths, silversmiths, coppersmiths, tanners, saddle-makers, wood carvers, cabinetmakers and swordsmiths. Even paper was made in the city, using a technique imported from China. Chain mail, carved ewers, ceramics and beautifully inlaid woodwork produced in the city were traded in the ports of the Mediterranean.

Samarkland had recently been fortified. In the ramparts were four great gates, symbolising the city's dependence on trade. It had a huge garrison, manned largely by Turkish mercenaries, so few of the inhabitants thought that it would suffer the same fate as Bukhara.

Genghis Khan was impressed by the defences, too. When he arrived in the spring of 1220, he camped outside the city and waited for reinforcements. Meanwhile, he deployed a curtain of troops round the city. When two of his sons turned up with thousands of prisoners, they decided the best ploy was to impress the enemy with their numbers. They took the prisoners' clothes from them and dressed them as Mongols. Then, under close guard and Mongol banners, they marched them towards the city walls.

The city's garrison charged the attackers. The Mongols turned and fled, leaving the unarmed prisoners to absorb the assault, then turned and counter-attacked, hacking though the Turkish mercenaries. After a severe thrashing the Turks deserted, leaving the city defenceless.

The town's leaders came out to talk to the Mongols. Genghis Khan promised that all those who left the city would be spared. Once they were gone, Samarkand was sacked; the die-hards who stayed on were butchered, and part of the city was set on fire. Genghis Khan considered the Turkish mercenary criminals. One Persian chronicler says 30,000 were massacred. Some 50,000 citizens bought their freedom with a ransom that totalled 200,000 dinars. Those too poor to pay the ransom were taken as slave labourers by the Mongol units. Craftsmen were sent to Mongolia. It was said that when those who had paid the ransom returned to Samarkand there were so few of them they could only repopulate a quarter of the city.

The capital of Khwarezam was not Samarkand but Urgench, 300 miles up the Amudar'ya River towards the Aral Sea. Again, it was defended by Turkish mercenaries. However, this time they were ready, having carefully stockpiled weapons, food and water, ready for a long siege.

Genghis Khan charged three of his sons to take Urgench. One of them, Jochi, was named ruler of Khwarezam, so it was in his interests not to destroy the city completely. With them were three of the Khan's most experience generals and 50,000 horsemen.

An emissary was sent demanding unconditional surrender. The offer was declined, so the Mongols laid siege to the city. There were no boulders in the area for the catapults, so prisoners were sent out to find mulberry trees and their trunks were sawn up to make ammunition. Meanwhile other prisoners, under fire from the city walls, began filling in the moat – it took 12 days. That done, sappers advanced under the cover of siege engines and started chipping away at the brickwork.

During these long preparations, two of the brothers fell out. One wanted everything done meticulously, while the other was more gung-ho. The dispute could have been disastrous. But Genghis Khan resolved the situation by putting the third brother in charge of the other two.

Soon after, the walls were breached. But, aware of what would happen to them if they were defeated, the defenders fought ferociously, house to house. Both sides used burning naphtha to set fire to houses where their foes took shelter, the consequence being high loss of life for the civilian inhabitants.

The Mongols were used to fighting huge sweeping battles; this sort of fighting therefore did not suit them and they paid a heavy price. Having taken one half of the city, they attacked the bridge over the Amudar'ya River that led to the other half, and were repulsed – this action alone cost them 3,000 men.

The Turkish mercenaries continued their stout defence from the ruins of the city, supported and supplied by the remaining inhabitants. After seven days, the Mongols lost their patience and torched the rest of the city. The Turks were forced to pull back but hundreds of civilians were burnt to death. Eventually, members of the city council indicated that they wanted to parley. One begged the Mongols to have mercy on the brave men who had defended the city. 'We have seen the might of your wrath; now show us the measure of your pity,' he said.

Unfortunately, the Mongols were in no mood for this kind of talk and the fighting continued.

'Everyone fought,' wrote an Arab historian, 'men, women and children, and they went on fighting until the Mongols had taken the entire town, killed all the inhabitants, and pillaged everything there was to be found. Then they opened the dam and the waters of the river flooded the city and destroyed it completely . . . Those who escaped from the massacre were drowned or buried under the rubble. And then nothing remained but ruins and waves.'

Genghis Khan was not at all happy about the destruction of Shah Mohammed's capital. The siege of Urgench had lasted six months; Mongolian losses were much higher than he was used to. Even worse, his sons had seized all the booty from what little remained of the city, without reserving any for their father. He refused to see them for three days. When he did, he lost his temper. Advisors calmed him down, pleading that his sons were young and inexperienced. They would soon toughen up if he sent them against the caliph of Baghdad.

Meanwhile, the Khan's generals pursued Shah Mohammed, whose troops deserted in droves. City after city fell to the Mongols until the whole of Khwarezam was in their hands. Shah Mohammed died of pleurisy on the shores of the Caspian in what is now Azerbaijan.

Genghis Khan took a summer break at the oasis of Nasaf, before going north to Termez. When the city refused to surrender, he lay siege to it for seven days. It fell and the usual massacre ensued. Everyone was disembowelled after one woman swallowed some pearls rather than hand them over.

Next he headed for the ancient city of Balkh, capital of the kingdom of Bactria in what is now northern Afghanistan. As a city, it had been known for 3,000 years. Alexander the Great had occupied it and married Princess Roxane there. But Genghis Khan was not interested in such niceties. When the city surrendered itself to him on the understanding that its citizens would go unmolested, he went back on his promise and put thousands to the sword. When he passed that way again in 1222, he massacred the survivors.

'Wherever there was a wall still standing, the Mongols tore it down,' said an Arab historian, 'and for a second time swept away all traces of civilisation from the region.'

A Chinese monk travelling through the region at the time did not record the destruction being that complete, but reported that the great city of Balkh was a ghost town with dogs barking in the street.

Genghis Khan spared some cities, but if there was the slightest sign of opposition, he was merciless. As well as massacring the inhabitants, he would destroy the irrigation system that had taken centuries to construct. Many cities ravaged by the Mongols were destroyed forever.

Nessa resisted. When it was taken, the inhabitants were ordered to tie themselves together outside the city walls while Mongol archers cut them down for target practice. Those only wounded were despatched by sabre. Some 70,000 in all were killed.

Occasionally, there were setbacks. When Genghis Khan's son-in-law, Toguchar, was besieging Neyshabur he was hit by a defender's arrow and mortally wounded. The Mongols lifted the siege, but laid waste all the surrounding villages in vengeance.

In February 1221, Genghis Khan's fourth son, Tolui, and 70,000 horsemen arrived in Merv, now called Mary, in Turkmeniya. It was a rich city famed for its ceramics, but its fortifications were particularly impressive. Tolui and 500 horsemen spent all day inspecting them. Twice he assaulted the city and was driven back, but the governor then surrendered, having received assurances that no one would come to harm.

Tolui did not keep his word: he evacuated the city and picked out 400 craftsmen and some children to keep as slaves – the rest were put to the sword. This was a formidable task. The population had to be divided up among the army units. Each man, it was said, had to kill between 300 and 400 people. One source says that Tolui left 700,000 corpses there. Another said he stopped counting after 1,300,000.

Tolui then went to Neyshabur to avenge Toguchar. The city tried to surrender but Tolui would have none of it. It was bombarded by boulders and incendiary bombs filled with naphtha. In two days, the walls were demolished completely and the inhabitants marched out. The craftsmen were separated out and sent off to Mongolia, then the slaughter began. Toguchar's widow and her entourage gleefully joined in. Again, everyone was disembowelled in case they had swallowed precious gems. Severed heads were stacked in pyramids. There were three – one for men's heads, one for women's heads, and one for children's. Not even the cats and dogs were left alive. The city was then flattened until there was hardly a trace that it had ever been there.

In Herat, after a siege that lasted eight days, only the mercenaries were massacred. Later, the populace revolted, killing the Mongol governor and the Khan's resident minister. In revenge, the Mongols slaughtered the population, then withdrew and waited. When survivors emerged from the rubble and those who had taken refuge in nearby caves returned, the Mongols went back and killed them too. One source says there were 1.3 million dead, another 2.4 million injured. 'Not a man, not an ear of corn; no scrap of food, not item of clothing remained,' it was said.

Mongol contingents were also sent back to Merv and Balkh to slaughter anyone who had returned to the cities they had laid waste. Next on the list was Bamiyan, where huge Buddhas were carved in the rocks. It was the jewel of Khwarezam, a stop off on the Silk Route and an unparalleled centre of culture. The story goes that the city was betrayed by Princess Lala Qatun whose father was trying to marry her off against her will; she sent word to Genghis Khan, telling him how the city's water supply could be turned off.

However, during the siege, Genghis Khan's grandson was killed. The Khan was so angered by the loss of his grandson that he did not even stop to put his helmet on before he started slaughtering the enemy. The boy's father was away at the time; when he returned the Khan rebuked his son falsely for having disobeyed him and asked his son whether he was now ready to obey any order his father gave him. His son swore he was.

'Well,' said the Khan. 'Your son has been killed and I order you not to lament.'

Revenge was taken in the normal way: the entire population was massacred. Even Princess Lala Qatun was not spared – she was stoned to death for her treachery.

After the death of Shah Mohammed, power passed to his son Prince Jalal a-Din. With an army of Turkish mercenaries and Kwarezamian conscripts numbering around 60,000, he held up in a fortress at Ghazi, 100 miles south of Kabul. The Mongols attacked but, after losing 1000 men, were forced to withdraw.

The Khan's adopted brother was in charge of the assault. Short of men, he thought he would fool Prince Jalal into believing he had more men than he had. He mounted straw dummies on horseback and rode them up to his camp as if they were a relief army. The ruse did not work – the Prince attacked. For the first time on Muslim territory, the Mongols suffered a defeat. The Muslim soldiers were said to have surpassed even the Mongols in their savagery, driving nails into the ears of their prisoners.

When Genghis Khan heard of this, he leapt into the saddle. It was said that with fresh troops he rode continuously for two days to reach Ghazi. They did not even stop to eat or drink, but rather – in the Mongol way – cut a nick in the back of their horse's neck each time they felt peckish and nourished themselves with the blood.

By the time they reached Ghazi, a dispute had broken out between the Turkish mercenaries and the local troops and Prince Jalal was forced to withdraw. The city's inhabitants were deported or killed and its defences destroyed.

The Prince planned to escape to the Punjab but was caught on his back to the river Indus. There he surrounded himself with a square of troops and made a stand. The Mongols steadily hacked away at his lines of defence. When he had only a handful of men left, the Prince made a break for it and jumped off a cliff on horseback into the river. Genghis Khan was full of admiration – first for how the Prince had saved his own life at the expense of those of his men's, and then for the leap. He was an example to all Mongols, the Khan said, and was allowed to escape. The men who had made the jump with the Prince were not accorded the same respect: Mongol archers rained arrows down on them in the water. Prince Jalal eventually found refuge with the Sultan of Delhi.

Genghis Khan only made a brief incursion into India, laying waste to a few villages around Lahore, but then turning back into Khwarezam to take a closer look at the land he had already conquered.

Meanwhile, following the death of Shah Mohammed, the Khan's general, Jebe, had moved on northwards into Georgia, defeating the Georgian cavalry who were supposed to be the mightiest in the region. Then he moved on into Russia.

At the Battle of Kalka, the Mongols were attacked by 80,000 knights under Prince Mstislav. The Mongols, numbering only 20,000, used their tried and tested tactic. After a short engagement, they withdrew, apparently in disorder. The Russians pursed them at high speed – this stretched out their army. Then, when they outnumbered the advanced guard, the Mongols turned and fought. When they rest of the army arrived, they would come upon a scene of appalling butchery, which usually put them off fighting. If not, the Mongols slaughtered them as well.

The Russian knights wore steel armour and had shields, axes, swords and lances, but they were heavy and slow compared to the Mongol horsemen, and were easy prey for the Mongolian archers. They were easily defeated and Prince Mstislav was captured. He was executed by being wrapped up in a carpet and suffocated; this was a sign that the Mongols held in him great respect – they would not shed his blood.

The rest of the Russian army were intimidated by Mstislav's defeat and withdrew. The Mongols went on to plunder the warehouses of Sudak in the Crimea; they looted the kingdom of the Bulgars, then turned for home, cutting a swathe through Kazahkstan.

Genghis Khan himself returned to Mongolia where he died on the shores of Lake Baikal in 1227. He left orders that, if anyone gazed on his coffin, the next coffin would be theirs.

In 1237, ten years after the death of Genghis Khan, the Mongolian 'Golden Horde' attacked Russia again, employing similarly barbarous tactics. In 1347, during the Siege of Caffa on the Crimea, they invented biological warfare, catapulting the corpses of plague victims over the walls to infect those within. The Mongols continued to plague the Russians for centuries. As a traditional Russian tale called *The Story of the Destruction of Ryazan* puts it: 'They devastated the churches of God and before the consecrated altars they spilt quantities of blood. And none was spared, all perished equally and drank the cup of death to the lees. No one remained to sob or weep for the dead – neither father nor mother for their children, nor children for their father and mother, neither brother for brother, nor cousin for cousin – for all without exception lay lifeless. And this happened in requital of our sins.'

2 ❖ Auto-da-Fé

In 1231, Pope Gregory IX set up the Inquisition to suppress widespread heresy. It went about its barbarous business mainly in northern Italy and southern France. However, when the Muslims were driven out of Spain the political authorities in Aragon and Castile were looking for a way to impose their authority on the rest of country and, in 1478, persuaded Pope Sixtus IV to authorise a separate Spanish Inquisition.

They set to work and the first *auto-da-fé* took place in Seville in 1481. Hundreds were burnt alive and the Spanish Inquisition was so savage that the Pope tried to ban it. But the civil authorities had found the Spanish Inquisition such a powerful political tool that they restored it and named their own Inquisitor-General. They chose the Dominican Tomás Torquemada who, in his 15-year career, was personally responsible for burning more than 2,000 people at the stake.

Tomás Torquemada was the nephew of the famous theologian Juan de Torquemada, who was made a cardinal for promoting the idea of papal infallibility. From an early age, Tomás was exceedingly pious. After a brilliant scholastic career, he joined the Dominicans. This was a disappointment to his father, a nobleman who wanted his only son to marry and continue the family line.

**Pope Gregory IX
(1142–1241).**

Torquemada withdrew to the Monastery of Santa Cruz in Segovia, where he lived an extremely austere life. He refused to eat meat and, unlike other Dominicans, he refused to wear linen under his coarse habit; if that was not chafing enough, he often resorted to wearing a hair shirt. And he always went barefoot.

As his reputation for piety spread, Torquemada was made confessor to Isabella, the sister of Henry IV. He got her to promise that if she were ever made queen, she would restore the Inquisition. She did become Queen and, good to her word, she re-introduced the Inquisition and made Torquemada its head.

In the Middle Ages many people joined the church for the wealth and power it brought them. Torquemada was not one of them. This made him all the more dangerous. What he wanted to do was force the austerity that he enjoyed on other people; he did not care how he did it. He also earned the title 'the Scourge of the Jews'. Though his own grandmother was Jewish, he persecuted Jews – even those who had converted to

Christianity – as heretics. One did not even have to be Jewish – it was enough that someone said one was.

As soon as he was made Inquisitor-General, Torquemada produced a new set of rules for the Inquisition – 28 articles. At each new place the Inquisition visited, an eloquent priest or one of the inquisitors would give a sermon. At the end of it, faithful Christians were to come forward and swear their allegiance to the Inquisition and promise to work for it. Anyone who had lost their faith or practised heresy – which included Jews and any remaining Muslims – was given 30 or 40 days to come to the Inquisition and confess. They would not be dealt with harshly – that is, they would not be burnt at the stake – provided their repentance was sincere and that they confessed, not only their own sins, but those of their neighbours.

There would, of course, be some punishment – those who had offended God's holy law could not expect to get off scot-free. They would have to perform penances and give up wearing jewellery and fine clothes; they were not to ride horses or bear arms, and they would be liable to forfeit some of their property to Queen Isabella and King Ferdinand to help in their Holy War against the Muslims in Granada.

Anyone guilty of heresy or apostasy who did not come forward during the period of grace, but came forward voluntarily later, would again be treated mercifully. They would simply have to surrender all their property and would be sentenced to life imprisonment – but no fire. This punishment could not be evaded – if you gave your property away beforehand, the Inquisition would seize it from whoever you had given it to.

The slaves of those condemned by the Inquisition would be freed – giving them ample incentive to inform on their master. Children who had become heretics due to the teachings of their parents were treated especially kindly. Provided they told the Inquisition of their parents' heresies, they would be given light penances and be taught the true faith. The children of those condemned by the Inquisition would be sent to monasteries and convents; the girls were supposed to be given a small dowry so that they could marry, but this never happened.

Anyone arrested for heresy or apostasy could ask for reconciliation with the church, but they would have to prove that their confession was sincere. The only way to do that was to inform on friends. If it were judged that their confession was not sincere, they would be handed over to the civil authorities and be put to death.

If a suspect fled, his name would be posted on the doors of all the churches in the area. He would be given 30 days to present himself to the Inquisition, otherwise he would be judged guilty of heresy. Those who had successfully fled the country were burnt in effigy, which did not hurt nearly as much.

There was no hiding place from the Inquisition: if a count or a duke refused to let the Inquisition into his realm, he would be found guilty of aiding and abetting heresy. Even death was no escape – if someone was found guilty after they were dead, their body would be dug up and their corpse burnt at the stake; their estate would naturally be forfeit.

Officers of the Inquisition were not allowed to take gifts from suspects. If they did, they would have to forfeit twice the value of the gift and might suffer excommunication – which would put paid to a lucrative career in the church. Torquemada reserved the right to sack inquisitors for other misdemeanours – such as not being harsh enough.

Torquemada took a broad definition of heresy. Besides the crime of being Jewish, bigamy was also a heretical sin as marriage was a sacrament. Sodomy was punished by burning, but ordinary, unmarried fooling around was okay, provided that the participants did not say it was all right – that would be contradicting the word of God.

One reason this was not included was that the Spanish priesthood was notoriously debauched. It was not until the sixteenth century that a screen was put in confessionals separating the priest and the penitent. Before that time licentious priests would lure attractive young women into the confession boxes and give them a few extra sins to confess. Torquemada would have loved to sweep this sort of behaviour from the church with his Inquisition but, by that time, Innocent VIII was Pope. He was a proud family man. His children lived with him in the Vatican, so he was hardly in a position to condemn amorous activity in those beneath him.

One priest was brought before the Inquisition because he had been sent to a convent as confessor and promptly seduced five nuns. But, he told the inquisition, he had been told to go the convent and take care of the nuns . . . and, as a good and faithful servant, he had done exactly that. Another priest was caught sodomising a 14-year-old boy in his care. As a priest, he was confined to a monastery for a year. The boy was not so lucky; he was made to wear a mitre full of feathers and whipped so severely that he died.

When a man or woman was suspected of heresy, they would be called to the Holy Office. All that was required to condemn a person was the testimony of two witnesses. The names of the witnesses were kept secret in case reprisals were taken against them. Theoretically, the accused could be represented by an advocate; in practice, no one was foolhardy enough to stand up to the Inquisition.

There were no guards at the Holy Office and so theoretically the accused could simply walk out; but that would invite condemnation as a heretic. Once accused by the Inquisition, there was very little hope of getting off. Both church and state wanted a uniformly Catholic country and the exchequer was eager to get its hands on as much confiscated property as possible. The odds were, of course, stacked against the accused. If a case was not proved, the suspect would have to undergo torture to see if they could clear the matter up by confessing. If they confessed, the confession would have to be repeated within three days.

Arrests often took place at night. *Alguazils* or familiars of the Inquisition would knock and, if there were any resistance, they would force entrance. The victim would be told to dress and they would leave immediately. The *alguazils* liked to work silently, bringing a painful gag for anyone tempted to cry out and alert their neighbours. It was shaped like a pear and was forced into the mouth. Screws then enlarged it, forcing the jaw open. Silence and secrecy made the *alguazils'* terror tactics more effective: everyone felt vulnerable.

Inside the Holy Office, everything was designed to intimidate the suspect. The 'trial' was held in a darkened room. The inquisitors wore white habits with black hoods and sat at a table swathed in black velvet; it had a crucifix, a Bible and six candles on it.

The trial would take place in camera, the public not being permitted to observe. A secretary would read the charges from a pulpit; there followed a long pause. Torquemada instructed his inquisitors to spend time examining papers before they spoke to the suspect as a method of instilling fear.

The prisoner would then be asked for their name and address, as well as whether they knew why they had been arrested. If the prisoner said they did not know why – which was usually the case – the inquisitor was instructed to study the papers before him once more.

After a while the prisoner would be asked if they had any enemies and whether they attended confession regularly. What was their diocese? Who was their confessor? When did he last go to confession?

Torquemada instructed his inquisitors not to be moved by anything the prisoner might do or say. Any sobbing, weeping, begging or heart-rending tales should be ignored – heretics were a crafty lot. Had they not pretended to be good Catholics while practising their heresy in secret? The inquisitors were reminded that the condemnation of one man might be the salvation of thousands. After all, heretics not only practised heresy themselves – they often persuaded others to follow in their diabolical ways.

If the prisoner stubbornly refused to be intimidated into confessing, the inquisitor was instructed to soften his expression. The prisoner was told that they were an errant child and, like a father, the inquisitor was merely trying to make them recognise the error of their ways. The Church was ready to forgive them and welcome them back, but first they had to unburden their soul by confessing and show true penitence, which, of course, meant revealing the names of those who, shared in their sin. Many fell into this trap and willingly provided more fodder for the Inquisition.

If the prisoner still refused to confess, they would be taken back to prison to think about it. If the suspect remained firm, the inquisitor would tell them that, although they appeared to be innocent, their jailers were not convinced. They would have to stay in prison, but would be moved to more comfortable quarters and be allowed visitors. Visitors would be sent by the Inquisition to encourage the prisoner to be careless in their talk. Prisoners were told that, if they confessed, they would get off with a light penance. An officer of the Inquisition was concealed so that they could overhear any conversation. They searched for any words that could be construed as an admission of heresy. Sometimes the suspect would be made to share a cell with another prisoner who was actually an agent of the Inquisition. The agent would talk openly of their own feigned heresy in the hope of entrapping the prisoner.

If all this failed, the prisoner would be taken back before the Inquisition and cross-examined at lightening speed. It would be long and wearisome interview. The inquisitor would try to force the suspect into contradicting themselves. For those quick-witted enough to avoid the inquisitor's snares there was but one reward – the torture chamber.

Torture was largely Torquemada's contribution to the Inquisition. It had been used against the Knights Templar in France in the fourteenth century, but successive popes had declared that it was unfair to force confessions out of men and women using torture that was so severe that if they did not confess they knew they would die. Torquemada had no such qualms.

He instructed that torture could be used in any case where heresy was 'half proven' – in other words, an accusation had been made but no confession had yet been extracted. Simply being brought before the Inquisition was enough. Being a good Christian, Torquemada said that no blood must be shed; however, he conceded that people did often die under torture. If this happened, the inquisitor must immediately seek absolution from a fellow priest. Torquemada gave all his priests the power to absolve one another of murder.

The inquisitors did not use the word torture – prisoners were simply put to The Question. There were five carefully thought-out stages to The Question. The first was the threat; the prisoner would already have heard about the cruel methods that the Inquisition employed, but the inquisitors felt it was their duty to remind the prisoner of the danger they faced in the hope that they would become weak with fear.

The second was the journey to the torture chamber. The victim would be taken ceremonially in a procession by candlelight. Also lighting the way would be braziers, which would take on their own terrifying significance. The torture chamber would be dark and dismal. The victims would be given a little time to glance around it and see the hideous devices that were employed; they would see them being used on other victims who had refused to confess; and they would see the torturers, who wore black hoods with eyeholes cut in them.

In the third stage, the prisoner would be seized and stripped, leaving them naked and vulnerable. The fourth stage was to introduce the victim to the particular instrument that was to be used on them and strap them on to it. Only then, in the fifth and final stage, would the pain begin.

It was against the law to repeat The Question. Once a victim had been tortured and survived, they could not be tortured again. However, there was no law against continuing the torture. It could go on day after day, week after week, with any interval merely being a 'suspension'.

Although the rack was used by the Inquisition, most prisoners were subjected to the hoist or water torture and, frequently, both. The victim's hands were tied behind their back and the rope was passed over a pulley – this was used to hoist the victim from the floor. If they did not confess after an hour or so, weights would be attached to their feet. If this still did not do the trick, the victims were to be let down with a jerk.

Next, they would be tied to a sloping trestle so their feet would be higher than their head. The head would be held in place with a band of metal. The nostrils would be sealed with wooden pegs and the jaw opened with piece of iron. A piece of linen would be put over their mouth and water would be poured down their throat, carrying the linen with it. The victim would swallow automatically pulling the linen into the gullet. They would cough and wretch and reach a state of semi-suffocation. When they struggled the ropes would cut into them. More and more water would be brought – up to eight jars were used.

Sometimes the Spanish Chair was also employed. This was an iron chair with metal bands that held the victim so they could not move. Their bare feet would be put in stocks next to a brazier. Their feet were covered in fat and slowly allowed to roast, more fat being applied from time to time so that the flesh did not burn away too quickly. Sometimes the victim had to be taken to the *auto-da-fé* in the chair because their feet had been completely burnt away. Flogging was also used and fingers and toes were cut off, usually one a day.

One Jew who converted to Christianity was delivered to the Inquisition by a servant whom he had whipped for stealing. He refused to confess to heresy. He had a linen bag tied over his head so tightly he almost suffocated. When it was taken off, he was asked to confess: he refused. Next, his thumbs were bound so tightly that blood spurted up from under the nails. His limbs were attached to pulleys and the ropes jerked violently so that his joints were dislocated. Then he was struck on the shins so viciously that he fainted with pain. Finally, he was tied up so tightly that the ropes cut into his flesh. He was only released when he had lost so much blood that his torturers feared he might die. Not that they cared, but it was much better for all concerned that, if people were going to die, they did so at the *auto-da-fé*. Public burning was a far more effective way of instilling the fear of God in other people. This particular man did not suffer that terrible fate. He was forced to wear the *sanbenito* – the garment of shame – for two years, then was banished from Seville.

A Scotsman named William Lithow was arrested in Malaga, accused of being a spy. As a Protestant he was taken before the Inquisition as a heretic. When he refused to convert to Catholicism, weights were put on his legs. The torture left him unable to walk. He was held in a prison overrun with vermin; his beard, his eyebrows and his eyelids were so infested that he could barely open his eyes. Every eight days, the vermin were swept off him. He was given a pint of water every other day. His cell had no bed, blanket, pillow or window.

After 47 days, he was taken by carriage to the torture chamber, where he was racked for five hours. His torturers were so clumsy that they took an inch of flesh off his heel. From then on, the carriage drew up outside his cell every morning at the same time, so that he would think he was being taken back to the rack. When he still refused to convert, he was kicked in the face by the inquisitor and sentenced to 11 different tortures. Finally, he was taken to Granada to be burnt.

Two slaves – a Turk and a black woman – were to look after him so that he would be well enough to be burnt. They were very kind to him and another servant, a Flemish boy, was so impressed by his courage that he got word to the English ambassador who rescued him.

The inquisitors were particularly fond of torturing attractive young women. In Cordova, one 15-year-old girl was stripped naked and scourged until she bore testimony against her mother.

In Toledo, a woman named Elvira del Campo was charged with not eating pork and putting out clean linen on a Saturday. Terrified of torture, she admitted that these were criminal acts, but denied any heretical intentions. The inquisitors were not satisfied. When they sent her to be tortured, she fell on her knees and begged them to tell her what they wanted her to say.

She was taken to the torture chamber where she was told to tell the truth, but she had nothing to say. She was stripped and asked again. Her suffering was detailed in the records of the Inquisition at Toledo.

'Señor,' she said. 'I have done all that is said of me and I bear false-witness against myself, for I do not want to see myself in such trouble. Please God, for I have done nothing.'

She was told not to bear false-witness against herself but to tell the truth. They began tying her arms.

'I have told the truth, what more do I have to tell?' she asked.

A cord was tied around her arms and was twisted until she screamed.

'Tell me what you want as I don't know what to say,' she said.

She was told to tell them what she had done. She had not done that. That was why she was being tortured.

'Loose the ropes, Señor,' she said, 'and tell me what I have to say. I do not know what I have done. Lord have mercy on this sinner.'

Another turn was made.

'Loosen the ropes a little so that I may remember what I have to tell,' she begged. 'I don't know what I have done. I did not eat pork for it made me sick. I have done everything they say. Loosen the ropes and I will tell the truth.'

Another turn of the cord was ordered.

'Loosen me and I will tell the truth,' she begged. 'I don't know what I have to tell. Loosen me for the sake of God. Tell me what I have to say. I did it, I did it. It hurts, Señor. I did it – I have nothing to tell. Oh, my arms. Release me and I will tell you everything.'

She was asked again what she did and she responded, 'I don't know, I don't eat pork because I don't like it.'

Asked why did she not like it, she replied, 'Loosen me, loosen me. Take me out of here and I will tell you. I will tell why I don't like it.'

She was then asked what she had done that was contrary to the Catholic faith and she replied, 'Take me out of here and tell me what to say. It hurts. Oh, my arms, my arms.' She repeated this over and over again.

Asked again what she had done against the one true faith, she said, 'I don't remember. Tell me what I have to say. Oh, wretched me. I will tell you anything you want, Señor. You are breaking my arms. Loosen me a little. I did everything I am accused of.'

She was then asked to tell them in detail what she had done. 'What do you want me to say? I did everything. Loosen me. I don't remember what I have to tell you. Don't you see that I am a weak woman? Oh! Oh! My arms are breaking.'

More turns were ordered and she cried. At this point, there were 16 turns in the cord. The pain was unendurable, but mercifully, when they tried to add another turn the rope broke.

She was put on the rack.

'Señores, why will you not tell me what I have to say?' she said as they strapped her on.

They told her to tell them what she had done wrong.

'I don't remember,' she said. 'Let me go. I did what the witnesses said.' She was asked what the witnesses had stated.

'Señor, I have told you, I do not remember,' she said. 'Señores, release me. I don't remember.'

Again, she was told to tell them.

'I don't know,' she said. 'Oh! Oh! You are tearing me to pieces. I have said I did it. Let me go.'

She was told to tell.

'Señor, it does not help me to say that I did it, and I have admitted that what I have done has brought me to this suffering,' she said. 'Señor, you know the truth. Señor, for God's sake have mercy on me. Oh Señor, take these things from my arms. Señor, release me, they are killing me.'

The cords tying her to the rack were tightened.

'Remind me of what I have to say for I don't know,' she begged. 'I said I did not eat pork – I only know that I don't eat it because I don't like it.'

She repeated this many times. Again, she was ordered to say why she did not like it.

'For the reason that the witnesses said. I don't know how to tell you. Miserable am I that I don't know how to tell you,' she said. 'I said I did it. My God, how can I find the words to tell you?'

She said that she didn't do it, so how could she tell them. 'You won't listen to me,' she said. 'You want to kill me. Release me and I will tell the truth.'

Again she was told to tell the truth and she said, 'I don't know how to say it. I have no memory. Lord, you are witness that if I knew how to say anything else I would say it. I have nothing more to say than that I did it and God knows it.'

She said this many times.

'Señor, Señor, nothing helps me. You, Lord, hear that I tell the truth and can say no more. They are tearing out my soul. Order them to loosen me.'

'I do not say that I did it. I said no more.' And then, 'Señor, I did it to observe the law.'

She was asked what law.

'The law that the witnesses say. I admit it all, Señor. I don't remember which law it was. Oh, wretched was the mother that bore me.'

Asked again what law she had meant, she said, 'If I knew what to say I would say it. Oh, Señor, I don't know what I have to say. Oh! Oh! You are killing me. If you would tell me what to say. Oh, Señor. Oh, my heart.'

She was asked whether she wished to tell the truth before they began the water torture. She said that she could not speak and that she was a sinner. The linen was then placed in her mouth.

'Take it away,' she screamed. 'I am strangling. I am sick.'

A jar of water was then poured down her throat. Afterwards she was told to tell the truth. She begged to be allowed to confess; she was dying. The inquisitor told her that the torture would continue until she told the truth. She had to tell it. Then she was repeatedly cross-questioned, but she said nothing. Seeing she was exhausted by the torture, the inquisitor ordered it to be suspended.

All this had been noted down by a secretary who attended the torture sessions. On this occasion, Elvira del Campo seems to have got off lightly.

Only one jar of water was poured down her throat and, according the secretary's meticulous notes, she did not scream or cry very much. But her sufferings were by no means over.

She was left for four days. By this time her limbs had stiffened, making any renewed torture doubly painful. Then she was brought back to the torture chamber. This time when she was stripped, she broke down completely and begged to be allowed to cover her nakedness. It made no difference. Her interrogation and torture continued. This time her replies were even less coherent than before. Eventually, she confessed to Judaism, repented and begged for mercy. The torture was suspended.

Legally, confessions extracted under torture were not valid. So, 24 hours later, she was taken back to the Holy Office, where her confession was read out. Under oath she had to swear that it was correct in every detail. If she did not, the suspended torture would be resumed. That done, she was reconciled to the Church at a public *auto-da-fé*.

There were other, worse, tortures. In the prison of the Inquisition at Toledo, a statue of the Virgin Mary covered with nails and blades was found. When a lever was pulled, the Virgin Mary's arms embraced the victim, whose naked flesh was pulled on to the spikes in a vicious mockery of the faith. Probably the most nauseating torture involved a number of mice that were placed on the victim's stomach. A large dish was put over them upside down, and a fire was lit on top of the bowl. As it grew hotter the mice would panic and try to get away from it. The only way out was for them to burrow through the victim's flesh.

The Holy Office were not allowed to take life, so when a suspect had admitted heresy they were handed over to the secular authorities as enemies of the state. The Inquisition, wanting its hands to be clean, said it 'abandoned' its victims in secular hands and beseeched the authorities to show mercy. However, the secular authorities did not dare to show mercy. If they did, they risked being hauled in front of the Inquisition and charged with heresy themselves.

Even the inquisitors admitted that mistakes were made. Thousands of good Catholics were falsely accused, tortured into making a confession and unjustly condemned to death at the *auto-da-fé*. But they were seen as privileged – they were being allowed to die for the faith. And for their glorious death, they would be admitted straight to paradise, so they had nothing to complain about.

The execution of heretics was no new thing. In the fourteenth century,

Pope Innocent IV had issued a Bull, instructing the governments of all Catholic countries that it was their duty to arrest and execute all heretics – or suffer excommunication and face charges of heresy themselves. The Spanish chose to do this in a particularly barbarous way.

Sometimes the Church was merciful. Some people who had been found guilty of heresy and asked to be reconciled with the church were spared. As an act of penitence, they had to be whipped half-naked though the streets in a procession to the local cathedral six Fridays in succession. After that, they would never be able to hold any rank or office, or wear fine clothes or jewellery. One fifth of their money would also be forfeit to the Inquisition. Unreconciled heretics, those who had relapsed into heresy and those the Inquisition did not choose to favour, suffered public burning at the *auto-da-fé*.

Auto-da-fé is the Portuguese for 'Act of Faith'. In Spanish it is *auto-de-fé* but, for historic reasons, the Portuguese variant has been adopted into the English language. These ghastly rituals took place on Sundays or other holy days, because more people would be able to watch.

The evening before the *auto* the heretics were brought before the Inquisition and told whether they would live or die. Every person condemned would then be allotted two priests to wrestle for their souls. Although the condemned were bound to die, it was still possible to save their souls. In that case, if they were reconciled with the church, they would be strangled before the flames reached them.

Everyone found guilty of heresy also had to wear a tall cap like a mitre called a *coraza*, and a *sanbenito*, a loose-fitting tunic made of yellow sackcloth that came down to the knees. It was a garment regularly worn by penitents. Those found guilty of lesser crimes than heresy would be sentenced to wear the sanbenito on Sundays, or for a specific period. Normally, they would have blood-red crosses sewn on them. But the *sanbenitos* worn by those facing the *auto-da-fé* were decorated with flames and devils prodding the fires with pitchforks. If the flames pointed downwards, the Inquisition had been merciful. The victim had repented of their heresy and would be strangled. If they pointed upwards, the victim was persisting in their heretical believes and would suffer the worst atrocity: they would be burnt to death. Burning was the favoured method as, technically, it did not spill blood.

The next morning at around six o'clock the victims were lined up outside the prison in their *sanbenitos* with a rope around their necks and their hands tied together. They marched off in a procession led by priests bearing green crosses – the symbol of the Inquisition – draped in black material. Next came the *alguazils*: as well as arresting suspects and visiting victims in jail, urging them to repent, they were charged with protecting the inquisitors who were not always popular figures in the community.

Following them was a priest carrying the Host. Over his head was a canopy of scarlet and gold carried by four men. When he approached, the men, women and children in the crowd had to fall to their knees. If they did not, they would be marked out as heretics.

Then came more *alguazils*, followed by lesser criminals, some of whom bore the marks of torture. The victims came next, each flanked by two Dominican friars in their white vestments and black hoods. In some cases, these men were still trying to save the soul of the victim. Following after were the bodies of those who had been found guilty of heresy after their death and had been dug up for punishment. After them were the effigies of those who had fled Spain rather than face the Inquisition, carried on green poles. The effigies wore the *sanbenitos* and *corazas* of the condemned.

Then came the inquisitors, flanked on one side by banners emblazoned with the arms of the pope, entwined with those of Ferdinand and Isabella. On the other side were the arms of the Inquisition. Behind came more *alguazils* and other minor officials. The entire procession was flanked by soldiers carrying halberds. Bringing up the rear was the crowd, who followed the procession to the cathedral square.

Once there, each victim was read a list of their crimes before a sermon was preached. Often there were several hundred of them and this process could take all day. The victims were made to sit on benches swathed in black crepe; the benches were set on a platform so the crowd could see those who had been condemned. Being good Catholics, the crowds shouted insults at the victims and humiliated them. It was not unusual to set fire to Jews' beards. This was called 'shaving the New Christians'. All the white, priests and monks harried the victims, still working hard to get last-minute repentance.

The inquisitors sat on another platform, surrounded by their black-draped green crosses. Incense burnt – a wise precaution, as there were usually a large number of freshly disinterred bodies around.

Mass was celebrated; then there was another sermon. Following that, the Grand Inquisitor stood up and led the crowd in the oath. The onlookers were required to fall to their knees and swear that they could defend the Holy Office against all its enemies. They would be faithful to it in life and in death; they would do whatever it asked of them; and they swore that they would pluck out their right eye or cut off their right hand if that was what it asked of them.

Ferdinand and Isabella refrained from saying this oath. So did the Spanish monarchs that succeeded them – with the exception of Philip II who was a zealot. It was at this point that the Church washed its hands of the victims. It had done all it could for the sinners. Now they abandoned them to the secular authorities for the punishment for heresy to be carried out. The charges were read out again, this time by the secular authorities. The Grand Inquisitor then made a public plea for mercy, asking disingenuously that their blood would not be spilt.

The secular authorities were deaf to these pleas and took the victims to the *quemadero* – the place of burning. This was a field where the stakes had already been set up and the faggots piled high. Having been tied to the stakes, the victims were asked if they wanted absolution; the lucky ones were garrotted, then the faggots were lit. Monks chanted; people cheered; the inquisitors feigned shock at the wickedness of the world; and the smell of roasting flesh permeated the air.

After condemning so many people to death, Torquemada himself died peacefully in his bed in 1498. He was a happy man: he had lived to see the Muslims expelled from Granada and his own persecution had resulted in the expulsion of the Jews from Spain in 1492. At the time, many people called him the 'Saviour of Spain' because he freed the country from the control of the Pope. Indeed, many of the Grand Inquisitors that followed him were worse than he was, but he had built the instrument through which they vented their sadism. In the end, the Spanish Inquisition weakened Spain and left it with a reputation for barbarism that it only threw off after the death of General Franco in 1975.

At its height, the Spanish Inquisition had 14 tribunals set up in Spain, Mexico and Peru. The Spanish Inquisition established itself in Sicily in 1517, but efforts to set one up in Naples and Milan failed. In 1522, the emperor Charles V introduced it to the Netherlands in an effort to stamp out Protestantism.

Napoleon attempted to suppress the inquisition when he occupied Spain in 1808 and it was finally halted in 1834. The last *auto-da-fé* took place in Mexico in 1850. Estimates of how many people perished in the *autos* vary wildly, but the number probably runs into the hundreds of thousands.

The majority were women, some of them in their nineties. Children as young as 12 or 13 were frequently burnt when their parents were found to be heretics. In 1659, two ten-year-old girls were burnt in Toledo.

Two elderly nuns were burnt alive in Evora in 1673 with the name of Jesus on their lips. They had lived blameless lives in a convent for over 40 years. Garcia d'Alarcon was said to be the most beautiful woman in the country when she was burnt by the Inquisition in Granada 1593. Isabelle, the wife of Francisco Dalos of Ciudad Real, first appeared before the inquisition at the age of 22. She was arraigned five more times and spent 18 years of her life in the prisons of the Inquisition. Her last trial began in 1665, when she was 80, and lasted until 1670. She was tortured three times and eventually died. The Inquisition then sentenced her to a double punishment. Her body was burnt, along with an effigy. Having neglected to confess before she expired in the torture chamber, she died in a state of sin.

One of the most famous victims of the *auto* in the New World was Doña Ana de Castro, a socialite in Lima. Her love affairs were legendary and it was said that she even shared her favours with the viceroy. It was possibly a rejected lover or a jealous rival who told the Inquisition she was secretly practising Judaism. She was burned in 1836.

In Sicily, a renegade Augustine Friar named Diego Lamattina got his revenge. In 1657 he was charged with being a heretical blasphemer, despiser of the sacraments and an insulter of sacred images. When he was in prison, he was visited by the Inquisitor General, whose brains he dashed out with his manacles.

Balthazar Lopez was an incorrigible joker. As court saddler in Castile, he had amassed a small fortune. After taking a trip abroad in 1645, he was arrested. Along with 56 others he faced the flame at the great *auto* held at Cuena in 1654. As they approached the *quemadero,* his confessor exhorted him to rejoice, as the gates of Paradise were soon to be opening freely for him.

'Freely,' scoffed Lopez. 'The confiscation of my property has cost me 200,000 ducats. Do you infer that I have been swindled?'

At the *brasero* – the brazier – he noticed that the executioner, Pedro de Alcalá, was making a clumsy job of strangling two of his fellow victims. 'Pedro,' Lopez said, 'If you can't strangle me better than you are doing to those two poor souls, I'd rather be burned alive.'

The executioner then tried to bind his feet.

'For God's sake,' said Lopez, finding this the final indignity. 'If you bind me, I won't believe in your Jesus.'

He threw down the crucifix he was holding. The priest finally managed to persuade him to take it back and ask for forgiveness. Then the executioner started to strangle him and the priest asked if he was truly repentant.

'Father,' said the dying man, 'is this any time to joke?'

3 ❖ The Destruction of the Aztecs

The conventional view of the Aztecs is that they were the most bloodthirsty people who ever existed. While it is true that they practised human sacrifice and would sometimes dress themselves in the flayed skins of their victims, this is by no means the whole story. The Aztecs were the last of the four great civilisations – the Olmec, Teotihuacán, Mayan and Aztlán – that had flourished in Mexico since the first millennium BC.

Their civilisation was destroyed by young Spanish nobleman Hernando Cortés in 1521. The Spanish considered the conquest of Mexico the last crusade. Battles against 'the infidel' were fresh in Spanish minds. Granada, the last great stronghold of the Moors, had only been recaptured by the Spanish in 1492. Muslims and Jews were expelled, and those who remained were forcibly converted.

Cortés conquered the Aztec empire with just 500 men, 16 horses and one canon. Almost as important was his mistress, a slave girl called Malinche, later baptised as Doña Marina. She spoke both Mayan and the Aztec language Natuatl, and acted crucially as his interpreter throughout the campaign.

The Aztecs had an inkling of their fate when between 1507 and 1510 strange ships were sighted off the coast of Mexico. Then came a series of ill omens – a comet appeared in the sky, lightning struck a temple and the sound of women weeping was heard at night. Although the Aztec ruler Motecuhzoma simply executed anyone who reported these portents of doom, it did no good.

A fatal flaw in the Aztecs' defence was their own legends. The Aztecs believed that the god Quetzalcoatl, the mythical ruler of Toltecs, the Aztec's precursors, had been exiled and would return in the year I Reed, according to the Aztec calendar. I Reed was 1519, when the Spaniards turned up, so Motecuhzoma assumed that the Spaniards were gods and that their ships were wooden temples.

He sent gold and magnificent costumes made out of feathers, in the hope that the gods would take the gifts and go. Instead, Cortés seized the messengers and put then in chains. He gave them a demonstration of his god-like powers by firing his canon, which made them faint. Cortés established himself at Veracruz and burnt his ships so that his men could not flee back to Cuba, then began his march on the Aztec capital, Tenochtitlán.

With armour, muskets, crossbows, swords and horses, the Spanish had overwhelming military superiority. War for the peoples of pre-Columbian Mexico was largely a ceremonial affair. They wore elaborate costumes and were armed only with a small sword made out of obsidian – volcanic glass.

Their object was to capture as many of the enemy as possible to use as human sacrifices later. If a leader was killed or a temple captured, the loser capitulated immediately and talks began over the amount of tribute that should be paid. Cortés did not play by these rules – he slaughtered as many as he could on the battlefield.

Motecuhzoma's only possible defence was guile. He tried to capture Cortés in an ambush at Cholula. But Cortés discovered the plan and massacred the citizens of Cholula. He destroyed the temple of Huitzilopochtli, the Aztec god of war, and set up an image of the Virgin Mary instead. It was a crucial psychological victory over the Aztec culture.

Cortés established an alliance with the people of Tlaxcala, who had only recently been conquered by Motecuhzoma. They rebelled and rallied to Cortés' cause.

Hearing what had happened at Cholula, other Aztec cities surrendered without a fight and Cortés marched on Tenochtitlán unopposed.

Motecuhzoma had no choice but to greet the Spanish graciously. He lodged Cortés in the palace of Axayacatl, Motecuhzoma's father, which was packed with gold ornaments. These were melted down; decorative stones and feathers they simply threw away. The gold was shipped back as bars directly to Charles V in Spain, bypassing Cortés's commander, the governor of Cuba, Diego Velázquez. Cortés also demanded that Motecuhzoma swear allegiance to Charles V of Spain. He would remain nominal ruler of the Aztecs while Cortés himself seized the reigns of power, with the aim of becoming viceroy.

To reassert his authority, Velázquez sent a force of over 1000 under Panfilo de Narváez to bring Cortés to heel. Leaving a small force under Pedro de Alvardo in Tenochtitlán, Cortés headed back to the coast where he defeated Narváez and used the troops to swell his own ranks.

Meanwhile, back in Tenochtitlán, the Aztecs were celebrating the festival of their war god Huitzilopochtli which, like all Aztec festivals, involved human sacrifice on an epic scale. Terrified by the extent of these bloodthirsty rituals, Alvardo's men turned on the Aztecs and slaughtered as many as 10,000 priests and worshippers. When Cortés returned to Tenochtitlán, he found the city in a state of open warfare. He tried to calm the situation by getting Motecuhzoma to talk to his people, but the Aztecs stoned Motecuhzoma to death as a traitor.

Cortés grabbed as much gold and treasure as his men could carry and tried to make a run for it. The Aztecs ambushed them and Cortés escaped with just 500 men. But in a monumental tactical error, the Aztecs did not pursue the Spanish and finish them off. This allowed Cortés to regroup. He turned back and laid siege to the city.

The Aztecs put up fierce resistance, but for months, they were starved and harried. Finally, they were defeated by an epidemic of smallpox brought by one of Narváez's soldiers. This killed Motecuhzoma's successor, his brother Cuitlahuac. Their cousin Cuahtemoc took over as emperor, but he was captured and tortured until he revealed fresh sources of gold. Later he was hanged on the pretext of treason against Charles V.

Many of the priests and Aztec soldiers preferred to die rather than surrender to the Spanish. In order to quell any resistance, Cortés demolished Tenochtitlán, building by building, using the rubble to fill in the city's canals. Mexico City was built on the ruins. The surviving Aztecs were used as slave labour in the gold and silver mines. They were decimated by two further epidemics of smallpox. Forcible conversion to Christianity destroyed what remained of their culture and they lost themselves in drink.

What little we know of the Aztecs comes from Cortés and his men who were more interested in booty than scholarship, and the Franciscan friar Bernardino de Sahagœn who circulated questionnaires among survivors of the onslaught in an attempt to learn something of the culture they had destroyed. His work was inhibited by the Inquisition who investigated him for being too pro-Indian and confiscated his writings which, fortunately, resurfaced in the eighteenth century.

4 ❖ The Black Hole of Calcutta

It was an inauspicious beginning to the British occupation of India, but an important one. Perhaps for some deep Freudian reason, the Black Hole of Calcutta is the stuff that myths are made of. It was the myth of the atrocity purportedly committed against innocent English men and women by the Nawab of Bengal in 1756 that allowed Britain to take over Bengal and, eventually, the whole of India.

The Seven Years War had spilled over both into North America and India where both Britain and France had trading concessions. The French held Hyderabad while the British held Calcutta and Madras, ceded by the French under the Treaty of Aix-la-Chapelle in 1748 in return for Cape Breton Island.

However, the old Nawab – or governor – of Bengal died in 1756. He was succeeded by his grandson who was both headstrong and vacillating. When he heard exaggerated reports that the British were fortifying Calcutta, he besieged the city. After four days, on 20 June 1756, it fell.

The foreign settlers were quite unprepared for the attack. Governor Drake and the majority of the English residents fled to the river and escaped on board ships. John Holwell, a council member of the East India Company, and 170 others retreated to the Company's headquarters' Fort William, which had been built in the early part of the century.

Accounts of what happened next are confused. A truce may have been called but, fearing treachery, Holwell opened fire on the Bengalis. The outraged Bengalis then took the fort, with some loss of life. Holwell was captured. The Nawab entered Fort William and ordered that the principal inhabitants be held overnight.

In all, 146 people were held. There were talks and the Nawab promised the captives his protection and good treatment. However, it seems that a drunken soldier killed one of the Nawab's men. When he found out about it, the Nawab asked where miscreants were usually held. He was told of the fort's guardroom – which was known as the Black Hole – a small room just 18 feet by 14 feet, between two arches of the outer wall. It was completely bricked in, except for two small barred windows that opened onto the courtyard. Usually, drunken soldiers were imprisoned in there until they sobered up.

At eight o'clock, when it was already dark, the Nawab ordered that all 146 captives, including one woman named Mary Carey, be jailed there. It is possible that the Nawab was unaware of the size of the jail.

It was a sultry Bengali night and Holwell and his companions were crammed in like sardines. The heat was intense and they took their clothes off – hats were waved around in an attempt to circulate the air. The guards passed them water, which they fought over. There were cries and groans from those at the back who were suffocating; some pleaded with the guards to be shot. Holwell sucked on his sleeve to keep his mouth wet. He later thought of drinking his own urine and considered slashing his wrists with a knife he had in his pocket.

By 11.30, Holwell noted that nearly everyone was delirious. He witnessed the death of the carpenter named Leech and the Reverend Gervase Bellamy who died hand in hand with his son. Holwell eventually collapsed and was pulled out from under a pile of corpses by Henry Lushington, a clerk, and John Cooke, a company secretary. They carried him to the window, where he recovered.

At 6 a.m., the doors were opened and they were let out. The 23 survivors included Holwell, Lushington, Cooke and Mary Carey. A total of 123 were dead. Their bodies were thrown in a ditch outside the east gate and covered with earth. Later, Holwell would erect an obelisk on the spot.

Cooke and Lushington made off to catch up with the English ships that were waiting down the river. Others stayed on but, after another incident involving a drunken soldier, all the British were ordered out on pain of having their noses cut off. Only Holwell and some of the soldiers stayed, held in irons. That, at least, is Holwell's story, which he wrote down in a letter to a friend on board the ship that took him back to England in 1757.

However, when Lushington and Cooke reached the English ships and reported to Governor Drake, they said nothing of what happened in the Black Hole. The soldiers held by the Nawab talked to some Frenchmen, but none of them mentioned the Black Hole either. The source of the story was Holwell's letters home; his story is full of inconsistencies and many doubted its authenticity.

Robert Clive – Clive of India – was in Madras at the time, but on 2 January 1757, he retook Calcutta. Clive defeated the Nawab's army, even

Suraj-Ud-Daula, the nawab of Bengal (1731–1757). He was the perpetrator of the Black Hole of Calcutta, where 123 people died from being held in atrocious conditions overnight.

though it vastly outnumbered his own, at Plassey in June 1757, then installed his own Nawab. This led to the virtual annexation of Bengal in 1765. In Clive's account of the conquest of Bengal, there is no mention of the Black Hole. He even referred to the Nawab as 'a man of courage and humanity', which was the general view. The Black Hole was certainly not used as an excuse for making war on him.

There was no official enquiry into the fall of Fort William until 1772 when a Select Committee of the House of Commons was set up. By then many of the survivors of the Black Hole had died. Others had made their fortunes with the East India Company.

In 1773, Cooke testified to the Select Committee. Up until this time, he had remained silent on the subject of the Black Hole. To the Committee, he confirmed Holwell's story; but then, he was not an unbiased witness – Cooke and Holwell had been friends long before the fall of Fort William. On one occasion, Cooke had put up bail for Holwell. The spoils of the Battle of Plassey had made Cooke a rich man, and by then, the story of the Black Hole of Calcutta had become the principal justification for British rule in India.

So if official versions of what atrocity took place in the Black Hole of Calcutta are not true, what did happen? It seems likely that, during the bungled truce, Holwell had ordered that the gate to the Fort be opened before he fired on the Bengalis. This prompted a massacre. A much smaller number of people than the 146 Holwell claimed were held in the Black Hole and some of them may have died there. But as the huge loss of life was plainly Holwell's fault, he exaggerated its significance, contending that many of the men who had died defending the Fort's walls had died in the prison. By the time his story circulated, it was in everyone's interests to go along with it.

5 ❖ The Middle Passage

When Europeans began colonising the Americas in the fifteenth and sixteenth centuries, they found their great projects there hampered by the shortage of labour. The indigenous people were not prepared to work for wages and they did not make good slaves – it was too easy for them to escape and live among their own people.

In Africa, however, the slave trade was already well established. As in most places in the world, an informal system of slavery had been established from the earliest times – those who lost a war became the slaves of those who won – but slaving became a commercial enterprise. As early as AD 650, Arab slave traders began taking African slaves to Arabia and beyond. In 1444, the Portuguese started taking slaves from West Africa, so when the Americas opened up, it seemed the natural place to find cheap labour.

At first, European ships would sail to the West African coast with manufactured goods that they would exchange for the slaves, who had been brought to the beaches by the local chieftains or traders. The slaves would be transported to the West Indies where the slave markets were. From there, they were taken to the islands' sugar plantations or on to North or South America. The ships would then return to Europe with cargoes of sugar, rum, tobacco and coffee. As these slaving voyages had three legs, they were known as the triangular trade.

For the American ships, the triangular trade was somewhat different. They sailed out of Boston, Massachusetts and Newport, Rhode Island, and were called 'rum boats' as they carried rum to Africa – Africans had come to like rum more than French brandy. The cargo was exchanged for slaves who, again, were taken to the West Indies, where they were exchanged for molasses. This was taken back to New England, where it was made into rum.

The journey across the Atlantic was called the 'Middle Passage'. Over 11 million Africans made the trip. This compares with over 18 million Africans who were taken eastwards by Arab traders. Nearly half of those who went to the New World were carried by the Portuguese and were taken directly to Brazil.

By the eighteenth century, when the transatlantic slave trade was at its zenith, slave ships were practically floating coffins. At any one time, the ships of half-a-dozen nations were moored off the coast of West Africa waiting to pick up slaves. In some places, such as the Bonny River in Nigeria, there could be as many as ten ships waiting. It could take months for a large ship to fill her holds. Along the Gold Coast, where the competition was greatest, ships would have to make numerous stops, sometimes buying slaves one or two at a time. The Portuguese traded further south out of Angola where they had the market to themselves and the waiting times were less.

Once the ship was moored and its sails furled, the crew would make 'house'. This involved tying spars between the masts to make the framework of a roof. On it, they would lay rush mats. Underneath, the 'house' was divided into two rooms. In one, the captain entertained kings, tribal headmen and other slave traders; the other was a receiving area for the slaves.

These roofs were not very good at keeping the rain out and they were hot and stuffy, especially as braziers were lit on deck. The crewmen were eager to make their stay off the coast as short as possible as they were prey

Slaves being transported from West Africa in 1444. The journey across the Atlantic was called the 'Middle Passage'.

to all sorts of tropical diseases. As there were rarely enough sailors to control the slaves, they tried to purchase Africans from different nations, so they could not easily organise a mutiny. Some captains picked out a few slaves to guard over the others, armed with a whip.

The slaves were brought on board in dugout canoes, manned by Krumen – fishermen from the Grain Coast who were expert at handling boats. The slaves were shackled in pairs with leg irons. Before they were purchases, they were given a rudimentary medical examination to make sure they were healthy. Special attention was paid to their teeth and any signs that they were ageing. Then their heads were shaved, their clothes taken away, and they were branded with a red-hot iron.

Once on board, the men were kept chained until the ship sailed, and sometimes for the entire voyage. Women and children were allowed to go free. On some ships sexual relations with the captives were forbidden. On most, the young women and girls were repeatedly raped by the sex-starved sailors.

The slaves were housed in the cargo hold. This was about five feet high, so it was impossible for most to stand upright. A worse method of cramming in even more of the human cargo was devised: a shelf six feet wide around the hold to hold a second tier of slaves. In larger ships, there were two shelves. These allowed slaves 20 inches of headroom. Slaves were packed in so tightly that they had to lie on their side rather than on their backs.

Some captains were, in the circumstances, kindly men. One, John Newton, went on to become a parish priest and composer of hymns; Hugh Crow boasted that he had black friends in the West Indies that had once been transported on his ship; but some were fiends, drunk with power. Captain McTaggart of the Alexander once had every one of his 50-man crew, except three, flogged. When one man jumped overboard to escape a flogging and was rescued from the sea, he was asked if he was not afraid of being eaten by sharks.

'I would prefer that to life on this ship,' he said.

Once out at sea, the slaves were brought up on deck every morning. Their shackles were attached to a chain running down the centre of the deck to stop them jumping overboard. A drummer, a piper or a man with a whip encouraged them to exercise. This was a mixed blessing. The heavy leg irons caused bruising and bleeding around the ankles; but few captains risked letting the slaves take them off.

The slaves were fed two meals a day of a coarse porridge made from maize of millet. Their diet was occasionally varied with beans, the kind fed to horses, and sometimes a little salted meat. When the slaves were out on deck, good captains had their quarters scrubbed out with vinegar, but many did not bother with this nicety. In rough weather, the slaves would not be let out – they would have to stay in the stuffy, dark, stinking hold day and night.

Ship's surgeon Alexander Falconbridge, who wrote several books about his experiences, said that each man had less space than he would have in his coffin. It was impossible to move through the hold without walking on someone. Falconbridge would take his shoes off to avoid injuring anyone. Slaves would bite his feet if they came near their faces.

The slaves had to move about to try and reach the lavatories – which amounted to no more than two or three large buckets for 100 men. They would have to manoeuvre themselves there with the man they were chained to. Many suffered from acute dysentery and were not up to this struggle. Not surprisingly, the smell of the slave ships was so foul that other ships would sail to windward of them. One slave captain, Richard Drake, would carry a bag full of camphor in his teeth as a nosegay.

Tarpaulins were spread over the gratings and vents to keep rain and spray out – they also kept the foul smell in. When it was warm, the conditions were so stuffy that many fainted. Falconbridge compared the conditions to those in a slaughterhouse.

Africans were particularly vulnerable to smallpox and epidemics raged through the holds. Others died of no apparent cause. Some went mad and others managed to kill themselves. One man on the Brookes, a slaver sailing out of Liverpool, tried to cut his throat the first night they were at sea. The surgeon sewed it up, but the next night the man tore out the stitches with his fingernails. The surgeon patched him up a second time and tied the man's hands behind his back. Then he refused to eat; he was threatened and punished, but it did no good. Within two weeks, he was dead. This was unusual. Those who could not be flogged into eating usually had a special device jammed between their teeth which forced their jaw open so that food could be pushed into their mouth.

Some slaves believed that if they died on the voyage, their spirit would return to their homeland, making suicide an attractive prospect. If they got the chance, they would jump overboard, often with a look of joy on their faces. One captain threatened to have the bodies of drowned slaves fished out and decapitated. Then, he said, their spirit would have to go home headless.

More commonly, death came from what the slavers called 'fixed melancholy'. This had no apparent cause except for the extreme misery of the conditions. Sailors believed that by some supreme act of will the Africans could simply hold their breath until they were dead. This is impossible, but it was noted that, although Africans often recovered from the other diseases on board ship – even smallpox – no one ever recovered from the 'fixed melancholy'.

The conditions were not always as bad as Alexander Falconbridge described. Slaves were a valuable cargo and, usually, everything possible would be done to keep them alive. The mortality rate was, in fact, higher among the sailors. They were not valuable and were prey to tropical diseases and scurvy as they were longer at sea.

Hugh Crow made several voyages without losing a single slave or seaman, but this was rare. An epidemic could kill hundreds before they reached the Caribbean. Occasionally, every slave would be dead before the vessel arrived. Anti-slavery campaigner Thomas Clarkson recorded 20 voyages where, of a total cargo of 7,904 slaves, 2,053 died. This is just over a quarter. More usually around one in eight died. The dead were thrown overboard and the slave ships were invariably followed by schools of sharks.

Mortality depended on the length of the voyage as conditions deteriorated day by day. The trip from the Gambia to Barbados took a mere six weeks; the journey from Angola to Cuba could take as long as three months, especially as ships often found themselves becalmed in the doldrums. In that case, ships ran low on food and water, worsening the conditions for slaves and crew alike.

There was the danger of shipwreck – slaves chained in pairs with heavy shackles were unlikely to survive. There were also pirates to contend with and privateers. Britain and France were regularly at war throughout the eighteenth century and the other's shipping and cargoes were considered fair game. In one case, a British ship's captain armed some of the slaves to repulse the French. He said that they fought with great spirit, but he sold them in Jamaica anyway.

On well-run slave ships, as they approached the West Indies, discipline was relaxed. Sometimes there was even a party with the African women dressed up in clothes that the sailors had given them, capering around. However, when they finally arrived in Kingston, Havana or Rio de Janeiro, they soon found there was no cause for celebration. The slaves had to undergo a humiliating physical inspection before being separated and sold at auction.

If there was a shortage of slaves at the time, there would be an unseemly scramble, with buyers swarming over the boats to try and secure the best of the cargo. Then the captains totted up their profits, scrubbed out the holds and filled them with produce, while the slaves were sent off to a life of servitude.

Occasionally, the slaves mutinied. In November 1749, the *Ann*, sailing out of Liverpool, moored off the coast of Guinea to pick up slaves. Six months later, she was still there. By this time, she had 60 slaves on board. Her crew of just 13 was ill and, in the middle of one night, the Africans turned on them. They seized the arms and ammunition and killed or wounded all the crewmen, except for two who hid. The Africans took over the ship and ran her aground, where she broke up, then jumped overboard and disappeared.

The *King David*, sailing out of Bristol, was also undermanned when she picked up a cargo of slaves from the Guinea coast in May 1750. Her captain was an easy-going man who did not keep the slaves in irons. One of the slaves had been a chief in his own country and spoke English well. The captain would sometimes invite him to his cabin for a chat. During these visits, the chief saw where the captain's weapons were stowed. Soon after the ship sailed, the chief and 15 of his men rushed the captain's cabin, seized the guns and took over the ship. The captain and five of the crew were killed; the rest shut themselves in the hold. The chief called for them to come out, saying they would not be killed. Those who surrendered were put in irons. However, the first mate refused to come out. A cabin boy was sent down to tell him that he would be cut to pieces if he did not give himself up. When the mate came out, he was clapped in irons like the rest of the crew. Then the Africans began throwing them overboard, but the chief stepped in to save the mate.

'If you throw him overboard, who will sail the ship?' he asked. He swore to kill any man who harmed the mate, who then sailed them to safety.

The most famous mutiny occurred on board the *Amistad*, which sailed out of Havana with a cargo of 53 slaves. Before being sold on in Honduras, the slaves were allowed on deck to 'refresh' them. A ship's cook, who was of mixed race, remarked that, when they arrived, they would be killed and their flesh salted and sold as meat. One of the slaves, whose named was Cinqué, led a revolt. He broke their chains and threw the captain overboard. The slaves' two owners were on board. Cinqué insisted that they sail back to Africa – eastwards, towards the morning sun. However, the slave-owners tricked him by sailing off course during the night. After two months, they grew short of food and water, and found themselves moored off Long Island.

At first, the US authorities thought that the *Amistad* was a smuggler. The ship was seized and the Africans were jailed in New Haven. The

Spanish ambassador in Washington demanded that both the ship and the cargo be returned to its owners. However, abolitionists in the US argued that the slaves should be freed. They persuaded the congressman and ex-President John Quincy Adams to represent the men. He took the case all the way to the Supreme Court and won. Cinqué and his companions were freed and returned to Sierra Leone.

However, it was not the slave mutinies that put an end to the transatlantic slave trade, but the atrocities committed by the slavers. One in particular caught the public imagination. On 6 September 1781, a British ship named the *Zong* left the Guinea coast bound for Jamaica. She carried a cargo of 440 slaves and a crew of 17. By the time she reached the Caribbean, the complement was down to 380 slaves and ten crewmen. Many were sick.

The *Zong* approached Jamaica on 27 November, but her captain, Luke Collingwood, steered away, saying that he mistook the island for another one. Two days later, he called the remains of his crew together and revealed his vicious plan. He proposed throwing overboard all the sick slaves. They were unlikely to recover he said, and they would fetch nothing at auction. His justification was that the ship was short of water and, by throwing some of the slaves overboard, he would be able to save the rest.

The real reason was an insurance swindle. Insurers would not pay out for a slave who died of natural causes, fearing that the slavers would simply let the slaves die. But the rule of the sea is that an insurer has to pay up for cargo thrown overboard if the reason for jettisoning it is to save the rest. Although, this rule was not written with a human cargo in mind, it still applied.

The mate, James Kelsal, objected. They were not short of water, he said, and they were near land. There was no justification for throwing anyone overboard. However, after he had made his protest, Kelsal said no more. He was one of the men who threw 54 living people into the sea. Three days later, after it had rained and replenished their stocks of water, they threw 42 more overboard. A week later, when they neared land, an additional 26 were drowned. To prevent them swimming ashore, their arms were bound before they were thrown. Another ten jumped overboard of their own accord.

A few days later, the *Zong* anchored in the harbour in Kingston, Jamaica, where the rest of the slaves were sold. Collingwood duly put in a claim for the 122 men and women he and his men had drowned and the ten who had killed themselves. However, the insurers were suspicious. They investigated the claim and found out what had happened.

The insurers refused to pay up for the drowned slaves and were sued by the owners. The owners won the case by arguing that throwing 133 slaves overboard was no different, in law, than throwing 133 horses overboard. The insurers appealed, and in a landmark decision, Lord Mansfield reversed the decision on the grounds that human beings – even slaves – could not be treated simply as goods.

The case set the campaign for the abolition of the slave trade rolling. There were even calls to charge the *Zong*'s officers with murder, but Collingwood died and so nothing came of it.

6 ❖ Reign of Terror

After the French Revolution, the government of the fledgling republic found itself embroiled in a civil war and under attack externally from Britain, Austria, Spain, Portugal, Prussia, Russia, Sardinia and Naples. In response, on 5 September 1793 – 9 Thermidor, Year I on the Revolutionary calendar – the republic issued a decree making 'terror' the order of the day. The enemies of the Revolution – nobles, churchmen and those suspected of hoarding food and private property – were to be eliminated. There followed a wave of atrocities known as the Reign of Terror.

The first plan was to send the revolutionary army from Paris out into the countryside with a mobile guillotine. Robespierre, who headed the all-powerful Committee of Public Safety, wanted an army of 500,000 men to do the job and so introduced conscription.

On 17 September, the Committee passed the Law of Suspects, allowing them to arrest and execute anyone suspected of harbouring anti-revolutionary views.

'A river of blood will now divide France from its enemies,' rejoiced Robespierre.

The Revolution was a product of the age of reason and organised religion was seen as the enemy. In line with this argument, the Committee sent agents out across the country to dechristianise the population. Churches and cemeteries were vandalised; the Bishop of Paris was forced to resign and Notre Dame was deconsecrated and renamed the Temple of Reason.

Lyon had rebelled against the Jacobins, but on 9 October, after a bloody bombardment, the revolutionaries retook the city and renamed it Ville-Affranchie – 'Liberated Town'. The houses of the rich were demolished and 20–30 rebels executed. Suspecting that the locals were being too lenient on their own, a revolutionary zealot named Mathieu Parein was sent to handle the situation. He ordered that those who had an income of 30,000 livres or more must hand it over immediately and that all vestiges of religion should be obliterated. Houses were searched and mass executions began.

The guillotine became overworked. On the eleventh of Nivôse, according the scrupulous accounts the Jacobins kept, 32 heads were severed in 25 minutes. A week later, 12 heads were severed in just five minutes. This was a messy way to dispose of political enemies; the residents of the Rue Lafont where the guillotine was set up kept complaining about the blood over-flowing from the drainage ditch that ran under the scaffold.

As an alternative, mass shootings took place. As many as 60 prisoners were tied together in a line and shot with cannon. Those who were not killed outright were finished of with bayonets, sabres and rifles. The chief butcher, an actor named Dorfeuille, wrote to Paris boasting that he had killed 113 Lyonnais in a single day. Three days later he butchered 209 and promised that another 400–500 would 'expiate their crimes with fire and shot'. This was an underestimate: by the time the killing had stopped, 1,905 were dead – and the victims were not restricted to the rich, the aristocratic and the clergy. The unemployed were also liquidated, along with anyone the Revolutionary Tribunal decided was a *'fanatique'*.

Marseilles – now Ville-Sans-Nom ('Town Without Name') – was similarly purged. After the insurrection in the Vendée, the local agent wrote to the Committee of Public Safety in Paris describing their reprisals.

'There is no more Vendée, citizens,' he said. 'It has just perished under our free sword along with its women and children. I have just buried it in the marshes and mud of Savenay. Following the orders you gave me I have crushed children under the feet of horses and massacred women who at least will give birth to no more brigands. I have no prisoners with which to reproach myself.'

The name Vendée was changed to Vengé – 'Avenged'.

A total of 200 prisoners were executed in Angers in December alone, 2000 at Saint-Florent. At Pont-de-Cé and Avrillé, 3000–4000 were shot in one long, relentless slaughter. At Nantes the guillotine was so overworked that a new method of execution, known as 'vertical deportation', was

Celebrations at the taking of the Bastille in Paris (14th July 1792).

developed. A flat-bottomed barrage would be holed below the waterline, then a plank nailed over the hole to keep the boat temporarily afloat; prisoners were put on the barge with their hands and feet tied. The barge would be taken out into the middle of the Loire where the executioner would pull out the plank and jump to safety on board a boat alongside. The barge would then go down, taking the prisoners with it. Anyone attempting to escape drowning would be sabred.

At first this form of execution was reserved for clerics and was known as a 'republican baptism'. Later the 'national bath' was more widely used. Prisoners were often stripped of their clothes first. Young men and young women were sometimes tied together naked and given a 'republican marriage'.

The revolutionary army spread out across the country, looking for sedition. They would slaughter men, women and children they suspected of harbouring anti-Jacobin sympathies. Crops were burned, farm animals slaughtered, barns and cottages demolished and woods torched; any town or village that had entertained anti-Jacobin troops would be razed.

Terrorists planned to put arsenic in wells and enquiries were made of a well-known chemist about the possibility of developing poison gas.

Next, 12 infernal columns were sent to 'pacify' the countryside by killing everyone in their path. Women were raped, children killed, both mutilated. Entire families were found swimming in their own blood: one impeccable republican lost three of his sons plus his son-in-law on the first visit of the Jacobins. They returned to massacre his remaining son, his wife and their 15-year-old daughter. To save ammunition, General Cordeiller ordered his men to use the sabre instead of a gun.

At Gonnord, General Crouzat forced 200 elderly people, along with mothers and children, to kneel in front of a pit they had dug; they were shot so that they fell into the grave. Some tried to make a break for it, but were struck down by the hammer of a local mason – 30 children and two women were buried alive when earth was shovelled into the pit.

In the Loire Valley, around 250,000 people were killed –a third of the population of the region – and that figure does not include those who lost their lives in the revolution or during the subsequent wars, fighting on the republican side.

In Paris, thanks to the Law of Suspects, the prisons were full to overflowing – the rich were made to pay for their board and lodging – the guillotine was being overworked too. A prostitute was executed for expressing royalist sentiments – trade had dropped off after the Revolution. Following her to the scaffold was the one-time playmate of Mozart, Marie-Antoinette, Queen of France. When one prisoner stabbed himself to death in front of the Revolutionary Tribunal, the court ordered that his corpse be guillotined anyway – revolutionary justice was not to be cheated.

The Revolution then began to consume its own. Anyone who opposed Robespierre was sentenced to 'look through the republican window' – that is, put his head through the frame of the guillotine. When the great hero of the Revolution, Georges Danton, tried to call a halt to the Terror, he too was arrested and sent to be ,shaved by the national razor,. Entire families were guillotined, the older members being forced to watch the younger being executed while awaiting their turn.

Robespierre was a prig. He saw himself as a missionary of virtue and believed he was using the guillotine as an instrument for the moral improvement of the nation. The dechristianisers, whom Robespierre viewed as immoral, paid for his views with their lives. He then instituted the Festival of the Supreme Being, in which he took the leading role. This was not a return to believing in God, he explained: nature was the 'Supreme Being'. However, many people wondered whether Robespierre really thought the Supreme Being was himself.

The new crimes of 'slandering patriotism, 'seeking to inspire discouragement', 'spreading false news', 'depraving morals', 'corrupting the public conscience' and 'impairing the purity and energy of the revolutionary government' were introduced. To speed up the course of justice, those accused were allowed no defence counsel and no witnesses would be called. The jury was made up of good citizens who were more than capable of coming to a fair and unbiased judgement without being distracted by such trifles. There were only two outcomes: acquittal or death. Given that Robespierre himself coined the slogan, 'Clemency is parricide,' this usually meant death. Executions jumped from five a day in the new revolutionary month of Germinal to 26 in Messidor.

However, things had been going well for the French army and the danger from abroad had eased. Some Republicans began to doubt the need for such Draconian measures. Anyone against this new Revolutionary Justice must have something to hide, Robespierre argued, and promptly investigated them. He was so busy organising the persecution he did not realise that, behind his back, leading Revolutionaries were mocking his cult of the Supreme Being.

On 26 July 1794 (8 Thermidor, Year III), Robespierre made a speech calling for 'more virtue' and his supporters called for his enemies to be sent '*à la guillotine*'. The next day, critics pointed out that Robespierre had departed from protocol: instead of speaking for the collective leadership, he had made a speech in his own name. Robespierre was lost for words at this accusation. In the silence a voice piped up, 'See, the blood of Danton chokes him.'

Quickly, his opponents moved against him. They knew if they did not, they would soon face the guillotine. Robespierre and his supporters were arrested. He could hardly ask for clemency. After a failed suicide attempt which left him bloodied, and his jaw shattered, Robespierre and 17 of his followers were guillotined. A fastidious little man, he went to the scaffold covered in blood. To give the blade an unimpeded fall, the executioner pulled off the paper bandage that was holding his jaw together. He yelped in pain, only to be silence by the falling blade.

During the Reign of Terror, over and above those who were slaughtered in the countryside, at least 300,000 people were arrested; 17,000 were officially executed. Many more died in prison or without trial.

7 ❖ Wounded Knee

The battle of Wounded Knee was the last battle of the Indian – that is, Native American – Wars. But it was not so much a battle as a massacre. The descendants of the Pilgrim Fathers and others wishing to live out their manifest destiny say that the US Cavalry went to Wounded Knee on 29 December 1890 to talk, not to fight. To them, the fact that 84 Sioux men and 62 Sioux women and children ended up dead was a tragedy; to the Indians it was an atrocity.

Wounded Knee was essentially the Cavalry's revenge for the Battle of the Little Big Horn, where General Custer and his entire command of 264 men had been wiped out by the Sioux. It had happened just a few days before 4 July 1876, the 100th anniversary of American Independence. That America's finest could be defeated by what the American people saw as a bunch of savages was a shock. Everyone clamoured for vengeance – the young nation's honour was at stake.

A few days later, Buffalo Bill shot down Chief Yellow Hand, taking 'the first scalp for Custer' and earning a considerable amount of fame into the bargain. Then General Miles began a winter campaign against the Indians. Rather than return to the reservation, the Sioux chief Sitting Bull fled to Canada. But Crazy Horse, who was low on supplies, led a procession of 800 braves into Fort Robinson, Nebraska, in an effort to save his people from starvation.

Crazy Horse had been one of the greatest Indian warriors and he found it difficult to adjust to life on the reservation. He did not trust the whites, who he thought were so evil that they would soon try to imprison the grass behind fences.

General Crook admired Crazy Horse and invited him to scout for him against his enemies the Nez Percé. It was a simply a strategy of divide and rule. Crazy Horse was keen: he sent word that he would fight until all the Nez Percé were dead. However, the message got distorted into an avowal to fight until all the whites were dead. The mix-up was straightened out, but afterwards the Cavalry found it impossible to trust him.

Crazy Horse's young wife died and he became increasingly restive. On the reservations, he found that jealous tribesmen spied on him and reported his every move to the authorities. He planned to leave but was first persuaded to attend a conference at Fort Robinson. Crazy Horse was on his guard – only the year before Sioux leaders had been murdered at Fort Keogh in Montana. When he arrived at the fort, Crazy Horse was informed that he would have to be locked in the guardhouse. He went for his weapons but even his own warriors tried to restrain him. In the resulting scuffle, a soldier stabbed him with a bayonet for 'resisting arrest'. He died that night.

In 1881, Sitting Bull returned to the United States and surrendered; but his warriors settled down to reservation life no better than Crazy Horse's followers. Then in 1888, the Ghost Dance came. A prophet named Wovoka who lived in the Nevada desert had had scarlet fever, which made him delirious. During a total eclipse of the sun he spoke with the Creator, who told him that the Indians had not come to the end of their trail. What they must do, the Creator said, was put aside the weapons of war and love one another. That way, they would have a special place in the afterlife. To herald the Judgement Day and the end of the world as they knew it, the Creator gave them the Ghost Dance, which had to be performed on five successive nights. The more often they did it, the sooner the Judgement Day would come.

By the time the Ghost Dance reached the Sioux, its prophecy had changed slightly. At Judgement Day, the suffering earth would die and with it, all the races of man. The whites, if they were reincarnated at all, would be reborn into a different world. But the Indians would be born back into the world of grasslands and buffalo, as it had been before the white man had come along. All the red people who had ever lived would be reborn in the flower of their youth, and heaven and earth would once again be in joyous harmony. When the Sioux danced the Ghost Dance, they chanted, 'We will live again.'

Soon 6000 Sioux were doing the Ghost Dance. As it seemed the one sure way to get rid of the whites, they danced until they dropped. This worried the Indian agents who did not understand that the Ghost Dance was a religious revival. They thought it was a new war dance. The US military grew nervous: they banned the Ghost Dance and sent more troops to the reservations.

The agents received word that some of the medicine men were making Ghost shirts which they said no bullet could penetrate. Most frighteningly

Dead bodies litter the ground on the battlefield of 'Wounded Knee' in South Dakota, USA.

of all, it was said that Sitting Bull was going to the Pine Ridge reservation in South Dakota, where he too would perform the Ghost Dance.

Sitting Bull was now 56 years old and a proud man. The Indian Bureau had tried to break his spirit by withholding his rations. In response, Sitting Bull showed his contempt for the bureau by refusing to report to the agents. The US military feared his strength and not without good reason – the Indians attributed their victory at Little Bighorn to Sitting Bull's Sun Dance. During that dance he had cut 50 pieces of flesh off various parts of his body. In the trance induced by this self-torture, he saw US soldiers falling from the skies into his camp like grasshoppers.

The authorities need not have worried. Having travelled widely with the Buffalo Bill Wild West Show, Sitting Bull had seen just how numerous the whites were and he knew that military victory against them was impossible. He wanted to explore the Ghost Dance for religious rather than political reasons. However, other Indians believed that after Sitting Bull danced the Ghost Dance the Sioux would have an even greater victory than the Little Bighorn. This could not be allowed.

Indian police were sent to Sitting Bull's house to prevent him going to Pine Ridge. They found the house unguarded and its occupant asleep. Sitting Bull was willing to go with them peacefully, but soon his followers gathered, warning him not to go. Some called him a coward. His 17-year-old son begged him to resist: he should remember what had happened to Crazy Horse. Suddenly, he refused to go. Everyone went for their guns – when the shooting stopped, Sitting Bull and his son were among the dead.

The news spread like a prairie fire. Fearing they would be massacred on the reservation, Sitting Bull's men fled, intending hide in the Bad Lands of Dakota. On the way they ran into Big Foot, who was returning to the agency for supplies with a troop of 100 ill and ageing warriors. Big Foot himself had pneumonia and was so ill he could not ride a horse. While they were talking, a cavalry troop under Colonel Forsyth caught up with them. Big Foot raised a white flag for a parley, but Forsyth insisted on his unconditional surrender and escorted his prisoner to the post office near a small stream called Wounded Knee Creek.

Forsyth called for reinforcements and soon nearly 500 men of the Seventh Cavalry – many of whom had been with Major Reno's party who had narrowly escaped the massacre at Little Bighorn – were guarding 350 sick and hungry Indians: 120 men and 230 women and children. There was no hope of escape, as the cavalry stationed men with machine-guns on the heights above the camp.

On 29 December, the order came to disarm the Indians. At a little past eight in the morning, the men and grown boys were called to a council. They sat in a semi-circle to the south of Big Foot's tent. Forsyth made a speech that was translated into their language, Lakotah. He said that they were safe now; the soldiers were their friends; they would be bringing more food and no one would go hungry. However, there had been trouble recently and to prevent any fighting starting accidentally, he was asking for their guns.

For the Indians, a gun was a symbol of manhood. As hunters, they needed them to survive, and they had heard of Indians handing over their guns only to be shot once they were disarmed. Two men went to confer with Big Foot, who told them to hand over their old weapons, but to keep the good ones.

The Indians handed over just two old rifles, claiming that was all they had. The soldiers did not believe them. Earlier, when they had caught up with the fleeing Indians, they had plenty of guns. Big Foot, who was bleeding from the nose, was brought outside and ordered to tell his braves to co-operate. He insisted they had no guns.

'The soldiers at Cheyenne River took them all away from us and burned them,' he told Forsyth. This was not true and Forsyth knew it.

'You tell Big Foot that yesterday at the time of his surrender his Indians were well armed,' Forsyth commanded his interpreter.

Big Foot stuck to his story and Forsyth ordered a search of the entire camp. Officers were sent to scour the tents and were told to use the utmost tact. Enlisted men were to search the outside area. They were not well disciplined and started tipping the contents of the Indians' wagons on the ground. They ripped open packs and took axes, hatchets, butchers' knives, and women's quilting awls – anything that could conceivably be used as a weapon.

The Indians understandably were tense and the situation got worse when the officers began searching the women, several of whom were hiding rifles under their skirts. Although this encounter passed without incident, the young men grew restless.

Yellow Bird, the medicine man, began to pray that their Ghost shirts would protect them. Then he began to dance. Something bad was about to happen, he said. There were many soldiers and many bullets, but the bullets would not hurt those wearing the Ghost shirts. He threw a cloud of dust in the air, saying that was how ineffective the bluecoats' bullets would be as the dust drifted away in the breeze. Besides, he said, 'I have lived long enough' – a traditional Sioux war cry. Forsyth ordered him to sit down.

By 9.30, the Cavalry had found 38 rifles, but only a few of them were good Winchesters; the rest were old and useless. The day before, the Indians had been armed to the teeth with good rifles. If they were not in the tents and not under the women's skirts, Forsyth reasoned, then the men must have them concealed under their blankets.

At that moment, Forsyth spotted an Indian with a rifle under his blanket and ordered a sergeant to seize it. Through an interpreter, he told the Indians they must hand over their rifles if they did not want to undergo the indignity of being searched.

About 20 older men came forward and opened their blankets to show they were unarmed. However, Yellow Bird started chanting again and the younger men held back. Major Whitside roughly ordered them to step forward. Some reluctantly did so. They did have rifles under their blankets.

Seeing the rifles being taken away, a young deaf troublemaker called Black Coyote leapt to his feet. He pulled a Winchester from under his blanket and waved it in the air, saying that he had given much money for his gun and was not going to give it up unless he got paid. While Yellow Bird chanted, another medicine man started singing a Ghost song and the other young men began to move away.

Tension grew. Forsyth tried to get one of the elders to calm the situation down. Black Coyote was trying to roll a cigarette; while he was distracted, two Cavalry sergeants tried to grab his gun. There was a scuffle; the gun pointed skywards and went off. At that precise moment, Yellow Bird threw another handful of dust in the air. The young braves took this as a sign, throwing off their blankets and levelling their guns; they were cut down by gunfire.

Big Foot caught a bullet in the head. Seeing her father fall, his daughter ran towards him. She was shot in the back and fell across him. Being badly deployed, as well as killing the Indians, the Cavalry hit each other in the crossfire.

The machine-guns on the ridge opened up, pumping explosive shells into the Indians' writhing bodies at a rate of 50 bullets a minute. It was reckoned that half the casualties occurred within the first minute. Survivors threw themselves on soldiers using knives, clubs, fists and teeth; but within two or three minutes the situation was impossible and the remainder fled. Once they were clear of the troops, the slaughter began in earnest. Fleeing Indians were simply gunned down; the explosive bullets set the tents on fire; a party of men, women and children trying to escape down the road to the south were slaughtered.

The remaining Indians tried to shelter in a ravine, but were shelled and cut to pieces by shrapnel.

Back in the camp, a young trooper saw an Indian disappear into a tent. Before anyone could stop him, he charged in too. A shot rang out.

'My God,' he screamed. 'I'm killed.'

The rest of his troops raked the tent with gunfire, then set it alight. When the burning canvas fell away, it revealed Yellow Bird, still defiant.

Some Indians escaped the ravine, but were caught up with later. Dead bodies were found up to two miles away. Survivors reported that women and children were enticed from hiding places in rocks only to be abused and murdered.

Outraged by what had happened, the Indians in the ravine came out guns blazing. One Indian bullet struck artillery Lieutenant Hawthorne who was up on the ridge. The bullet hit his pocket watch, which saved his life, but the workings of the watch were scattered throughout his body and five operations were required to remove them all.

The Indians' last stand was futile; they were shot down like dogs. When the guns eventually fell silent, any Indians remaining alive were told to come out – they would not be harmed. When a wounded man staggered out, he was shot. Colonel Forsyth then stepped in and ordered no further shooting.

The injured were taken to a field hospital. There were 51 Indians, 37 soldiers and two civilians – an interpreter who had had his nose cut off and a priest – wounded. The bluecoats had lost 25, largely as a result of 'friendly fire'. The Indians had lost 146 and the troopers proudly boasted that they had avenged Custer.

8 ❖ King Leopold and the Congo

Belgium was only established as a nation in 1831, so it was a late starter in the imperialist race. Nevertheless, its second king, Leopold II, was an ambitious man. Like the rest of Europe, he turned his eyes to Africa. He paid Henry Morton Stanley – the rescuer of Dr Livingston – to explore the Congo, which led to the establishment of the Congo Free State, under the sovereignty of Leopold, in 1885. However, reports of the atrocities committed in Leopold's name there appalled the world and forced him to hand over the Congo in 1908.

The Congo was rich in ivory, but even richer in 'black ivory' – slaves. Although the British had outlawed slavery in 1833 and put the Royal Navy in the Atlantic to stop the western trade, trade to the east still flourished. Indeed, slavery was only outlawed in the Arabian Peninsular in 1970.

Although Leopold publicly issued great anti-slavery edicts, he was playing a double game. He made Tippu Tip, a slave trader from Zanzibar, governor of the Congo's eastern province. At the same time, he also bought the 'freedom' of several thousand of Tippu Tip's slaves and press-ganged them into the Force Publique, the Congo's militia, where they remained, essentially, slaves. They were then used to enslave the rest of the population.

We have an eyewitness account of what it was like to be taken into slavery by Leopold's men. It comes from a woman named Ilanga and was recorded by an American who published it at the turn of the century. Ilanga told him, 'Our village is called Waniendo, after our chief Niendo . . . It is a large village near a small stream, and is surrounded by large fields of cassava, maize and other foods. We all worked hard in the fields and we always had plenty to eat . . . We never had war in our country, and the men did not have many weapons except knives . . .

'We were all busy in the fields hoeing, as it was the rainy season when the weeds sprang up quickly, when a runner came to the village saying that a large band of men was coming. They all wore red caps and blue cloth, and carried guns and long knives. Many white men were with them and their chief was Kibalanga.'

This was the African name for the Force Publique officer Oscar Michaux, who had been decorated personally by King Leopold. Niendo called the elders to his house, while drums were beaten to summon the people back to the village. They discussed the matter for a long time. Eventually it was decided that the people should go back to the fields and bring groundnuts, plantains and cassava for the soldiers who were coming, and goats and chickens for the white men. The women went out with baskets, filled them and put them by the road. Niendo thought that, by giving the visitors a lot of food, they might pass by without harming his people.

'And so it proved to be,' said Ilanga. 'When the white men and their warriors had gone, we went again to our work, and were hoping they would not return. But, a short time later, they did. As before, we brought them great heaps of food, but this time Kibalanga did not move away immediately. He camped near our village, and his soldiers came and stole our fowls and goats and tore up our cassava. But we did not mind that as long as they did not harm us.

'Next morning, soon after the sun rose over the hill, a large band of soldiers came to the village, and we all went into the houses and sat down. We were not seated long when the soldiers came rushing in shouting and threatening Niendo with their guns. They ran into the houses and dragged the people out. Three or four came to our house and caught hold of me, my husband Oleka and my sister Katinga. We were all crying, for we knew that we were to be taken away as slaves. The soldiers beat us with the iron sticks from their guns and forced us to march to the camp of Kibalanga. He

King Leopold II of Belgium.

ordered the women to be tied up, ten to each cord. The men were tied up the same way, separately. When we were all collected – there were many from other villages we did not know, and many from Waniendo – the soldiers brought baskets of food for us to carry, some of which contained smoked human flesh . . .

We then set off marching very quickly. My sister Katinga had her baby in her arms, and was not forced to carry a basket. But my husband Oleka was made to carry a goat. We marched until the afternoon, when we camped near a stream. We were glad to be able to have a drink there because we were very thirsty. But the soldiers gave us nothing to eat . . . The next day we continued the march, and when we camped at noon were given some maize and plantains, which had been taken from near a deserted village – the people had run away. It continued like this for five days. Then the soldiers took my sister's baby and threw it on the grass, leaving it to die, and made her carry some cooking pots that they had found in a deserted village. On the sixth day we became very weak from lack of food and from constant marching and from sleeping on damp grass. My husband, who marched behind with a goat, could not stand up any longer. So he sat down beside the path and refused to walk any more. The soldiers beat him, but still he refused to move. Then one of them struck him on the head with the butt of his rifle and he sprawled on the ground. One of the soldiers caught the goat, while two or three others stuck the long knives they put on the end of their guns into my husband. I saw blood spurt out, and then saw him no more. We had passed over the brow of a hill and he was out of sight. Many of the young men were killed in the same way . . . After marching for ten days, we came to the great water . . . and were taken in canoes across to the white men's town at Nyangwe.'

Later Leopold ordered that the children should be separated from their parents and organised into three children's colonies where they would be taught Christianity and be trained as soldiers. But the missionaries and the colonies said that they should only take orphans. The Force Publique took this as an excuse to butcher their parents then force march the children to the colonies. Thousands perished: of a column of 108 boys on a forced march to a state colony at Boma in 1892, only 62 made it to their destination. And eight of them died in the next few weeks. The colonies themselves were rife with disease and their mortality rate was 50 per cent. Still, some survived to make soldiers.

In 1839, American inventor Charles Goodyear accidentally spilt sulphur onto some hot rubber on his stove. The result was a substance that did not turn stiff when it was cold or go gooey and smelly when it was hot – both of which had been major problems for the manufactures of rubber boots and coats. Then in 1885, John Dunlop fitted a pneumatic tyre to his son's tricycle wheel. His new company set off the craze for bicycles and he had developed the tyre just in time for the coming of the automobile.

Rubber was not just needed for car tyres, but also tubing, hoses and gaskets. And the new telegraph, telephone and electrical companies needed rubber for insulation. In the 1890s, therefore, there was a rubber boom – and the Congo was full of wild rubber, which came from vines, rather than trees. However, it would need vast manpower to harvest it.

Collecting the rubber from vines was an arduous business. Labourers would have to stay in the flooding forests for days on end. The sap from the vines had to be coagulated; this was done by spreading it on the arms and chest until it hardened. When it was ripped off, it took the body hair with it. Needless to say, this was painful; no amount of trinkets could induce the Africans to do it. What is more, as the job had to be done out in the jungle, one could not simply shackle a bunch of men and set them to work under an overseer.

More brutal methods had to be adopted. The British vice consul in 1899 explained, 'The Force Publique would arrive in canoes at a village, the inhabitants of which invariably bolted on their arrival. The soldiers were then landed, and commenced looting, taking all the chickens, grain, etc., out of the houses. After this they attacked the natives until able to seize their women. These women were kept as hostages until the chief of the district brought the required number of kilograms of rubber. The rubber having been brought, the women were sold back to their owners for a couple of goats apiece, and so [they] continued from village to village.'

The wife of any man refusing to collect rubber would be killed. She might die anyway as the conditions were harsh and food scarce in the stockades where they were held. The soldiers guarding the women would take the prettiest and rape them.

Although hostage taking was not a policy announced in Brussels, this method of collecting rubber is recommended by the official manuals handed out in Africa. Once the system got going, every village was assigned a quota. This was usually three to four kilos of dried rubber per adult male per fortnight, which essentially meant full-time work for the men. Not only was this barbaric, it was self-defeating – instead of tapping the vine so that it continued to live, the collectors tore down the vine in the scramble to make the quotas.

Hundreds of thousands of men were conscripted in this way. They were overseen by the Force Publique who built garrisons throughout the rubber-growing areas. Men had to carry their heavy load of rubber for miles to deliver it to the company agents. They would get paid in trinkets or a few spoonfuls of salt. One chief was paid in people: he was told he could eat them, kill them, or use them as slaves – anything he liked.

When a village resisted, the Force Publique would be employed to ter-rorise them. Ten hostages would be taken, tied up in a tent with big stones and pushed in a river. The women would then be raped. Sometimes, the Force Publique would simply shoot everyone in order to intimidate other villages. However, the Force Publique were strict with their ammunition. They did not want their troops to go wasting it on hunting or shooting for recreation. So for every bullet they were issued, the soldiers would have to return one right hand. Sometimes, when a man did a little hunting and shot an animal, he would cut off the hand of a living man.

In 1894, one Belgian officer, Léon Fiévez, explained what he did when the local villages failed to supply his troops with what he demanded. 'One example was enough; 100 heads cut off, and there have been plenty of sup-plies around the station ever since,' he said. 'My goal is ultimately human-itarian. I killed 100 people . . . but allowed 500 others to live.'

Leopold was ambitious for the Congo. He wanted to open the country up and planned to build a railway. Of the 540 Chinese construction work-ers brought in from Hong Kong and Macao in 1892, 300 died on the job or ran away into the forests. Several hundred workers came in from Barba-dos, thinking they were being taken somewhere else. When they realised they were in the Congo, they rioted, at which point the soldiers opened fire on them. The survivors were taken to the railhead and put to work.

Tropical diseases, lack of food, no shelter, relentless floggings, engines that ran off the track and boxcars full of dynamite that exploded, cost the lives of nearly 2000 men in the eight-year construction of the first stretch of track.

Missionaries who had seen Africans slaughtered and piles of severed hands began publishing articles in the European papers. Leopold asked the heads of the missionary societies to come and talk to him instead, as deal-ing with the press with was 'toujours désagréable'. However, the missionar-ies persisted.

In 1897, a Swedish Baptist missionary told a meeting in London that Force Publique soldiers were actually rewarded for the number of hands they brought in. Some said they were paid money. Another soldier told him, 'The Commissioner has promised us if we have plenty of hands he will shorten our service. I have bought in plenty of hands already, and I expect my time of service will soon be finished.'

The British press was already gunning for Leopold. In 1895, a Belgian officer had 'dared to kill an Englishman' – actually, the victim was an Irishman who had 'gone native' and married an African woman. His ivory business challenged Leopold's monopoly, so the Force Publique was sent in. They hanged the Briton and the London press howled in outrage.

Leopold countered the bad press he was getting by creating a Commission for the Protection of the Natives, comprising six Belgian Catholics and six foreign missionaries. It was a public relations coup. Universally greeted as a good thing, Leopold had cleverly picked commissioners who lived so far apart that the commission only met twice and then only three members attended.

The world's fair took place in Brussels in 1897. The Belgian exhibit included 267 Africans brought from the Congo. They were depicted as living happily in an African village set up for them in a park in Brussels. Just to make sure they were happy, 90 of them were members of the Force Publique. At a gala dinner, a black sergeant proposed a toast to King Leopold.

As the vines died, the Africans found it increasingly difficult to fulfil their quotas which, in any case, were always being raised. The Budja tribe rebelled, killing 30 soldiers, then fled. A punitive expedition was sent against them, led by an American rubber agent named Edgar Canisius. 'As our party moved through village after village, a party of men had been detailed with torches to fire every hut,' he wrote. 'As we progressed, a line of smoke hung over the jungle for many miles, announcing to the natives far and wide that civilisation was dawning.'

Under Canisius's command were 50 soldiers and 30 porters carrying their supplies.

'We marched though native clearings, where the trunks of large trees lay by hundreds across our path,' he said. 'Over these we had to climb, the trail seeming to lead to the top of every high anthill within range. The porters had an especially hard time, for many of them were chained together by the neck. They carried out boxes slung on poles, and when one fell down he usually brought down all his companions on the same chain. Many of the poor wretches became so exhausted by this kind of marching that they could be urged forward only by blows from the butt-ends of rifles. Some had their shoulders so chafed by the poles that they literally shrieked with pain.'

By the time he caught up with the Budjas, the porters were done for so his prisoners had to take over. 'All were compelled to carry heavy loads, each of which had previously required two men to transport . . . until they finally succumbed to starvation and smallpox.'

This process took too long though and, as the fighting grew worse, Canisius's men began shooting their prisoners, 30 at a time. Summing up the campaign, Canisius said, 'We had undergone six weeks of painful marching and had killed over 900 native men, women and children.' And why? For the prospect of 'adding fully 20 tons of rubber to the monthly crop.'

Roger Casement, the Irish nationalist later executed for treason, was at that time working for the Foreign Office. He was sent to the Congo as consul and reported back on the brutalities he had witnessed. He discovered that soldiers did not just cut off the hands of their victims: when accused of killing only women, they castrated their victims to prove otherwise.

Casement's reports provoke a debate in Parliament, but when this did not move the matter on as he had hoped, Casement went public. Newspapers across Europe began reporting the atrocities in the Congo. Stories emerged of mass murder, where entire villages and towns had been wiped out, brutal beatings, mutilations, rapes, mass starvation and epidemics of smallpox and other diseases the whites had brought. In all, ten million people died as a result of Leopold's reign.

The situation looked so dire that show trials of particularly brutal Belgian rubber agents were staged in the Congo. Their defence was that the natives were lazy; how else, without terror tactics, were they to be made to work? Most were acquitted. Those found guilty escaped with light sentences.

The king of the Belgians seemed to be riding out the storm, until the 65-year-old Leopold took up with a 16-year-old prostitute. She was the love of his life, but she cost him the love of his people and made him a ridiculous figure in the eyes of the world, especially when he took her with him to Queen Victoria's funeral in 1901.

Social reformer Edmund Morel set up the Congo Reform Association with branches throughout the United Kingdom. Even Sunday members would be regaled with reports of atrocities received from eyewitnesses. This one came from a missionary, the Reverend John Harris. 'Lined up were 40 emaciated sons of an African village, each carrying his little basket of rubber. The toll of rubber is weighed and accepted, but four baskets were short of the demand. The order is brutally short and sharp. Quickly the first defaulter is seized by four lusty executioners, thrown on the bare ground, pinioned hands and feet, whilst a fifth steps forward carrying a long whip of twisted hippo hide. Swiftly and with cessation the whip falls, and the sharp corrugated edges cut deep into the flesh – on back, shoulders and buttocks blood spurts from a dozen places. In vain the victim twists in the grip of the executioners, and then the whip cuts other parts of the quivering body – and in the case of one of the four, upon the most sensitive parts of the human frame. The 100 lashes each left four inert bodies bloody and quivering on the shimmering sand of the rubber collecting point.

'Following hard upon this decisive incident was another. Breakfast was just finished when an African father rushed up the veranda steps of our mud house and laid upon the ground the hand and foot of his little daughter, whose age could not have been more than five years.'

Morel took his campaign to the US, where Leopold paid lobbyists in Washington to defend his case. But when one was discovered trying bribe members of Congress, atrocities in the Congo began to make the front pages.

To try and stem the tide of criticism, Leopold set up a new Commission of Enquiry with three judges – one Belgian, one Swiss, one Italian. Again, he picked shrewdly: the judges knew no African languages, nor did they speak enough English to talk to the highly critical British and American missionaries who were leading the international campaign. Moreover, the Italian, Baron Giacomo Nisco, had been chief judge in the Congo. He was convinced of the need for stern discipline and had let off Belgian officers found guilty of atrocities with light sentences.

Nevertheless, the evidence collected was so overwhelming it could not be ignored. They collected 370 depositions, one from Chief Lontulu of Bolima, who had been flogged, held hostage and set to work in chains. He laid on the table of the commission 110 twigs, one for each of his tribe who had been murdered in the quest for rubber. He divided the twigs into four piles – one for tribal nobles, one for men, one for women and one for children. Then he put a name to each of the twigs.

The testimony of Chief Lontulu and the other witnesses was so damning that the governor-general, the man nominally responsible for the system, slit his throat. During the account of one atrocity one of the judges broke down and wept.

The commissioners returned to Europe and wrote their report. It was damning, but Leopold still had one trick up his sleeve. The day before the report was published every major newspaper in England got a document purporting to be a 'complete and authentic résumé of the report'. It came from the West African Missionary Association. The newspapers were delighted. Not only did it give them a one-day jump on the big story of the week, but also it was in English. Associated Press sent it on to the US.

However, when the report itself came out, the papers realised that they had been tricked – the summary was nowhere near as damning as the report itself. They then discovered that the West African Missionary Association did not actually exist and the 'summary' had been delivered by a Belgian priest whose church had recently been given a large donation by Leopold.

The full report detailed one atrocity after another – fatal beatings, random killings, senseless acts of cruelty. One woman who was making bricks had clay forced into her vagina by the overseer. All the Belgian agent said was, 'If you die working for me, they'll throw you in the river.' There was page after page after page on the severing of hands.

Nobody could doubt the authenticity of the evidence: there were numerous witnesses to each atrocity and the witnesses had risked their lives giving testimony to the commission. One man reported that, when he and a companion had been on their way to testify, they had been seized by a Belgian officer and hung from a tree for several days. Then they were beaten around the neck and private parts with a stick. His companion died and his body was thrown in the river.

Britain and the US began to put pressure on the Belgian government, but they did not own the Congo – Leopold did. They attempted to buy it from him. During the negotiations, they asked to see the balance sheets. When government auditors examined the books, they discovered that the 32 million francs the government had lent Leopold were missing. They suspected he had given the money to his teenage mistress. The money was written off along with 110 million francs-worth of debt, much of it in the form of bonds given to Leopold's teenage mistress and the king's other lovers. Moreover, Leopold received another 100 million francs in compensation; but his atrocity-studded rule in the Congo was over.

9 ❖ The Death of the Romanovs

The Romanovs had ruled Russia for 400 years. By the end of the nineteenth century, their empire stretched from the borders of Poland to the Sea of Japan. But even that was not enough for Nicholas II. He tried to extend his empire further in the east, aiming to seize China, Tibet and Persia. His ambitions were thwarted by defeat in the Russo-Japanese War of 1904–05.

This weakened him at home and he was forced to give up his autocratic power to become a constitutional monarch answerable, in theory, to a parliament or Duma. However, this did not suit him, so he allied himself with right-wing extremists and, in 1907, dissolved the Duma. His ambitions to extend his Empire into the Balkans led, in some measure, to World War I – though, when it broke out, he did try and stop the confrontation between the great powers. He took control of the war effort while his wife Alexandra handled domestic government. She fell under the influence of the mad monk Rasputin, who became so unpopular he was assassinated. Nicholas's mishandling of the war led to riots in 1917, following which, his government lost control in St Petersburg, then Russia's capital. Politicians from the Duma formed a provisional government. Meanwhile, Bolshevik workers and soldiers began to form themselves into committees known as Soviets.

The generals had lost confidence in Nicholas. When the Duma insisted that he abdicate, they concurred, seeing it as the only way to prevent civil war. On 15 March 1917, Nicholas abdicated in favour of his brother the Grand Duke Michael. The 13-year-old Tsarevich Aleksei was too young to take over and suffered from haemophilia. However, on 16 March, the Duma decided the formation of the Soviets meant that the continuation of the monarchy in any form was impossible and they persuaded Grand Duke Michael not to assume the throne.

On 21 March, Nicholas was arrested, as were Alexandra and the rest of the family. Although they were allowed to stay in their palace, they were guarded by soldiers, who had suffered because of Nicholas's incompetent leadership at the front.

The provisional government arranged for the Tsar and his family to go into exile in Britain. The British government agreed, but King George V, the Tsar's cousin, stepped in, asking how the Tsar intended to support himself in Britain. The socialist movement was strong in the UK; the war was dragging on and George feared giving sanctuary to the hated Tsar might bring the British monarchy down too.

In August, the provisional government moved the Tsar and his family to Tobolsk, a provincial backwater between the Urals and western Siberia. There they would be safe from the turbulent politics of St Petersburg.

The people in Tobolsk were courteous to the Romanovs, as were most of the troops that guarded them there. They would even play cards with Nicholas and the children. However, in November 1917, the royal family's fate was sealed when the Bolsheviks overthrew the provisional government. In January 1918, they closed the Duma, as they only controlled a quarter of the votes there. Furthermore, in March, they signed a peace treaty with the Germans, ending Russia's involvement in World War I.

With no voice in the Duma, non-communists had no way to oppose Bolshevism. Civil war was therefore inevitable, and it broke out in spring 1918. The Bolsheviks had already shown they were ruthless. Many of them had suffered under Nicholas's repressive regime – it seemed unlikely that he could survive.

Bolshevism was not widespread in Siberia, except for in one place – Yekaterinburg – the capital of the 'Red Urals'. The Soviets there had nationalised the mines even before Moscow had fallen to the Bolsheviks. The Yekaterinburg commissars were determined that the Romanovs would not escape.

The party leadership in Moscow sent for the Tsar, but on his way there he was intercepted by an armed detachment of Bolsheviks from Yekaterinburg, who seized the royal family and took them there. They were greeted by a large crowd shouting insults and the Bolshevik authorities had to threaten the use of force before the crowd would let them through safely. The Romanovs were taken to a house that had been confiscated from a wealthy merchant called Ipatiev, which was now known as the House of Special Purpose. A number of royal aides were taken and shot on suspicion of being involved with counter-revolutionary plots to free the royal family from there.

Instead of being guarded by soldiers, the Romanovs were watched day and night by a special Red Guard recruited from the local factories. The

Tsar Nicholas II and his family as they sit on a rooftop. This picture was taken during their captivity from 1917–1918. Second on the left sits Anastasia, thought to be the only remaining survivor of the family.

Tsar and his family were not permitted to talk to their guards, who were rude and abusive and pilfered their belongings. Nicholas was denounced as a bloodsucker. Female members of the royal family were not allowed to the lavatory by themselves but had to be escorted by a male guard. The walls of the house were covered with lewd graffiti, a lot of it showing Rasputin and Alexandra having sex in various positions while Nicholas looked on. One piece of doggerel went:

Our Russian Tsar called Nick

Was dragged off the throne by his prick.

As the war against the counter-revolutionaries heated up, the language of Lenin and the other leading Bolsheviks turned increasingly to class war and violence. The words 'purge' and 'cleansing' were soon being used to justify murder. In Yekaterinburg, local anarchists demanded that the Bolsheviks hand over the Tsar so they could kill him. There was at least one-armed attempt to abduct Nicholas and assassinate him. After that, the anarchists were rounded up.

The Tsar received several letters from army officers who said that they were organising an escape. These may have been part of a plot that would allow the guards to kill the Romanovs while they were fleeing; but they built up the family's hopes. On more than one occasion, they stayed up all night fully clothed, believing they were about to be saved. Fearing that there may indeed be plots to free the Tsar, the deputy head of the Yekaterinburg Cheka – or secret police – Yalov Yurovsky, was appointed head of the Romanovs' guard. He was a convinced communist and a cruel man. He brought with him Grigori Nikulin, who Yurovsky described as his 'son' and who was certainly the executor of his will. Nikulin was an experienced killer; his first act when he arrived at the House of Special Purpose was to shoot Prince Dolgorukov, Nicholas's trusted aide-de-camp.

As soon as Yurovsky arrived, he fired the men who were pilfering from the Romanovs and brought in his own men from the Cheka. These men were not known to the locals and were referred to as Latvians, not surprising, as ethnic Latvians played an important role in the Cheka. In fact, they were Germans, Austrians, Hungarian Magyars and Russians. Discipline was tightened.

In Moscow, Lenin was making plans to put Nicholas on trial. He wanted the proceedings broadcast on radio across Russia, with Leon Trotsky as prosecutor. But things were turning against the Bolsheviks: many people saw their peace treaty with Germany as an act of treason – cowardly at the very least – and there began to be strikes against Bolshevik rule. Even the revolutionary writer Maxim Gorky was condemning Lenin and Trotsky for having betrayed socialism.

There were other threats too. Allied troops had arrived at Murmansk; the Japanese had taken Vladivostok and 30,000 Czech soldiers rebelled when the communists tried to disarm them. The Czech Legion moved eastwards down the trans-Siberian railway in the hope that ships would pick them up from Vladivostok and deliver them to the Western Front. They took Samara, while an anti-Bolshevik government was formed in Omsk. Yekaterinburg was midway between Samara and Omsk, and looked set to fall – a trial would now be impossible.

It is not known who gave the order for the execution. It could have come from the leadership in Moscow – the communists in Yekaterinburg still talked of arranging a trial, but that may have been a bluff. 'Trial' could simply have been a code word for 'execution'. Nevertheless, in the House of Special Purpose, preparations were made for the killings. An orthodox priest was allowed to visit the Romanovs; the family sang hymns together and prayed.

Yurovsky claimed that an order came at 6 p.m. on 16 July 1918 telling him to 'exterminate the Romanovs', though he said it came from Perm, not Moscow. Yurovsky was none too fussy, though. He already referred to his Cheka guards as 'the execution squad', and had told his chief of staff, P.Z. Medvedev, to bring revolvers that morning as he planned to execute the whole family that night.

The family was told that they were going to be moved so they should not go to bed that night. At 2 a.m., they were summoned to the basement – there was some disorder in the town and they would be safer down there.

Once they were safely in the basement, Yurovsky, Nikulin and ten other men entered. Yurovsky read a death warrant. The lorry that was going to carry away their bodies revved outside to cover the sound of shooting. Yurovsky pulled a revolver and shot the Tsar at point-blank range. With a second revolver he shot the Tsarevich Aleksei, who had just turned 14. The boy groaned in pain and Yurovsky emptied the rest of the bullets into him.

Alexandra and her four daughters fell to their knees while the other men opened up on them, although two Hungarians refused to shoot the women. The Tsar's doctor was also shot, along with his manservant Trup. The Tsarina's maid Demidova was not hit by the first volley, so the men came at her with bayonets which she sought to parry with a cushion. She died in agony. The children's spaniel, Jimmy, was also killed, his head smashed in with a rifle butt.

The Tsar's daughters did not die immediately – they had sewn valuable jewellery inside their corsets to give them money in case they escaped, and the bullets ricocheted off it, leaving the girls in agony. The political commissar, P.Z. Ermakov, stood on the arms of the Grand Duchess Anastasia and stabbed her repeatedly with a bayonet. During the 1930s, he was wheeled out as a hero of the revolution, a role model for Soviet youth.

The bodies were loaded onto the lorry and Ermakov took them to some mine shafts nearby. The drunken guards there stripped the Grand Duchesses to gloat over the young girls' naked bodies. When they burnt the women's clothes, to their surprise and delight, they found the jewellery. Then they threw the bodies down the mine, followed by grenades.

Yurovsky was furious when he discovered that the guards had told the whole town where the Tsar and his family lay buried. The White Russians would take Yekaterinburg in a matter of days and he had promised Moscow that the bodies would never be found.

The next night, Yurovsky went back to the mine shaft with his most trusted men and recovered the Romanovs' bodies. The plan was to dump them down another, deeper shaft; but the lorry got stuck in the mud on the way, so they buried them where they were. Just in case the Whites discovered the corpses, the bodies of the Tsarevich Aleksei and one of the women were buried separately. In addition, the faces of all the corpses were smashed and disfigured. This proved unnecessary and it was not until 1976 that anyone suspected where the Romanovs were buried.

Yurovsky reported to Moscow that the deed was done. However, the Bolsheviks only announced that Nicholas had been killed. Alexandra and Aleksei had been moved to a safe place, the official announcement said – the authorities were not sure how the people would react to the murder of women and children.

Immediately after the atrocity, witnesses came forward to say that Alexandra and her children were seen on a train on their way to Perm. More often, witnesses spoke of a young woman alone, clearly injured and traumatised. She was thought to be the Grand Duchess Anastasia. Soon after, reports said, she was arrested by the Cheka, raped and murdered. Nevertheless, several young women turned up in the West claiming to have been Anastasia, though none managed to substantiate her claim. A man claiming to be Aleksei and bearing some of the distinguishing marks of the Tsarevich turned up in Baghdad, but he soon disappeared into obscurity.

After the Tsar and his immediate family were murdered, the rest of their entourage, including their servants, who had remained behind at Tobolsk, were killed. The Grand Duke Michael had already been shot in Perm on 12 June; the rest of the Grand Ducal party had been taken to Alapayevsk where, on the day after the Tsar was killed, they too were murdered. They were taken by cart to nearby mine shafts and thrown in. The Grand Duke Sergius put up a fight and was shot dead first; the rest were thrown in alive. Afterwards, planks and dynamite were thrown in. When the bodies were recovered, they all had grave head wounds. Some died instantly, but some may have lived on for hours.

The Czechs captured Yekaterinburg on 25 July. Almost immediately, they found the charred remains of the Romanovs' clothes and other possessions, and began an investigation. They quickly concluded that the entire family had been massacred. Surprisingly, most of the perpetrators did not fare well at the hands of their comrades. 28 of the people involved in the murders were arrested by the Bolsheviks and five of them were executed by the Soviet government in September 1919 for their part in it.

10 ❖ Massacre at Amritsar

After the annexation of Bengal, British conquests in the subcontinent continued rapidly. The Hindu Marathas were defeated in 1818 and when the Sikh kingdom in the Punjab fell in 1849 the whole of the subcontinent was under the control of the British East India Company. Following the Indian Mutiny in 1857–58, the British government in London took over.

In the 1890s, thousands of Sikhs moved to the west coast of Canada and the United States looking for better jobs and higher wages. They faced a hostile reaction from white workers and the Canadian immigration laws hurt their pride. Inspired by the Irish struggle for Home Rule, they began to seek some way of freeing India from British domination.

During World War I, India rallied to the British cause in the hope that their loyalty would win political concessions. Indian Muslims were in two minds about the war, though: they were loyal to Britain, yet Britain was not just fighting Germany, but also the Ottoman Empire. The Sultan of Turkey was Caliph – head of Muslims worldwide – and he called a jihad, or holy war, against the British in India.

India sent millions of pounds to help the British war effort and the Sikhs, with their fearsome military tradition, sent fighting men. Although they made up only seven per cent of the population of India, over half the troops who volunteered came from the Punjab. When they returned from the war, they were changed men. They were not prepared to go back to being second class citizens in their own country.

A worldwide flu epidemic struck; there was a drought, which bought on a famine; plague and cholera broke out in several parts of India. Exhausted by the war, the British had neither the money nor the organisation to respond to such disasters.

In 1918, the British parliament rushed through legislation ending direct rule and giving India a limited form of self-government. However, instead of letting the Indian people decide things for themselves, government was put into the hands of the Imperial Legislative Council. Those organising 'criminal conspiracies connected with the revolutionary movements in India' were cracked down on. They could be arrested without a warrant, held without trial and, if tried, had no right of appeal. The Indian press was outraged, but despite protests from all quarters, the bill was enacted.

Mahatma Gandhi wrote to the viceroy informing him that he intended to start a campaign of civil disobedience. The government ignored him. The first protest day was to be 30 March 1919, but was later changed to 6 April. For 24 hours, no one would work; all shops, offices, factories and markets would be closed. People would fast, giving themselves over to discipline and self-purification, and attend public meetings.

In many places, people observed the first protest day on 30 March. In Delhi, the police tried to halt a procession, by opening fire. When a crowd gathered in front of the Town Hall, they opened fire again. Eight people were killed and many more wounded.

On 6 April, the whole of India was closed down. This time the police took no action and the day of protest remained peaceful.

The Punjab was ruled with an iron hand by Lieutenant-Governor Sir Michael O'Dwyer, who was fanatically opposed to political reform. He banned newspapers and excluded political leaders. During the war he had used press-gang techniques to recruit soldiers and he had little respect for the law. This caused enormous resentment. However, everything remained calm in the Punjab until the first week of April 1919.

On 29 March, a meeting was held at Jallianwala Bagh in Amritsar, which was the administrative centre of the Punjab. Home to the Golden Temple, Amritsar is a holy city and the centre of Sikhism. The Jallianwala Bagh was private property, held in common by a number of people. A walled rectangle about 250 yards long and 200 yards wide, it had once been a garden – and is again. But then it was open ground used for fairs and public meetings. The entrance was through a narrow lane which opened out onto a patch of raised ground that overlooked the rest of the Bagh.

Two local leaders spoke at the meeting. They said they had did not want to hurt the police as protesters did in Europe. To use violence, they said, was a moral degradation. Instead, they urged the crowd to follow Gandhi's dictum: 'Do not injure anyone but be ready to be injured.' The meeting went ahead without incident.

The following day, the whole of Amritsar was closed down and, in the afternoon, another meeting was held in the Jallianwala Bagh. It called for Hindu-Muslim unity, though once again the speakers urged the crowd to maintain the strategy of non-violence.

On 6 April, Amritsar was brought to a standstill for a second time. Muslims, Hindus and Sikhs all stayed away from work and 50,000 attended a protest meeting. The next day, Gandhi left Bombay for Delhi and Amritsar. He got as far as Palwal, where he was served with a written order banning him from Delhi and the Punjab; he was arrested and taken back to Bombay.

The Hindu festival of Ram Naumi was on 9 April. Muslims joined in as a gesture of solidarity. This worried the British, who had always used the Machiavellian tactic of 'divide and rule'. Observing the festivities, the Deputy Commissioner of Amritsar Miles Irving said, 'There will soon be a row here.'

Mohatma Gandhi with his wife. He was the Indian nationalist leader of the Indian National Congress's campaign of passive non-cooperation.

The following day, he invited the local leaders who had addressed the meetings at the Jallianwala Bagh to his bungalow, where they were arrested and thrown out of Amritsar. When news of the arrests spread through the city, a crowd marched on the Deputy Commissioner's house. They met numerous Europeans on the way, but harmed no one. The procession was stopped at a railway bridge that was guarded by the army. The protesters said that they only wanted to go to the Deputy Commissioner's house to lodge a protest. Despite the fact that they were unarmed, the soldiers opened fire and many people were killed and wounded.

The crowd returned to collect the bodies. This time they carried lathis or Indian quarterstaffs, but some lawyers tried to calm them. The Deputy Commissioner and the police gathered in force on the other side of the bridge. Some protesters threw stones at the police, who opened fire without warning.

The crowd scattered and rampaged through the city, some attacking the telegraph building. The telegraph master was dragged from his office and had to be rescued by the army. Rioters stormed the railway goods yard – the station superintendent was beaten up and barely escaped with his life. A guard was not so lucky and died on the spot. The manager and assistant manager of the National Bank were killed and the building was set on fire. The manager of the Alliance Bank was also killed; his bank and a local store were looted, and a lady missionary was knocked unconscious.

On 10 April, the Commissioner of the Lahore district, A.J.W. Kitchin arrived. He toured the city and reported back to the Lieutenant-Governor that the situation was beyond control. Miles Irving was told to hand control of the city over to the army. Brigadier-General Reginald Dyer, commander at Jullundur, took over; his first move was to arrest prominent Nationalists.

On 11 April, the people wanted a funeral procession to bury their dead. At first Dyer banned it, then let it proceed on the condition that it dispersed at 2 p.m. The procession went ahead, was peaceful and dispersed on time. Even so, Dyer cracked down all the harder on the city. The next day, he stationed armed men at strategic points throughout Amritsar and cut off water and electricity supplies.

Baisakhi, the Indian new year was on 13 April. To Sikhs it was even more significant: it was the day that Gobind Singh Ji – the tenth and last guru of Sikhism – found the Khalsa. This is the dominant order of Sikhism, with its familiar beards and turbans. It is the militant order, responsible for throwing off the tyranny of the Moguls. On 13 April, people from all over the Punjab flocked to Amritsar. Some 20,000 men, women and children assembled in the Jallianwala Bagh, but Dyer had issued a curfew and banned any procession.

'Any gathering of four men,' said the order, 'would be looked upon and treated as an unlawful assembly and dispersed by force of arms, if necessary.'

The proclamation was read out publicly, but not all parts of the city were covered and most people did not hear it.

At 4 p.m., General Dyer took a tour of the city to see if his order was being obeyed. He took with him an escort of 50 men – armed with rifles and kukris – and two armoured cars. Half the men were Gurkhas; the other half came from the 54th Sikh Frontier Force and the 59th Rifle Frontier Force. At about 5 p.m., he arrived at the Jallianwala Bagh. Seeing the public meeting there, he deployed 25 of his men to the left and 25 to the right.

The meeting was peaceful. Some local leaders were sitting on the stage; one of them was reading a poem. The huge crowd listened attentively.

Some saw the soldiers and began to panic. 'Don't be afraid,' said the speaker. 'The army is not going to fire on innocent people.'

But they were.

Without warning, Dyer gave the order to fire – he had been there just 30 seconds. The soldiers shot down the unarmed crowds, who were caught in a death trap. Dyer's men blocked the exit. Some people had the presence of mind to throw themselves flat on the ground. Others, in panic, ran this way and that and were cut down.

The Times correspondent Sir Valentine Chirol described the scene like this. 'One cannot possibly realise the frightfulness of it until one has actually looked upon the Jallianwala Bagh – a waste space frequently used for fairs and public meetings, about the size perhaps of Trafalgar Square, and closed in almost entirely by walls, above which rise the backs of native houses facing into the congested streets of the city. I entered by the narrow lane by which General Dyer entered with about 50 rifles. I stood on the same rising ground on which he stood when, without a word of warning, he opened fire at about 100 yards' range upon a dense crowd, collected mainly in the lower and more distant part of the enclosure around a platform from which speeches were being delivered. The crowd was estimated by him at 6,000, by others at 10,000 and more, practically unarmed, and all quite defenceless. The panic-stricken multitude broke at once but for ten consecutive minutes he kept up a merciless fusillade on that seething mass of humanity, caught like rats in the trap.'

The crowd broke into two. Dyer would order his men to fire on one group, then the other. Between fusillades, one could hear the low moaning of the wounded. In their effort to get away, the crowd converged, trampling each other; Dyer aimed fire at them. Men went down, others clambered over them. Some were hit again and again. In places the dead and wounded lay in heaps, so that those who were only wounded would find themselves buried beneath a dozen others.

Still the firing continued. Hundreds tried to scale the walls, at some placed just five feet high, at others seven feet or ten. They would run at them, trying to gain a hold on the smooth surface. Some almost reached the top when others, fighting to get away, pulled them down. The Jallianwala Bagh had turned from a peaceful meeting place into a screaming hell.

At the official enquiry, Dyer admitted that, as far as he knew, they had committed no crime. He claimed that he feared that his force would be attacked, though he had no information that a single individual was armed. They were going to use *lathis* he said; but no one saw anyone carrying them. Sergeant Anderson, Dyer's bodyguard, was certainly not afraid.

'I saw nothing to be afraid of,' he said. 'I had no fear that the crowd would come on us.'

The only reason Dyer's men stopped firing after ten minutes was because they had run out of ammunition: 1,650 rounds had been fired. Dyer told the inquiry, 'It was unlikely that a man shooting into the crowd would miss.'

If the passage had been wider, he said, he would have taken the armoured cars in. The fire had not been indiscriminate, he maintained. From time to time, he checked his fire and 'directed it upon places where the crowd was thickest'. He had made up his mind to punish the demonstrators for having assembled.

The fire was directed towards people who were running away and at those who were lying flat and posed no possible threat. 12 men trying to shelter behind a tree found themselves spotted by soldiers and cut down. There was a well in the Jallianwala Bagh and over 100 corpses were found down it. They had to be removed when the stink became unbearable.

At 5.15 p.m., Dyer ordered his men to shoulder their arms and march off. They left 381 corpses and another 16,000 wounded. 'The corpses were ten to 12 feet high in some places,' an eyewitness said.

That night the curfew was strictly enforced and 1000 wounded were left lying in the Jallianwala Bagh overnight. Asked why he had left the wounded to their own devices, Dyer said that he had done his duty and it was not his job to render aid. The wounded could go to hospital, he said. But they could not – he had imposed a curfew.

A number of women, many wives of the dead, defied the curfew and tended the wounded, but there were too few of them even to give water to all those who needed it. The next morning relatives removed the bodies, which were cremated five or six at a time. Other bodies lay out in the Jallianwala Bagh all the next day and were consumed by vultures and jackals.

Miles Irving was delighted. Once Dyer had fired on the mob, he said, 'the whole rebellion collapsed.'

Dyer had not finished his cruelty against the people. He declared Martial Law and instigated the infamous 'Crawling Order'. In the hours when Indians were allowed out of their houses, between six in the morning and eight at night, they had to crawl. This was enforced at bayonet point. People had not so much to crawl as to wriggle along on their bellies. Even the smallest offence was punished by flogging. Large numbers of people were arrested, tortured and humiliated, while special tribunals meted out summary justice.

The authorities cracked down right across the Punjab. Professors were arrested; students were forced to walk up to 16 miles a day for a roll call and children as young as five were made to salute the Union Jack; a marriage party was flogged; Hindus and Muslims were left handcuffed together; Indian's cars were confiscated; property was destroyed; along with crawling orders there were skipping orders. Aeroplanes and Lewis guns were employed against unarmed civilians.

Winston Churchill condemned these actions. The crawling order, he said, 'violated every canon of civilisation'. But, Churchill said, 'one treacherous fact stands out: the slaughter of nearly 400 . . . That is an episode which appears to me to be without precedent or parallel in the modern history of the British Empire.'

The authorities had tried to cover it up. One woman who lost her husband in the Jallianwala Bagh reported that constables had come to her house four months later and offered her 25,000 rupees if she would forget all about it. More money would be forthcoming later. She declined the offer, saying she would prefer to remember.

Churchill's condemnation in the House of Commons ensured that the atrocity at Amritsar could not be covered up. Many moderate Indians began to hanker for self-government. The massacre had shaken their belief in British 'fair play'. Although it took another 26 years and another word war – in which Indian troops, yet again, played a major part – before India gained its independence, the massacre in the Jallianwala Bagh sounded the death knell of the Raj.

The Jallianwala Bagh is now a place of pilgrimage. In 1997, during an official visit to India, the Queen went to Jallianwala Bagh and publicly apologised for what General Dyer had done there in her grandfather's name.

11 ❖ Guernica

Guernica is a small market town in the Basque country, 30 kilometres north-east of Bilbao in northern Spain. To the Basques it is a spiritual home. Their historic parliament building is there; and in its grounds there is an oak tree that is the symbol of Basque culture and independence. When the Spanish Civil War broke out in 1936, its 6,000 inhabitants stayed loyal to the Republican government, who promised the Basques self-government. By contrast, General Franco, whose Nationalist army invaded from Morocco, aimed to keep the whole of Spain under the direct control of Madrid.

Until the end of March 1937, the struggle for Spain centred on Madrid. The war seemed a long way away. Guernica was protected by three battalions of Basque troops and the inhabitants felt safe. However, fearing that Franco, their fascist brother, might lose, both Hitler and Mussolini secretly sent troops to help him. It was a way for the two dictators to give their men battle experience before the war that to them seemed inevitable. Along with 5000 ground troops, Hitler sent his Condor Legion. They were hand-picked airmen who would spearhead his revolutionary new strategy of *Blitzkrieg* that allowed him to overrun most of Western Europe in a matter of months.

It was the Legion's commander in Spain who persuaded Franco to begin a new offensive in the north. The mountains that separated the Basque country from the rest of the country would have made conventional warfare a long and tedious process. Guns would have to be manoeu-

Guernica, Northern Spain. The small market town in Basque country is destroyed in the Spanish Civil War.

vred across the rugged terrain to soften up the opposition every time it took up a new defensive position. But under the *Blitzkrieg* strategy, the Condor Legion would act as aerial artillery, pounding the enemy before they had a chance to dig in. This would keep the front fluid and the Nationalists' motorised infantry could easily outrun the ill-equipped Republicans.

The *Blitzkrieg* was also used to terrorise the civilian population. Once the planes had dropped their deadly load, civilians knew that Nationalist troops would not be far behind. Franco's formidable troops from Morocco had a fearsome reputation. Stories spread of men being shot after surrender and women being forced to strip at gunpoint and submit themselves to rape.

As the Nationalists attacked, the population fled. Refugees jammed the roads, making it harder for the Republicans to withdraw and regroup. Refugees poured into Guernica, believing that there they would be safe. It was renowned worldwide as a historic centre of culture and democracy – surely the enemy would respect that.

By 25 April 1937, the Nationalists were just 20 miles from Guernica. But between them and the town was rugged terrain and thousands of Basque troops to provide protection for the inhabitants. Or so the Guernicans thought.

Monday 26 April was a market day. Although the livestock market had been suspended for the duration of the war, the street market was in full swing. At 4.30 p.m., the bells of Santa María Church began to toll. People were puzzled by this. By the time they realised that it was an air-raid warning, a single Heinkel 111 bomber was directly overhead. Some people ran for the cellars that had been designated as air-raid shelters. Others took refuge in the church of Santa María and, naively, in the railway station plaza.

The plane climbed high in the sky, then came screaming earthwards. This was only a practice run, giving the bombardier a chance to identify the target – the Rentería Bridge across the River Mundaca. Again, the plane was climbing, and the anti-aircraft gunners, who had identified the plane as fascist, found that they could not elevate their guns high enough to see it off with ack-ack fire. By this time, the plane seemed to be retreating. The soldiers defending the town got to their feet and cheered. But now the aircraft turned and began the run again, this time dropping its bombs.

Even though the navigator on board the Heinkel was supposed to have been one of the most experienced bombardiers in the Condor Legion, the 3,000 pounds worth of bombs landed hundreds of yards from the Rentería Bridge, near the railway station plaza in the centre of town.

One 550-pound bomb sliced off the front of the Julián Hotel. The rubble engulfed a group of children playing in the street outside. Another bomb hit the back of the station, which collapsed. Others fell in the station plaza killing both the people waiting for the next Bilbao train and those who had sought refuge there, believing it to be a place of safety. No one knows how many people there were in the plaza, but it was probably 300–400.

One eyewitness saw a bomb hit a group of women and children. 'They were lifted high into the air, maybe 20 feet or so,' he said, 'and they started breaking up. Legs, arms, heads, and bits and pieces flying everywhere.'

Some corpses had been decapitated; others were stripped of their clothing by the blast. Many, though dead, did not have a mark on them – the force of the blast had simply collapsed their lungs. The air was full of the screams of the wounded and bereaved. Survivors took no notice of the dismembered corpses and they tried to drag the injured free of the debris. Soldiers left their posts to help; people came out of the shelters – no one was expecting another attack.

However, the rest of the squadron – nine Heinkels with a fighter escort of six Messerchmitt 109s – were circling over the village of Garay, ten miles south of Guernica. At 4.40, they lined up and moved in.

Ten minutes later they began their descent along the River Mundaca. They came in lower this time, as the first attack had drawn negligible flak. They were so low that people on the ground could see the crewmen. Spotters also noticed that the planes were spread out in a wide formation. This meant they were not planning to attack one specific target. They aimed to destroy the whole town using the technique of 'carpet bombing' perfected by the Condor Legion during its attack on Oviedo the previous September.

The first three Heinkels came in at 2,000 feet. Travelling at 170 miles an hour, they made an elusive target. After spraying the skies with an ineffective burst of gunfire, one young machine-gunner dropped his weapon and started taking pictures of the raid. His photographs later formed a vital part of the propaganda war.

The first plane had dropped high explosives. The next three dropped incendiary bombs: a cluster hit a sweet factory, setting vats of boiling sugar on fire, along with the hair and overalls of the girls who worked there. Women came running out into the street, living balls of fire.

People still had no idea what had hit them. The factory manager walked calmly back in through the flames to rescue a fish he had bought for the meeting of his cookery club the following day. He simply could not believe that things would not continue as normal. Another eyewitness saw an old woman sitting outside her front door peeling potatoes with bombs dropping all around her. When she had finished, she got up and walked calmly indoors.

Two more waves of bombers came in, each plane dropping 3,000 pounds of explosives. One bomb hit a house where a girl was celebrating her 15th birthday with her widowed mother. The house collapsed, killing them; but by some freak circumstance, her birthday cake ended up sitting, unscathed, on top of the pile of rubble that had buried them.

The incendiaries exploded with a white flash, then flared, burning fiercely and scattering red and white fragments of Thermite. One landed in a bull pen in the market place, where two bullocks were sprayed with burning Thermite. Maddened with pain, they broke free and went charging through the burning stalls and burning people, before falling to their deaths in a bomb crater.

Fire tore through the canvas-roofed stalls. There was no way to stop it. The concrete roof of the fire station had collapsed, flattening the fire tender to a third of its original height. Firemen had to do what they could with buckets. A stable collapsed, so completely that it was three days before the body of the stable boy was recovered, mingled with the remains of two dray horses.

Mercifully, some of the bombs did not explode. The canisters were recovered and their German markings later displayed by the Basque government to show the world who had been responsible.

Sadly, that was not the end of the tragedy at Guernica. Next came ten Heinkels who peppered the town with more incendiaries. Junkers swept in at 200 feet, spraying the town with machine-gun fire and cutting down those who tried to escape. A mother who had left her house to tend to an injured girl was cut down. Seeing this, her three children rushed screaming from the house and were likewise cut down.

A group of 15 boys had taken shelter in a thick concrete pipe that carried flood water away from the town. They should have been safe, but four incendiaries fell at the mouth. The heat cracked the concrete and tons of earth collapsed on them. Their bodies were only found two weeks later after a flash flood washed them from their resting place.

The Heinkels flew back and forth, combing the streets for someone to kill. It was estimated that 50 people were hit in one strafing alone. Condor pilots swooped in on single figures fleeing down the street, shooting them and dropping grenades. The Heinkels lingered for half an hour before, low on ammunition and gas, they turned for home. They left at six, one and a half hours after the first attack.

Throughout the onslaught, the Rentería Bridge remained intact. People sheltering under it considered themselves very lucky indeed. Little did they know that worse was yet to come. At six, the main bomber force took off, 23 Junker 52s, carrying 100,000 pounds of high explosives between them, forming over Garay.

During this brief respite, the fire brigade started digging people out of collapsed buildings. They had just enough time to rescue one small girl. Lines of people with buckets tried to dowse the flames, while Guernica's Carmelite Convent was turned into a makeshift hospital. It was filled with dying people calling for absolution, but no priest to oblige.

Father Eusebio had heard that his church had been hit. He ran to see it and found it intact. Earlier in the day he had intended to take a photograph of it. His old plate camera was standing on its tripod outside. He ran to it, determined to make a record of the destruction of his town. As he reached it, he just had time to turn it skyward and see three Junkers through the viewfinder. He snapped the shutter, pulled out the plate and fled. Behind the Junkers, the sky was black with bombers. Moments later the church was hit by incendiaries and the camera consumed.

The first salvo of bombs hit a restaurant and a bank. People in the street and cows that had escaped from their pens were blown to pieces. Houses collapsed like packs of cards. Several bombs simultaneously made a direct hit on an air-raid shelter in Calle Santa María, hurling bodies out into the street. In other shelters, people were asphyxiated by the lack of air. In the shelter of a basement in a house in Calle Allende Salazar, all 20 occupants died, suffocated by smoke. Their unmarked bodies were discovered four days later. The Town Hall took three direct hits and three floors collapsed on the shelter beneath. One young woman crawled to safely. Over her shoulder she saw a hand and thought someone was trying to hold her back, only to discover that a severed arm had got caught in her belt. The moment she struggled free, the rest of the building collapsed, sealing the entrance to the shelter.

Father Eusebio led a mother and her five daughters to the Rentería Bridge while buildings collapsed and people were blown to bits all around them. He told them that their only chance was to get out of town. He himself went back into town to warn the people in the church of Santa María. After seeing his own church destroyed, he realised that German airmen were no respecters of the Catholic faith, although now they were not even bothering to aim. The Junkers were high up and the town was obscured by dust; the bombardiers could not see their target, so dropped their loads indiscriminately. The pilots claimed it would have been dangerous to take them back to the airfield with them.

Baker Antonio Arazamagni saw a bomb hit his bakery. The building bulged outwards slightly, then collapsed on his prized Ford. He decided it was time to get out of Guernica.

There was only one legitimate target in the town – an arms factory. The owner was pro-Franco and believed that was why his factory was saved. In fact, the German pilots did not know about the factory or his sympathies. It was left unscathed because the line the bombers took across the town did not pass over it, and the fighters did not bother strafing it because the factory was built out of solid concrete. Nevertheless, the owner had the smile wiped off his face when a German bomb hit his mansion 100 yards away.

After the smoke from the first squadron's attack had cleared, the lead planes of the second squadron could see the Rentería Bridge and went in for the kill. They unloaded their high explosives and a shower of smaller incendiaries. Not one bomb hit the bridge – they simply rained down on the battered town once more. By this time, terror had given way to exhaustion among those who huddled in the shelters. Human beings, it seems, can become accustomed to anything – even aerial bombing.

Father Eusebio was right about the Germans' attitude to the church. One 550-pound high-explosive bomb hit the local Augustine monastery, blowing it to smithereens. An incendiary dropped through the roof of the church of Santa María, landing in the chapel of Our Lady of Begonia and knocking Our Lady to the ground. Father Iturran was in the pulpit, leading the packed congregation in prayer, but Father Eusebio was on hand. He grabbed a vase and emptied its contents over the canister. The incendiary gave off clouds of smoke, but no flames.

'Bring more water,' yelled Father Eusebio.

People began to panic.

'If our Lord could work a miracle by turning water into wine,' said Father Iturran, 'then perhaps he will allow us to use wine as water.'

The incendiary was snuffed out with communion wine and Iturran's calm words stemmed the panic.

Soon after 6.30 p.m., the last of the Junkers climbed away from the town. This last attack had killed a further 200 people, injuring 400 more. Three-quarters of the buildings in Guernica had been destroyed – or soon would be, by flames. The Rentería Bridge was still intact.

After the planes had gone, Father Eusebio counted out 60 seconds then instructed the congregation to get out. They streamed down the Calle San Juan, across the Rentería Bridge, up the Arteaga road to the safety of the caves in the rocky hillside. Over 500 found safety there.

Others were caught out on the roads. As civilians streamed out of the town, they were joined by deserting soldiers. They slowed their pace to those of the refugees, figuring that, from the air, it would be impossible to tell the difference between soldiers and civilians. It made no difference: a squadron of six Messerschmitts strafed them anyway. They came in so low that those on the road stood no chance.

At 7 p.m., the Heinkel 51s, refuelled and re-armed, returned. After strafing those on the roads, they turned their attention back to the town. On the ground the anti-aircraft gunners were out of ammunition, but the Heinkels made no attempt to attack them. Instead, they strafed the ruins, moving backwards and forwards, sometimes in pairs, sometimes in a long line, sometimes in close formation as if they were trying out new tactics.

Eventually, at 7.30 p.m., they turned for home. The attack on Guernica was over. After a few minutes, a woman named María Ortuza emerged. She had been hiding under the corpse of a dead donkey, which had protected her from the strafing. She walked up to the Church of Santa María and looked out over the town, desperately searching for a sign of life 'to show I was not alone'.

She wandered the town for some time. Suddenly, she saw a horse rear up in flames. It had probably been dead for some time, but the heat of the fire made its muscles contract. As the flames consumed it, the animal fell back. Shortly afterwards she heard the voice of a man who was trapped under a pile of rubble. He had been lucky: moments before the building had collapsed on him, the street had cracked apart. He had fallen down a sewer, which protected him. With him was a young woman who had not been so fortunate. Her bones stuck out through her light cotton dress; she was dead and already her body had begun to smell.

In all, 1,654 were killed in the attack and 889 wounded. Many of the bodies lay face down, having been hit from behind while running away.

Miraculously, the houses of the rich on the western slopes of the town were largely intact. The rich supported Franco and it was rumoured that they had been spared intentionally. Townspeople scoured the buildings, looking for 'traitors' on whom to take revenge. But the rich had already fled. In fact, no orders had been given to spare them; they had been spared by chance because of the northeast-to-southwest bombing run across the town.

That night the Condor Legion celebrated in the brothels of Vitoria. Their leader, Lieutenant Colonel Wolfram von Richthofen, cousin of the World War I fighter ace, secretly reported to Berlin that the concentrated attack on Guernica was 'the greatest success'. On Thursday, 29 April 1936, the Nationalists reached Guernica. Spanish, Italian and Moroccan troops marched over the Rentería Bridge at about 8.30 a.m. They met some resistance – five Nationalist soldiers were killed and 28 wounded – but by 10.30 a.m., Franco's flag flew over the parliament building. The troops behaved well, even setting up a field kitchen to feed the survivors.

That night, Franco's headquarters issued a statement saying that Guernica had been burnt by retreating Republicans and that it was a lie to 'attribute this atrocity to our noble and heroic air force'. The Spanish Church backed the story and the professor of theology in Rome said, 'The truth is there is not a single German in Spain.'

However, the photograph Father Eusebio took to Bilbao the following day and the unexploded incendiaries showed this to be a lie.

Although the war dragged on for another two years, the Republican soldiers retreating from Guernica knew that their cause was lost. Their raggle-taggle army was not up to fighting such a ruthless enemy. Having taken Guernica, the Nationalists now had a new arms factory that, by fluke, had escaped the bombing.

When the painter Pablo Picasso heard about the bombing of Guernica, he was appalled. A communist, his sympathies lay with the Republicans. He was no stranger to the regions, having been brought up in nearby Galicia. He condemned the German attack in a huge painting entitled *Guernica*, which became one of the great icons of pacifism. In 1940, when Germans marched into Paris, they came to his studio where the painting was leaning against the wall.

A German officer pointed at it and demanded, 'Did you do that?'

Picasso replied, 'No, you did.'

12 ❖ The Rape of Nanking

Since the 1870s, Japan had sought to expand into the mainland of Asia. Firstly, it took over Korea. Then, after a short war with Russia, it established a toehold in Manchuria. In World War I Japan sided with the Allies against the Germans and demanded that China cede its German concessions to the growing Japanese Empire. Being weak and without allies, China had no choice.

The Versailles Peace Conference rewarded Japan for backing the winners in World War I with more concessions in China. In 1931, the Japanese consolidated their hold on Manchuria and, when the Chinese objected, firebombed an entire district of Shanghai. The Chinese appealed to the League of Nations, which found in China's favour. Japan promptly withdrew from the league. China was further weakened by the fall of the last Emperor of the Manchu Dynasty, so Japan swallowed up Mongolia and parts of China's Hebei province.

Up until this time, the Japanese military had been constrained by a civilian government at home. But in 1936, the military seized power in Tokyo and signed a pact with Nazi Germany. Then in 1937, the Japanese commanders in Manchuria decided to 'solve the Chinese question once and for all' and launched a full-scale invasion.

In August 1937, Beijing fell; in November, Shanghai was taken. From there, the Japanese moved up the Yangzi towards Nanking, then the capital of the Chinese Republic. The Chinese government quickly withdrew to Wuhan while Generalissimo Chiang Kai-Shek considered the situation. Nanking, he quickly decided, was indefensible. He suggested declaring it an open city, so the Japanese would have no excuse for butchering its citizens. Although its loss would be a psychological blow to China, it would have no effect on the overall military situation. His chiefs of staffs agreed.

There was one dissenting voice though. General Tang Shengzhi point out that Nanking contained the mausoleum of President Sun Yat-Sen, then considered the father of the nation. Tang said that if they did not sacrifice one or two big generals, how would they be able to account to the father of the nation in heaven? Honour had to be satisfied.

Chiang Kai-Shek was delighted: Tang got the job. Despite his noble sentiment Tang's defence of Nanking made no difference. The Japanese were making their way towards the city unopposed. Japanese pilots – who, in the Samurai tradition, carried a sword instead of a parachute – were indiscriminately bombing and machine-gunning unarmed civilians for the fun of it.

The Japanese, under General Matsui Iwane, army looted Suzhou on the way. An American missionary fleeing the fighting reported that he had to drive slowly to avoid running over the dead bodies that were strewn across the road. Matsui's forces were within sight of Nanking on 5 December. On 7 December, Chiang Kai-Shek flew out, after destroying all the petrol and ammunition that could not be saved.

'I intend to defend Nanking to the last man,' General Tang told an American observer. 'The Japanese will eventually capture the city, but they will pay a high price for it.'

This was mere hubris, the Americans concluded. The mechanised Japanese forces were unstoppable.

On 9 December, a Japanese plane dropped a letter from General Matsui. It was addressed to General Tang, demanding his surrender within 24 hours. Matsui pointed out that he would be hard on those who resisted, but would be 'kind and generous to non-combatants and to Chinese troops who entertained no enmity to Japan'. When he received no reply, the Japanese began shelling. It was a precision bombardment: the shells fell in a straight line that advanced 25 yards every half minute.

Soon the 100,000-strong garrison of Chinese troops was routed. The retreat was disorganised. Officers and men fled as they could. However, acting without orders, a small group of fanatically patriotic Chinese troops put machine-guns on the top of the city walls and strafed the men fleeing the city.

The gates to the city were then locked. Nevertheless, both soldiers and civilians still tried to escape. Access to the Xiaguan gate, which opened on to the river, was down a 70-foot long tunnel. Two military vehicles collided in it and burst into flames. Refuges fleeing the fire met those fleeing the city. Thousands were suffocated or trampled underfoot. Those who emerged were machine-gunned by the Japanese. Two Americans who went through the tunnel the next day reported having to drive over bodies 'two or three feet deep'. By the time the city fell on 13 December, 40,000 were dead.

The Japanese Victory Parade at Nanking.

Throughout the fighting, Japanese planes had been dropping pamphlets promising the citizens of Nanking the protection of the invading army and telling them that they would be allowed to live in peace under Japanese occupation. However, when General Matsui drove in triumph through the city gates, it became clear that these were empty promises. Although the General himself showed traditional restraint, behind him on a high-stepping white horse came Colonel Hashimoto. He was one of the new breed of arrogant super-patriots.

Even worse was the field commander of the occupying force, Lieutenant-General Prince Asaka Yasuhiko, who was married to the Emperor's aunt. As a royal, he brooked no opposition. It was he who gave the orders for the first massacres.

He was not alone in his lust for blood. The Japanese press carried news of two sub-lieutenants who held a Samurai contest to see who would be the first to kill 100 Chinese using their swords. Both reached 100, but they could not decide who had got there first, so they continued to 150. One of them had to drop out when his sword was damaged by 'cutting a Chinese in half, helmet and all'; but the contest was only a friendly and the loser declared it to have been 'fun'.

Once inside the city, bloodthirsty victory celebrations began. The Chinese municipal authorities had fled and the Japanese organised no new ones. Law and order broke down. Japanese soldiers got down to the business of getting drunk, looting, raping woman and killing anyone who got in their way. Even though the Japanese troops could do pretty much what they liked, the generals were soon complaining that these 'celebrations' were taking place under the eyes of neutral observers. Some of these were Germans. One even handed over Nazi armbands and decorations to make the Japanese soldiers and officers stop committing atrocities – in his presence at least.

Nanking was the temporary home to 250,000 refugees from Shanghai. The refugees were terrified of the Japanese, but anyone who ran away was bayoneted or shot. Just 27 foreign missionaries, doctors and teachers had stayed on. They tried to organise what they hoped would be a 'safety zone', believing that the Japanese authorities would soon restore order. Instead, Nanking became what many of them described as 'a living hell'.

While the foreigners did as much as they could to protect the populace, the citizens of Nanking were robbed of their last possessions. They were lined up and shot, or used for bayonet practice. Even the homes of foreign dignitaries were looted and foreign flags torn down and insulted. When complaints were made to the Japanese Embassy, they were received politely, but nothing was done. A victorious army must have its spoils.

Some tried desperately to keep a record of the atrocities. On 18 December, for example, the following complaints were logged.

'One teahouse master's daughter, aged 17, was raped by seven Japanese soldiers and she died on the 18th. Last night three Japanese soldiers raped four girls between six and ten o'clock. In number 5 Moh Kan Road, one old man reported his daughter was brutally raped by several Japanese soldiers.

'There are about 540 refugees crowded in number 83 and 85 on Guangzhou Road. Since the 13th up to the 17th those houses have been searched and robbed many times a day by Japanese soldiers in groups of three or five. Today the soldiers are looting the places mentioned above continually. At present, women of younger ages are forced to go with the soldiers every night by sending motor trucks to take them. They are released the next morning. More than 30 women and girls have been raped. The women and children are crying the whole night through. Conditions inside the compound are worse than can be described.'

One girl scratched a Japanese soldier while he was raping her. He stuck a bayonet into her neck and severed the muscles on one side.

Two days afterwards a 17-year-old married girl, who was nine months pregnant, was raped by two Japanese soldiers at 7.30 in the evening. An hour and a half later her labour pains began; the baby was born at midnight. 'Mother is hysterical,' the report said, 'but the baby is doing well.'

Some 140 refugees were dowsed with petrol and set on fire. Only one survived, and his eyes were burnt out.

On Christmas Day, the Japanese began the registration of refugees at the university. Disarmed Chinese soldiers were told that they could join labour details. Instead, the soldiers were grouped together and used for bayonet practice or simply machine-gunned. Meanwhile, the death toll of unarmed civilians climbed to 40,000. Some had been buried alive or roasted to death over fires. Yet even death did not end the horror: Japanese soldiers found it good sport to toss a grenade into a pile of dead bodies.

Still the complaints of rape poured in. A German observer estimated that there were 20,000 cases in all. On the university campus, girls as young as 11 and women as old as 53 were violated. Elsewhere it was reported that two women of 72 and 76 were raped repeatedly in broad daylight. When soldiers came to attack a 62-year-old woman, she complained that she was too old to be raped. One soldier responded by jamming a stick up her vagina instead. After a 60-year-old woman was gang-raped, one of the soldiers told her to 'clean his penis with her mouth'. Her grandson was stabbed twice for crying.

One doctor reported that a 14-year-old girl who had not yet reached puberty was raped so brutally that she needed surgical intervention; four soldiers gang-raped a girl of ten; one man had both his legs broken with a rifle butt when he refused to supply a girl for a soldier; and when a young man of about 17 told a soldier that there was no girl in the house for him to rape, the youth was taken and sodomised.

These rapes were not just perpetrated by drunken soldiers on the rampage – the officers indulged themselves freely too. One foreign resident reported that six women had been take to wash clothes for Japanese officers. That was their daytime occupation – at night they were repeatedly raped. The older women were raped between ten and 20 times, the younger women 40 times a night.

A group of officers drove up to the university one night, held the night-watchman up against the wall and raped three of the women. One was just 12. Another one was carried off by the officers.

Anyone who opposed the soldiers, including children, was bayoneted or shot. If a woman resisted, she risked being bayoneted. One woman had her five-month-old baby next to her while she was being raped. When it cried, the soldier raping her smothered it to death.

The foreigners attempting to maintain the 'safety zone' eventually managed to get the Japanese to post sentries around the compound. But this did no good. The sentries went in and raped the women instead.

The rape of Nanking was only brought to a halt when venereal disease began to get out of hand – syphilitic men do not make good soldiers. One Chinese woman was admitted to hospital with virulent forms of syphilis, gonorrhoea and genital chancroids. She had been imprisoned by Japanese soldiers in their quarters, and they raped her seven to ten times a day for six weeks.

The Japanese authorities solved the problem by opening brothels, staffed by Chinese women who had been forced into prostitution. This was the beginning of the forced military prostitution that turned millions of enslaved Chinese, Koreans, Malays, Filipinos and captured Europeans into 'comfort women' throughout World War II.

After the orgy was over, General Matsui held a service for the 300 Japanese who had died. He used it to berate his officers. Later he told an American correspondent that 'the Japanese army is probably the most undisciplined army in the world today'. He found this shameful. During the Russo-Japanese War of 1904, Japanese troops were renowned for their high standard of discipline and the scrupulous treatment of civilians and prisoners of war. But at that time, the officers had come from Samurai families with high codes of honour. The new officer corps was full of swaggering fascists like Colonel Hashimoto.

This new breed sought to justify their actions on the grounds that the Chinese had done the same to them. True, Chinese militiamen had mutinied against their Japanese officers at Tongxian on 29 July, two-thirds of the 380 Japanese in the city had been killed and all Japanese buildings burnt. Japanese soldiers had been tortured and Japanese women impaled on stakes. The Chinese also cut the ears or noses off the Japanese on battlefields to prevent their souls finding a resting place. But these atrocities were nothing compared to the wholesale barbarity that the Japanese inflicted on occupied China.

As regards the rape, Japanese apologists claim that it occurred because Matsui's front-line troops were middle-aged men who were 'more likely to get out of hand with women'. This is not true – when new recruits arrived in China, they were appalled at the atrocities, but the Japanese army took pains to habituate its men into practising the most barbaric torture on the Chinese as a matter of course. Mass executions were used as to terrorise the civilian population and mass rape was a way to humiliate the Chinese.

News of the rape of Nanking soon got out. The world was appalled. Prince Asaka Yasuhiko was recalled to Tokyo where the Emperor ordered that especially good treatment should be meted out to the inhabitants of Nanking. It was too late.

13 ❖ Massacre in the Katyn Forest

After Nazi Germany and the Soviet Union signed a non-aggression pact in 1939, Hitler was free to invade Poland, beginning World War II. Yet at the same time as Germany seized the western part of the country, the Soviet Union seized the east. As a result, 250,000 Polish military personnel fell into Russian hands.

When Germany attacked the Soviet Union in June 1941, the government in Moscow found itself allied to Great Britain and the Polish government in exile in London. Stalin agreed to let a Polish army be formed on Soviet territory under General Wladyslaw Anders, who asked the Soviets to hand over the 15,000 Polish officers they had once held in camps at Smolensk to form the nucleus of his command. After an embarrassed silence, the Soviets could not hand them over. They told Anders that, in December 1941, most of the prisoners had escaped to Manchuria and could not be located. Their whereabouts was a mystery.

However, on 13 April 1943, the Germans announced that they had discovered mass graves containing Polish officers in the Katyn forest near Smolensk. A total of 4,443 corpses were unearthed. They had been shot from behind, piled in stacks and buried. Investigators determined that they were General Anders' missing officers who, the Germans claimed, had been executed by the Soviets in 1940.

A propaganda war ensued. The Soviets said that the Polish officers had been engaged in construction work to the west of Smolensk when the Germans arrived in August 1941 and that they had killed them. But both German and Red Cross investigators produced evidence that they had been killed in 1940.

The Polish government in exile asked the International Committee of the Red Cross to provide official reports on the fate of the Polish prisoners that they had held. The Soviet government refused to co-operate and, on 25 April 1943, broke off diplomatic relations with the Polish government in London. The Soviets then established a rival Polish government in exile, comprised entirely of communists.

After the war the Katyn massacre remained a thorn in the side of Polish-Soviet relations. The Soviet Union continued to insist that the Polish officers had been killed by the Germans and the communist government in Warsaw had no choice but to accept this. However, when a non-communist coalition came to power in Poland in 1989, they shifted the blame to the Soviets. Finally, in April 1990, Soviet President Mikhail Gorbachev admitted that the Soviet secret police, the NKVD, was responsible for the massacre.

The following is an account of what happened. In the autumn of 1939, the Soviets assembled what they held of the Polish military in 138 camps. The officers were separated and imprisoned in the old Russian Orthodox monasteries at Kozelsk and Starobelsk. Each prisoner was interviewed and investigated. Next, those who had served in the Polish intelligence services, military policemen, border guards and even some local policemen were segregated and transferred to the monastery at Ostashkov.

The Soviet authorities provided the prisoners with a meagre ration, just about enough to sustain a man. Generals were allowed to keep their batmen, though. The prisoners were allowed to run their own kitchen and organise work parties to clear snow, but anyone who showed real leadership qualities was arrested and held incommunicado.

The State Jewellery Trust visited the prisoners to buy their watches, fountain pens and jewellery from them. The money could be spent on additional food. Religious services were held surreptitiously. Nevertheless, morale remained high.

Unlike other prisoner-of-war camps, these three camps were run, not by military units, but by the dreaded NKVD, the forerunner of the KGB.

Officials look over bodies found in mass graves in the Katyn forest.

The men were interrogated over and over again. NKVD officers tried to indoctrinate them . . . to little effect. Not only did the Polish prisoners refuse to embrace communist ideology openly among their fellow prisoners, they also refused to do so privately during interrogations. By March 1940, the NKVD had given up. They decided that there were only 448 of the 15,000 Poles they could use. Some of them were communists, who eventually formed the core of the Polish Red Army. Others were ethnic Germans, some of whom were handed over to the German authorities. The rest could be useful in some way or, in some way or another, could not be considered class enemies.

The Katyn forest lay to the west of Kozelsk. In April 1940, the men in the camp there were told they were being sent home. Lists were drawn up for those who were about to depart. The men picked then had to line up and return any equipment given to them by the camp authorities. In a second building their personal possessions were returned to them. Everything was checked carefully. By this time, the departing men were segregated from those waiting behind and were not allowed to communicate with them. The selected men were then given a good meal, and a ration of bread and three herrings wrapped in white paper for the trip. For the men from the camp it seemed like heaven – white paper alone was an unimaginable luxury.

The generals were the first to go. When they left the camp, the NKVD officers formed a guard of honour. At Starobelsk, a military band played up-tempo tunes. The other officers followed later in groups of 50 to 360 men. There was no discernible pattern as to who went in which group, though officers with leadership qualities tended to be sent first. When those who remained behind asked the NKVD privately why this was, they were told that they should count themselves lucky still to be in the camp.

From Ostashkov and Starobelsk, the men were taken in closed trucks to waiting trains. From Kozelsk, they were marched to the nearby railway station. The column was closely guarded by NKVD men with guns and dogs. Some Poles began to wonder why such security precautions were needed if they were really going home.

At the station, they were loaded into closed prison carriages and taken to the railway station at Gnezdovo, a mile and three-quarters from the Katyn graves. The first batch had no idea where they were going, but the shadows of the telegraph poles they could glimpse through the tiny windows near the roof of the carriage told them they were going north-west –

towards Poland. Those that followed found messages concerning their destination scratched into the wooden walls of the carriages.

The journey took two or three days, depending on the rail traffic. When they disembarked at Gnezdovo, they were searched; money and valuables were confiscated. Groups of 20–30 at a time were taken in buses into the forest. They were gagged – their arms were tied behind their backs and the rope looped around their necks so that, if they struggled, they would choke themselves.

The mass graves had already been dug. The Polish officers were brought six at a time and forced to kneel on the edge of the grave. Below them were layers of dead bodies, stacked neatly head to toe. Two NKVD men then walked down the line. One shot each Pole in the back of the head; the other kicked the corpse in the small of the back so it fell into the grave. While the NKVD men went to get six more prisoners, Russian peasants standing on the corpses below pushed the fresh ones into place. This went on hour after hour, day after day until finally the pits were full – then they were covered over.

It was a well-oiled killing machine run by NKVD specialists. Each prisoner was shot through the occipital bone in the back of the head and the bullet emerged from the forehead, extinguishing life instantly. It is therefore all the more amazing that one Polish officer taken to the Katyn forest survived and escaped.

His name was Lieutenant-Colonel Eugenjusz Andrei Komorowski. In September 1939, escaping from the invading Germans, he had ridden with some trepidation towards the Russian lines. He was with General Boleslaw Olszyna-Wilczynski, the Military Commander of Grodno who aimed to surrender to the Russians rather than the Germans. When he tried to do so, he was shot by the Russians while a Polish farmer and his wife looked on and laughed.

Eventually, Komorowski ended up in the camp at Kozelsk. He was scheduled to leave on 28 April 1940. As they marched out of the camp they were met by a huge force of NKVD men and warned that any man trying to escape would be shot. The NKVD kept up a constant barrage of insults at the Poles, whom they considered inferior.

It had rained the night before and the column had to ford a swollen stream. The banks were muddy and the men could not get a grip to stand up. As they slid around, the guards grew angry, causing the Poles to fear that they were going to be fired upon there and then.

One guard lashed out at a Pole with his rifle butt and someone shouted, 'Kill the guards! They're planning to murder us all.'

The Poles attacked the NKVD men, who responded with machine-gun fire. Many of the Poles were killed. Komorowski was hit in the right shoulder and right thigh – the bullets knocked him to the ground and he passed out.

When he came to, he felt a gentle rocking and heard the clack of wheel; he was on a train. He also smelt the overpowering smell of human excrement; warm liquid was dripping from above, onto his head and face; there was a weight on top of him and everything around him felt soft.

He realised that he was in a railway truck full of corpses. Blood was seeping out of the man stacked on top of him. The dead men had emptied their bowels, making the awful stench. Yet somehow he was alive. He could breathe and see just the tiniest shaft of light; then he slid back into unconsciousness.

Next time he awoke he could smell a new smell – rotting flesh. It was lighter this time and he could see among the corpses friends from the camp. This time he felt pain: his right shoulder was on fire; he felt sure he had broken bones; and pain was coming from his upper thigh. He prayed that no vital organ had been hit.

Afraid that he was going to die in this stinking compartment, he turned his thoughts to life, to his wife and the other beautiful women he had known.

The train clacked to a stop. Outside he heard voices. The doors squeaked. He could hear men being ordered out and told to get on the buses. Later, he heard the door of his compartment being opened.

'Drag the bastards out,' a voice demanded. 'The truck is coming.'

Komorowski played dead. As they lifted him out, two Russians discussed whether to steal his smart Polish army boots.

'Do you want to be shot?' said one of them. 'They're to be buried in Katyn with boots and papers so that no trace of them will ever be found.'

Outside it was cold. They dragged him along like a rag doll and lay him on the ground. After a while a truck arrived and the corpses were flung onto it. Komorowski counted fourteen thuds as they landed. Luckily, he was the last.

The truck bumped up a hill and through a gate. Komorowski saw barbed wire and started to shiver in the cold air. But he managed to get the tremble under control by the time they reached a wooden lodge. Beyond it he saw a group of Polish officers. The truck slowed. An NKVD officer examined the corpses and directed the truck to the right, deeper into the forest.

It came to a halt by a mass grave, where Komorowski could see Russian peasants walking on the corpses; there were more bodies than he could count. He lay still and watched while his brother officers were murdered and saw how they were stacked so that the grave would hold the maximum number of bodies. Weak from loss of blood and the horror of what had happened to him, Komorowski could not fully take in what he was seeing. Suddenly, a wave of nausea swept over him; he struggled not to vomit.

He closed eyes and tried to block out what he had seen; he struggled to keep the smell of rotting flesh out of his nostrils. The grave must have been open for days. Somehow, he resisted vomiting; somehow, he resisted screaming; somehow, he resisted weeping. He lay there silently until the NKVD mass murderers had finished their day's work. Then the peasants came to unload the truck. Komorowski was lucky again – he was thrown face down on top of the last man to be killed. His body was still warm. No one was put on top of him.

It was late and the peasants decided to cover the corpses with earth the next day. Then they drove off in the truck. He heard other cars, buses and trucks drive off; the forest fell silent. Komorowski lay there on top of layer upon layer of his dead comrades and wept.

A cold wind ruffled the back of his hair. Gingerly, he raised his head. Then he realised, suddenly, that he did not have to lie still and play dead. Why would the NKVD leave anyone to guard the dead?

He thought of his wife again. In his imagination, she told him to muster all his strength to get out of there before the Russians came back again. Somehow he pulled himself out of the grave and stumbled towards some trees. He looked for the North Star. He reckoned the station was to the south, so he would go north until he was out of the area, then turn west and head for Poland.

His progress was slow: he was in considerable pain. In the darkness, with tears in his eyes, he kept bumping into trees; but every so often, he found a clearing, checked the position of the pole star and continued his halting journey.

Eventually he reached a river and waded through its freezing water. Cold, hungry and weak from loss of sleep, he kept blacking out.

Eventually, he snagged his coat on a barbed wire fence. He cut his hands trying to free himself and eventually gave up and fell asleep. When he awoke there was a fog. He climbed the fence and, looking back, the fog was lifting and he could see the peasants turning up for work at the lodge. This stirred him on.

His situation seemed hopeless. Nevertheless, in his pocket he found a bar of chocolate and a can of herring he had bought from the camp shop with the money from his watch. He ate the chocolate, then smashed the tin open with a rock. Some of the oil splashed on some leaves, but he picked them up and licked it off. The food gave him renewed strength and he hobbled on.

The sun came out and dried off his clothes; it also helped him navigate. He reached a barn where he washed his wounds in a pail of water. He was lucky that the two bullets that had hit him had passed right through. He drank some milk direct from the teat of a cow and found an old smock and some baggy trousers, which he changed into.

Out in the forest again, he made a fire, burnt his uniform and papers, and buried his boot. He travelled on barefoot foraging for food. A few days later, he found a pair of old boots in a barn, and stole them.

Avoiding houses, he entered barns only to sleep in at night. However, soon he realised that he would need other people's help if he were to survive. One evening, he climbed up on to the porch of a remote house and begged the people inside for help. Eventually, they let him in, fed him, tended his wounds and said they would let him sleep in the loft for one night; but once he had gone to sleep, they went to fetch the police. Fortunately, Komorowski was a light sleeper. He heard the man of the house saddle his horse and he escaped.

He made his way across Russia, stealing food wherever he could. Then one day, he heard people speaking Polish. He was back in Poland, but that was not the end of his troubles: if he stopped and asked people for help, he could endanger their lives; and there was always a possibility that the people he spoke to would be Russian Poles whose sympathies were with the occupying forces.

Eventually, he reached the farmhouse where General Boleslaw Olszyna-Wilczynski had been shot and went in to see the couple who had ingratiated themselves with the Russians by laughing. They were not pleased to see him – there was a violent row and Komorowski killed them both. He felt no remorse and left the bodies on the kitchen floor as he helped himself to their food. Then he blew out the light and went to bed.

In the morning, he stole the man's papers and a suit, then headed on to Grodno. Presenting the papers at the sentry post outside town, he distracted the guard with a few words of Russian. When he reached home he received the worst shock of all: he found another couple living his apartment who told him that his wife had been shot by the Russians. The grief drove him temporarily insane, before he decided he wanted revenge. He determined to leave Poland so that he could fight. Most of all, he wanted to tell the world what had happened to his comrades in the Katyn forest.

He headed for Rumania with the idea of travelling on to Paris, but by the time he got there, Paris had fallen to the Germans. So, he headed for Switzerland, crossing Hungary and Czechoslovakia by hoboing on trains. In his numbed mental state, he took incredible risks, but the fact that he had exhibited no fear seemed to help him. Komorowski rode freight trains across Austria, then walked across the border into Switzerland. There he gave himself up to a policeman who took him to the Red Cross. They fattened him up and informed the Polish authorities. When two Polish officers turned up, they did not believe that he had come all the way from Russia, preferring to believe that he had escaped from a German camp – they flew him to London. By then, his mind had wiped all memory of the horrors of the Katyn forest. It was years before the full truth of the atrocity he had witnessed came back to him.

But a mystery still remains. The Germans only found 4,443 bodies in the mass graves at Katyn. The men in the mass graves were all from the camp at Kozelsk. What had happened to the other 10,000 or so who had been in the camps at Ostashkov and Starobelsk? Some witnesses say that at least 6,000 of them were taken to Archangel and put on barges, which were floated out into the White Sea. The barges were then sunk by artillery fire and the men drowned in the freezing water.

An NKVD document dated 10 June 1940 indicates that the men were murdered and buried in mass graves at Bologyne and Dergachi in the Ukraine. In 1991, a mass grave was found at Piatikhatki, near Kharkov, which was thought to contain the bodies of the men from Starobelsk; but the KGB only allowed the exhumation of 140 bodies there. Apparently, no one knows where the rest of the Polish officers were buried. They don't even know where the ones who were massacred in the Katyn forest are: in April 1944, Soviet earth moving machines were photographed at work in Katyn, removing the bodies and destroying the graves. However, Katyn is where the memorial to all 15,000 of the missing Polish officers stands.

So why did the Soviets slaughter these men? The Soviets, naturally, wanted to convert the Poles to communism. As they marched into eastern Poland, planes dropped pamphlets telling Polish soldiers to rebel against their officers and kill them. Although this failed, once the Soviet forces had rounded up the Polish army and separated the officers, they had in their hands the entire middle class who had run pre-war Poland. If they wanted to rule Poland – which they did effectively from 1945–1989 – the task would be made a lot easier if they simply liquidated anyone who might oppose them.

14 ❖ The Liquidation of the Warsaw Ghetto

The Nazis had proved that they were capable of mass murder at Babi Yar and numerous other places across occupied areas of the Soviet Union and the Baltic States. At least this suffering was mercifully brief. The torture of the people in the Warsaw Ghetto dragged on for four years and some 500,000 people were lost.

Between 1918 and 1939, the Jewish population of Warsaw became the largest concentration of Jews in Europe and the second largest in the world, after New York. When the Germans occupied the city on 7 September 1939, there were around 380,000 Jews in Warsaw, making up some 30 per cent of the population. The situation grew ugly immediately: many Poles were anti-Semitic and knew what their new German overlords expected of them. Jews soon found themselves subject to kicking and punching on the streets. They were thrown out of their homes and kidnapped for forced labour. Women were raped and people murdered by Polish rowdies as well as by the Germans themselves.

As early as November 1939, the Germans made it clear to the Jews what was going to happen to them. Special 'educational' camps were going to be set up for them. Only one thing would be taught there: how to die.

In the meantime, all Jews had to wear armbands with the Star of David on them. This made it easier for the violent anti-Semite element of the Polish population to know whom to attack. Jews were also issued with identification papers marked prominently with the word 'Jude'. All Jewish

During the clearing of the Warsaw Ghettos, German soldiers watch over the men, women and children as they leave.

assets of over 2,000 zloty per family were confiscated and, later, it became illegal for any Jew to earn more than 500 zloty a month – at a time when the price of bread rose to 40 zloty a pound. It became illegal for Jews to make bread, to buy from or sell to 'Aryans', to own gold or jewellery, to ride on trains or trolley-cars or to leave the city without special permits. Jewish doctors were not allowed to treat 'Aryan' patients, nor were Jewish patients allowed to seek the help of 'Aryan' doctors.

Jews were regularly robbed, beaten and murdered on the streets, with no sanction against their assailants. They lived in constant fear of the only punishment for even the slightest infraction of the regulations – death. However, even carefully obeying the rules was no protection, as the regulations were constantly being tightened. Jews were persecuted, humiliated and subjected to ruthless acts of terror. All Jews bore responsibility for what any one Jew did. Hence, early in November 1939, all 53 of the male inhabitants of an apartment house at 9 Nalewski Street were summarily shot because one of the tenants had struck a policeman.

Actions such as these sent a wave of panic through the Jewish population. The constant degradation left them feeling dehumanised; they were systematically robbed of the self-confidence to fight back.

In January 1940, the *Seuchensperrgebiet* – or 'area threatened by typhus' – was established, and was to be designated a Jewish area. The Germans decided that the world had to know that they were not the only ones who hated Jews. Over Easter 1940, a number of pogroms were arranged. In Warsaw, the German Air Corps paid Polish hoods four zloty a day to beat up and murder Jews. For the first three days, the hoodlums ran amok, unopposed; but on the fourth day, the Jews fought back. This resulted in running battles. The Jews published a mimeographed newspaper called *The Bulletin* to celebrate the event – the triumph was brief.

In November 1940, the Germans established the Warsaw Ghetto. Jews living outside the *Seuchensperrgebiet* were forced to move into it. Houses vacated by Jews were locked and their contents given to Polish merchants and peddlers. Poles living within the boundaries of the ghetto were ordered out, as the walls and barbed wire surrounding it grew higher day by day. By 15 November, it was sealed completely. Two weeks later, shops and small factories inside the ghetto were closed, meaning that Jews no longer had any way of making a living and were cut off from any contact with Jewish communities elsewhere.

The ghetto population was swelled by thousands of Jews being moved in from neighbouring towns. They were allowed to bring nothing with them. Many who knew no one in Warsaw died of malnutrition on the streets. The place became impossibly overcrowded. In spring 1941, the population peaked at 450,000 in just 307 hectares. Hunger and overcrowding brought with it disease and people, wrapped in filthy rags, their bodies impossibly swollen or covered with open wounds could be seen on the streets.

No newspapers were allowed in the ghetto, so the inmates knew nothing of the outside world. Only life inside the ghetto existed. For most, this meant somehow trying to get by on the meagre rations of soup and bread doled out by public kitchens. Some lived on potatoes recovered from garbage pits and begged pieces of bread; but those who still had a little money lost themselves in the chit-chat of pavement cafés and the dance music of the nightclubs. This contrast between the poor and the rich, who grew fat on 'food smuggled in from "Aryan" sections', was exploited by the Germans, who used photographs from the ghetto in their propaganda.

Every day the situation deteriorated. Children and old people begged on the streets. Some six-year-old boys crawled though the barbed wire to beg for food on the outside – entire families were supported this way. Often a single shot rang out, indicating the death of another under-aged food-smuggler.

Starving shadows of boys became known as 'catchers'. They would snatch parcels from passers-by and devour their contents while they were running away. In their haste, they sometimes stuffed themselves with soap or uncooked peas, with disastrous results.

The Germans had organised the Jewish Community Council to try and give some semblance of order to this chaos. This comprised well-respected figures of the Jewish community, who had been forced to join on pain of death. The Germans also instituted a Jewish Police Force to maintain law and order, increasing the risks for the food smugglers and the catchers.

Deaths rose from 898 in January 1941 to 5,560 in January 1939. In all, 100,000 Jews died inside the ghetto, largely from starvation and disease. Some simply fell down in the street and stayed there. Those who died at home fared little better: they were stripped so that their clothes could be sold and their bodies left outside the house. Every morning, between 4 and 5 a.m., the Jewish Community Council sent round carts to pick up the bodies. They could be seen stacked high with naked corpses, heads and limbs bobbing up and down as the carts rumbled down the uneven streets.

Those who died were soon replaced by Jews who had been rounded up in other parts of Poland. The ghetto was so overcrowded that newcomers had to camp on the streets, or would have to go to the 'points'. These were the large unheated rooms of synagogues or disused factories. Hundreds of people would be living in each room with no washing facilities. Whole families were given enough room for one person to sleep in – usually a straw mattress on the ground. Some did not have the strength to rise. The Jewish Community Council provided only one slop of 'water soup' a day. The walls were filthy and mildewed.

Not surprisingly, typhus raged in the ghetto. The hospitals were full to bursting point: 150 people a day were being admitted to a single ward. The sick and dying were two or three to a bed, with others on the floor. Doctors could not keep up; those who were dying were urged to get on with it to make room for the next patient. The gravediggers could not dig fast enough. Even though hundreds of corpses were buried in every grave, hundreds more had to lie around, filling the area with a sweet, sickly odour. The epidemic grew out of all control, at one point as many as two per cent of the population dying every month.

Then came the news that, during November and December 1940, some

40,000 Jews of Lodz, another 40,000 from Pomerania and other areas that were going to be incorporated into Germany, along with several hundred gypsies, had been gassed in Chelmno. The victims had been told that they were being taken there to work. When they arrived in Chelmno, they were ordered to strip and given a towel and soap, having been told they were going to have a shower. It was a cruel hoax. As the Jews were transported in trucks towards mass graves in the woods near Chelmno, exhaust gas was pumped into the sealed vehicles. At the woods, Jewish gravediggers – under the watchful eyes of SS guards – unloaded the bodies and buried them, knowing they would be next.

Three people who had, miraculously, escaped brought the news to the Warsaw Ghetto. Most people did not believe them – the inhabitants of the ghetto were clinging to life so tenaciously that they could not comprehend how people could have died in such a fashion. Some of the youth groups, particularly the young communists, believed the stories, though. They noticed that German terror was increasing and decided they would not go meekly to their deaths like the people at Chelmno. They began to organise propaganda to alert the other inmates of the ghetto to the danger, and they smuggled the news abroad, along with a demand that retaliation be taken against the Germans. The communist delegate to the Polish government in exile in London broadcast the news to the world, but few people believed it.

When Germany attacked the Soviet Union in the summer of 1941, the Jews of the ghetto began to hear of mass shootings of Jews in Wilno, Slonim, Bialystok and Baranowicze. Tens of thousands of Jews were being slaughtered. Again, most of those inside the ghetto refused to believe it, or put it down to the antics of drunken soldiers rather than an organised policy of extermination.

At this point, the youth groups decided that they must organise resistance. They sent messages to the Polish Underground to ask for arms and in the meantime, they began training. Several thousand were involved in the resistance movement, though they were organised into cells of between five and seven. They established a co-operative barber's, a tailor's shop and a cobbler's as a front. Youth groups organised a choir, educational courses and put on plays to try to keep the cultural life of the ghetto going. They also produced one weekly and six monthly magazines in an effort to maintain morale.

On one occasion, the girl who was smuggling 40 mimeographed copies of *The Bulletin* was stopped by the Polish police. She pretended to be an ordinary smuggler and offered them a bribe of 500 zloty. This was an unusually high offer and therefore made them suspicious. They asked to see the 'merchandise' and from under the girl's skirt fell not food or stockings, but printed sheets. They were just about to take her to the Gestapo when a colleague, seeing she was in trouble, started a scuffle. The police ran off to stop it, leaving the girl to drop the 500 zloty and run for her life.

The Germans grew angry with the number of Jews managing to slip out of the ghetto to get a little bread or a few pennies. They established special courts to try any one caught on the 'Aryan side'. On 12 February 1941, 17 people, including three women and four children, were executed for leaving the ghetto. Cries were heard from the Jewish jail on Geisha Street from the 700 other prisoners waiting to be tried for the same offence.

Just in case the message had not got through, the German Commissar of the ghetto, Dr Auerswald, filled the ghetto with posters announcing the executions. The ghetto was so intimidated that no protest was made, but things still got worse. The Germans began shooting passers-by in the street for no reason. Between ten and 15 a day were slaughtered randomly. One particularly sadistic policeman claimed to have killed over 300 people in a month. More than half of them were children.

The Jewish Police were used to rounding up people for forced labour. The Germans maintained that the people being sent to labour camps were lucky. Although the conditions were harsh, it did give them the opportunity to survive the war. Forced labourers were even allowed to write to their families. However, when the letters arrived, they were full of stories of the mass killing of Jews. Again, the people remaining in the ghetto could not believe what they were being told. Even when they heard of the liquidation of the ghetto in Lublin, the people in Warsaw refused to believe it was going to happen to them.

People tried to convince one another that not even the Nazis would murder 300,000 people when there was a labour shortage – that the Germans were taking people from the Warsaw Ghetto for forced labour showed that they needed manpower.

What they did not know was that there had been a change of policy in Berlin. Although the Germans had shot tens of thousands of people at Babi Yar and other places throughout the occupied areas of the Soviet Union and the Baltic states, it was not a very efficient method of slaughter. On 20 January 1942, SS *ObergruppenfŸhrer* Reinhard Heydric, Adolf Eichmann and others met in the Berlin suburb of Grossen-Wannseee, where they came up with what they called the 'final solution' to the 'Jewish question'. They planned to round up all Jews in occupied Europe and ship them to camps in the east where they would be systematically exterminated.

In the Warsaw Ghetto, the terror tactics continued. On the night of 17 April 1942, over 50 of the Jewish Community Council's workers were dragged from their beds by German officers and shot in the streets. The ghetto was shocked, hysterical, but the inhabitants concluded that this brutal action was aimed at the political leaders who urged resistance. On 19 April, a special edition of the resistance paper *Der Weker* was published, explaining that this was part of the German policy of systematic extermination of the Jews. It urged the people of the Warsaw Ghetto not to go to their deaths as meekly as those in Lublin or Chelmno had. However, the activists still had not managed to get any guns and their words fell on deaf ears.

Guns were promised, though. The Polish socialists said that a shipment of 100 pistols, a few dozen rifles and some grenades would arrive shortly. The communists in the ghetto organised more military training and tried to work out a plan of action in case the Germans stormed the ghetto.

Their task was not made any the easier by the fact that they were always losing members. Between 18 April and 22 July, the Germans entered the ghetto every night and killed ten or 15 people. None of the activists slept in their own beds. The whole ghetto was unsettled by the Germans' habit of shooting people from one group one night and another the next – smugglers, merchants, workers, and professional people.

Other random acts of violence terrorised the people into absolute subordination. A Polish policeman saw three children sitting one in front of another in front of the hospital and killed all three with a single shot. A German watched as a pregnant woman tripped and fell as she crossed the road. Instead of helping her up, he shot her. Every morning a man, shackled, was flung out of an Opel car on Orla Street and shot. It was a Jew who had been caught on the 'Aryan side'.

The Germans adopted a new tactic to stop smuggling. They would dress up as Jews with Star of David armbands and hide machine-guns in burlap bags. Thinking they were safe, smugglers would scale the ghetto walls, only to be gunned down.

In mid-May 1942, 110 people arrested for being on the 'Aryan side' were executed. The prisoners were led out of the central jail into special trucks – to be gassed. Only one of the accused protested. A woman stopped on the steps of the trucks and shouted, 'I will die, but your death will be much worse.' Again, Dr Auerswald put up posters announcing the 'just punishment' of these 110 'criminals'.

In mid-July, the rumour circulated that the Deportation Board had arrived and that between 20,000 and 60,000 inmates of the ghetto were to be taken to build fortifications. Supposedly, the Germans planned to take all the ghettos' unemployed, leaving only those who had jobs. Those who had had enough money to sit in cafés all day quickly became clerks and mechanics. The women became seamstresses and the price of sewing machines went through the roof. Many paid what little they had to get work, but it did them no good.

On 20 July 1942, the doctors were rounded up, along with the managers of the Jewish Mutual Aid Committee and a number of the Jewish Community Council. They were locked up.

On 22 July, the Deportation Board arrived at the headquarters of the Jewish Community Council. They brought news – it was a small matter really: all unproductive Jews were going to be deported somewhere to the east. *OberscharfŶhrer* Hoefle dictated a proclamation that appeared under the Jewish Community Council's name on white posters the following morning. It said that all Jews, except those who worked for the Germans, the Jewish Community Council or the Jewish Mutual Aid Committee, would be deported. The Jewish police would be the agency responsible for organising this and they would report directly to the Deportation Board.

On the first day, 2,000 prisoners from the central jail, along with beggars and starving people picked up on the streets, were taken. From then on, the quota was to be 6,000 a day.

The following afternoon the activists met. Without guns, they decided, resistance was impossible. Their clear duty was to save as many people as they could. They thought they might be able to get help from their contacts inside the Jewish police, but it was too late. Germans and Ukrainians had moved in and surrounded a block on Muranowska Street. They took over 2,000, enough to fill the shortfall in the daily quota. Even those with papers saying they were working for the Germans were taken. From then on, the Germans said they would look after the 'technical details' of the deportations themselves.

In a meeting on the 23 July, the communists began urging resistance.

But the majority feared that any actions might be provocative. If they handed over the required quota of Jews every day, the Germans might leave the rest of them alone, they argued. Still, the inhabitants of the ghetto did not believe that they were all going to be killed and those who thought that there might be some possibility of saving themselves willingly condemned others.

However, Adam Czerniaków, chairman of the Jewish Community Council, committed suicide. He knew that deportation meant that hundreds of thousands of Jews from the ghetto were heading for the gas chambers and he refused to take responsibility for it. Activists condemned him. He was a voice of considerable authority in the ghetto, they said; he should have made it his business to inform everyone, particularly the Jewish police, of the fate awaiting deportees. Instead, the communists rushed out an issue of their paper *On Guard*, warning people of the fate that awaited them and urging them to resist by any means at their disposal.

By the fifth day, the resistance knew for certain what was happening to those who were deported. A Polish contact had followed one of the transports to Sokolow. There he was told by a local railway worker that it had taken the branch line to Treblinka. Every day freight trains were taken down that branch, full of people from Warsaw: they came back empty. No consignment of food was ever sent down that line and civilians were forbidden to go anywhere near Treblinka railway station. The Pole also met two naked Jews who had somehow escaped. They told him about the mass extermination that was going on at a camp outside Treblinka.

Another edition of *On Guard* was prepared, explaining in full what deportees could expect; no one believed it. At the same time, the Germans began giving three kilograms of bread and one kilogram of marmalade to anyone who voluntarily registered for 'deportation'. It was a brilliant ruse. Ghetto inmates said, 'Why would they feed people they intend to murder?' Their hungry stomachs got the better of their reason. Thousands took the short walk down to the *Umschlagplatz* of their own volition. They waited in line in their hundreds; the transports had to be doubled to accommodate the demand: 12,000 people were deported daily, but still the trains could not accommodate them all.

Once all the volunteers had gone and the children's homes and refugee shelters had been emptied, the ghetto was emptied block by block. People with knapsacks would move from street to street, trying to guess which block was going to be cleared next.

The clearance was done by the Polish police, the Ukrainians and the Jewish police. The Polish police isolated the block; the Ukrainians surrounded the house; and the Jewish police would walk into the courtyards and summon the inhabitants.

'All Jews must come down. Only 30 kilograms of baggage is allowed,' they would say. 'Those remaining behind will be shot.'

People would come running, pulling on their clothes and carrying everything they could grab. They would assemble, trembling, in front of the houses. No talking was allowed. Then the Ukrainians would go in and search the apartments. According to regulations, the doors of the apartments had to be left open. If not, the Ukrainians would break them down with a boot or a rifle butt. There would be shots as anyone left inside was killed. Then they would move on to the next house.

The people in the street would be formed into columns. Any passer-by who had mistakenly walked down the wrong street would be taken too. The column would be marched off, with old people and children who had to be carried bringing up the rear. Outside the area cordoned off by the Polish police, relatives would desperately try to find their loved ones.

The column would be marched to the *Umschlag* or deportation point. The tall wall surrounding it had one narrow entrance, guarded by the Polish police. The deportees would hold out their identification papers and be told *rechts* – meaning life – or *links* – meaning death. Although argument was futile, people held out other papers, trying to prove how useful they would be to German industry. It made no difference. The gendarme's decision was quite arbitrary. Sometimes he ordered people to show him their hands and let all those with small hands live. Other days, he picked all the blondes to die. In the morning, short people might live; in the afternoon, only the tall survived.

The *Umschlagplatz* was filled with more than enough people for four days' transports. They were left to camp out in the square or in the surrounding derelict buildings for four or five days before they were loaded into cattle trucks. Some people wore merely a housecoat or nightgown. Every inch of free space was filled. There were no toilet facilities – everything was covered in urine and excrement.

The people were given no food; on the second day, the hunger pains became unbearable. There was no water either; people's lips cracked. While waiting, children sickened and people became smaller and greyer. By now, they had no doubt as to what their fate would be.

The Germans were clever enough to tantalise those they had con-demned to die with a glimmer of hope. They set up a children's hospital and an emergency aid station. The staff were clad in white coats and given working certificates. The personnel were changed twice a day, so it appeared that, if you had a white coat, you could walk in and out. White coats were soon fetching fabulous prices in the ghetto. Some nurses took strange children in their arms and walked out with them. If they were sick, older people could be sent to hospital or direct to the cemetery. Healthy people were also sometimes smuggled out in ambulances. But the Ger-mans got wise and checked the condition of the sick. Those found fit had their legs broken without an anaesthetic.

It was possible to get the Jewish police to smuggle one out, if they were bribed enough. But those who escaped usually appeared in the *Umschlag-platz* two, or possibly three, times before they ran out of money and had to board the train like everybody else.

Some people, who did escape from the *Umschlagplatz*, survived. Others who were brave enough to come to the *Umschlagplatz* to try and help get someone else out were swept onto the trains themselves.

The transports left every morning and evening, so twice a day the crowd was rounded up and forced into the cattle trucks. To survive this, you had to be as far from the trucks as possible. The Ukrainians would encircle the square and force the people towards the train; thousands of people would be crushed together. Resist and the Ukrainians shot you. They could not miss at that range and with thousands of people huddled together, they would probably kill another one or two besides.

People would squeeze into the doorway of the hospital or take to the upper floors of the surrounding buildings; but the Ukrainians would run about, chasing them out like wild beasts. Some hid in the attics; three girls who hid up there for five days were eventually smuggled out by nurses.

The Ukrainians did not have to exert themselves too much, though. No matter how many escaped, there were always enough to pack the cattle trucks. Indeed, the people had to be beaten with rifle butts before the doors could be closed. Those who escaped that shipment would simply wait in the *Umschlagplatz*. They would either go on the next shipment or the one after that . . . or starve.

The resistance groups were losing a lot of their men. Still, they started to fight back. They set a few fires and beat up the commander of the Jewish police. They also tried to place their people with German firms in a vain effort to save them.

By the middle of August 1942, there were only 120,000 left in the ghetto – 300,000 had been taken to Treblinka to be gassed. There came a short pause in the deportations while the Germans started liquidating what remained of the Jewish settlements in nearby towns.

Then the deportations from the ghetto started again. This time they were hard to avoid as cleared areas had been sealed off and the ghetto was now much smaller. The people left had become more skilled at hiding, so the Germans gave every Jewish policeman a quota. They each had to prove seven 'heads' a day. Whereas before the Jewish police had sometimes been helpful, they were now inflexible. They would grab women with babies in their arms, snatch stray children or tear the white coat off a 'doctor'. If they did not come up with their quota, they would be on the train to Treblinka themselves.

On 6 September 1942, the remaining inhabitants of the ghetto were ordered to move into the area bounded by just four streets. There the final registration would take place. The people remained in the small rectangular block for two days. Yet, even now the Germans did not leave them completely without hope. Some would go to German firms; along with members of the Jewish Community Council, they were issued with numbered slips that guaranteed them – for the moment – life. Instead of offering any last-minute resistance, everyone without a slip thought of only one thing – how to get one.

Finally, those with slips were marched away to the firms where they would be billeted. The rest were taken to the *Umschlagplatz*. The last to be taken there were the families of the Jewish police.

There was no escape from the *Umschlagplatz* now. Sick adults and children brought from the hospitals were left lying in the empty halls. They relieved themselves where they lay as there was no one to help them. Nurses sought out their parents and gave them an overdose of morphine. One doctor poured cyanide into the mouths of sick children, saving them the horrors of the train ride to Treblinka. In two days, 60,000 people were deported to certain death. On 12 September 1942, the liquidation of the Polish ghetto was over.

Those left alive were some 33,400 Jews working in German factories and 3,000 employees of the Jewish Community Council. However, there were more hidden in cellars, attics and in any other corner the Ukrainians had not bothered to look. Building work began: new walls were put up to divide the ghetto into three. Jewish workers from nearby factories were billeted there. They were forbidden to communicate with one another and were forced to work at least 12 hours a day without a break. The food was minimal and soon there was another outbreak of typhus.

The garbage carriers and gravediggers became rich, smuggling out what valuables remained to sell on the 'Aryan side' under piles of garbage or in coffins. What was left of the resistance groups in the ghetto joined forces in the Jewish Fighting Organisation or, in Polish, ZOB. They organised themselves this time according to the sector they were billeted to, rather than along political lines. They heard that Polish resistance groups were now forming in the forests and they even managed to get some pistols from Polish communists. These they used to attack senior figures in the Jewish police.

ZOB also attacked Jewish foremen who had been harsh with the slave labourers under their care. During one attack, three ZOB men were arrested, but others disarmed the German guards and freed them.

In mid-November several hundred more Jews were deported, ostensibly to the concentration camp at Lublin. During the train journey, a ZOB man broke the bars on the carriage window, pushed six women out and jumped out himself. Before, such an escape had been impossible – the escapees would have been held back by others, fearful of the vengeance the Germans might wreak. Now everyone realised the deportation meant death and it was better to die honourably.

In December 1942, ZOB received ten pistols from the Polish Home Army, which had recently formed. They planned to take revenge on the Jewish police, but on 18 January, they found the ghetto surrounded again as the Germans started a second liquidation. This time, however, they were not unopposed. ZOB put up barricades and, for the first time in the ghetto, offered armed resistance. There was a full-scale battle on the streets and many ZOB men were killed. Realising that they were not ready to take on the Germans in this way – they did not have the weapons for it – they resorted to guerrilla tactics. Four guerrilla actions were organised, one of which attacked the SS. Again, it cost ZOB lives.

One ZOB battle group was caught unarmed by the Germans. They were taken to the *Umschlagplatz*, where their leader addressed them. When they were ordered to get on to the train, not a single man moved. Van Oeppen, the chief of Treblinka, shot all 60 himself, on the spot. Tragic though this was, it was an inspiration to others.

Both Polish and Jewish public opinion were altered by these ghetto battles. The halo of omnipotence had been ripped from the heads of the Germans and they were frustrated by these actions. At last, people realised that it was possible to oppose the Germans' will and might.

Although the resistance was puny, rumours began to circulate outside the ghetto that there were hundreds of dead Germans inside. Word spread throughout Warsaw that ZOB was invincible. The Polish Underground was so impressed that they sent 50 pistols and 50 hand grenades. ZOB organised itself into a tight military outfit with sentries and guard posts manned 24 hours a day – they did not intend to get caught napping by the Germans again.

Once more, the German propaganda machine got to work. Two of the Warsaw factories were to be moved to Jewish 'reservations where productive Jews devotedly working for the Germans would be able to live through the war in peace'. In February 1943, 12 Jewish foremen arrived from the concentration camp in Lublin and tried to persuade the Jews of the Warsaw Ghetto to volunteer. The working conditions in Lublin were 'excellent', they said. That night ZOB surrounded the Lublin men's quarters and forced them out of the ghetto.

ZOB began putting its own proclamations on the ghetto walls. When the Germans tried to counter this, ZOB seized their posters from the printing shop and destroyed them: ZOB was now in control of the ghetto. Again, plans were announced, saying that German factories were being evacuated to 'Jewish reservations'. At one joinery shop, only 25 out of the 1,000 Jewish workers volunteered to go. ZOB burned down the joinery shop, causing one million zlotys-worth of damage. The Germans issued a statement saying the fire had been started by a parachutist, but no one in the ghetto had any doubt about who was really behind it.

The next factory, a brush maker's, was to be moved in March. Out of its 3,500 Jewish workers, not one registered to go. When the machinery was being moved, ZOB planted incendiary bombs with delayed action fuses so the machines burnt up on their way.

ZOB now had the backing of the whole ghetto, which supplied them with food. Money was donated to buy arms and ammunition, and they taxed those who would not pay voluntarily. Even the Jewish Community Council was taxed. The money was then smuggled over to the 'Aryan side' where weapons and explosives were bought. These were then smuggled back into the ghetto like other contraband – Polish policemen were bribed to look the other way as heavy packages were hurled over the wall. Inside the ghetto, the Jewish police had no say any more.

Petrol was smuggled in to make Molotov cocktails and explosives were used to manufacture hand grenades. Soon every member of ZOB was armed with a pistol with ten to 15 rounds of ammunition, four or five hand grenades, and four or five Molotov cocktails. Each area had two or three rifles and there was one machine-gun for the entire ghetto.

ZOB now decided to rid the ghetto of all those who had collaborated with the Germans. Death sentences were pronounced on all Jewish Gestapo agents; those who were not killed, fled. Later, when four Gestapo agents entered the ghetto, three were killed and the fourth badly wounded.

Realising that those remaining in the ghetto were not going to go to their deaths voluntarily, the Germans began arresting people for minor offences. However, when ZOB heard that the people caught were going to be deported, they raided the jailhouse and freed them.

The Germans then tried arresting people en masse, loading them onto trucks and taking them direct to the *Umschlagplatz*; ZOB stopped the trucks and freed them. Finally, the Germans got so frustrated that they decided to forcibly liquidate the remainder of the ghetto, no matter what the cost.

At 2 a.m. on 19 April 1943, ZOB observation posts reported that the Germans were coming. German and Polish policemen surrounded the ghetto at 30-yard intervals. Within fifteen minutes, ZOB had manned its defensive positions. The inhabitants of the ghetto were warned and fled to pre-arranged shelters and hiding places in cellars and attics.

At 4 a.m., German soldiers arrived in threes and fours, hoping not to arouse the suspicion of the population. Once in the middle of the ghetto, they formed in companies and platoons. At 7 a.m., motorised detachments, including a number of tanks and armoured vehicles, entered the ghetto. Field guns were set up around the walls. SS men came marching in, their goose-stepping boots ringing down the silent streets of the ghetto – the mastery of their situation seemed complete.

However, they had chosen to form at exactly the wrong place – the intersection of Mila and Zamenhofa Streets. ZOB had been waiting for just such an opportunity, and they were manning all four corners of the inter-section. They rained gunfire and hand-grenades down on the SS men. Even the machine-gun opened up on them, sparingly – ammunition had to be conserved. The SS tried to retreat, but found themselves cut off. Those still alive tried to find shelter in doorways, but were fired on from all sides. A tank was called up to cover the retreat; it was hit with a Molotov cocktail and burned out. Not one German left the area alive.

Another group of Germans tried to enter the ghetto, but they were pinned down. After dozens were killed and wounded, they were forced to withdraw.

In Muranoski Square, the partisans were cornered. But they fought so ferociously that they repulsed the attack, capturing two German machine-guns and burning out a second tank. By 2 p.m., there was not a single German left alive in the ghetto. It was ZOB's first complete victory.

For the next 24 hours the ghetto was bombed and shelled. Then at 2 p.m. on 20 April, the SS turned up again in close formation. As they waited for the gate into the ghetto to be opened, a partisan set off a remote-controlled mine – 100 SS men were killed. The rest withdrew under showers of gunfire.

Two hours later, the Germans attacked again, this time in a loose formation. Although 30 Germans entered the ghetto, only a handful re-emerged; the Germans were forced to withdraw. They tried to attack again in several points around the ghetto but met with ferocious opposition – every house round the perimeter of the ghetto was now a fortress.

At this point the Germans changed tactics. They sent emissaries – three officers with machine-guns lowered and white rosettes in their buttonholes – who suggested a 15-minute truce to remove their dead and wounded. They also offered all the inhabitants of the ghetto safe passage to labour camps in the Jewish reservations. They would even be allowed to take their belongings with them. The response from ZOB was gunfire.

In one area, the Germans were taking such heavy casualties that, by dusk, they resorted to setting the buildings on fire. ZOB partisans were forced to withdraw, but their retreat was blocked by a wall. A gap in it was the only way to the central ghetto, but it was guarded on three sides by German and Polish police, and Ukrainians. Half the group managed to slip through in the darkness before the Germans found a searchlight and trained it on the wall. One well-aimed shot put the light out and the rest of the partisans escaped.

The ordinary inhabitants of the ghetto were not so lucky. Thousands perished in the flames; others ran out into the courtyards where they were seized by the Germans or killed on the spot. Hundreds committed suicide by jumping from the fourth or fifth storeys of apartment houses – some mothers jumped with their children to save them from the flames. The only consolation was that these scenes of horror were witnessed by thousands of Poles who lived in the surrounding area.

The Germans thought that such horrendous loss of life would subdue the ghetto. They announced a deadline for the inhabitants to report to collection points for deportation: no one turned up. The partisans now began to take the battle to the enemy. They tried to disrupt troop movements into the central ghetto; from balconies, windows and rooftops, they showered SS trucks with bombs. One such vehicle saw all but five of the 60 SS men it was carrying killed. ZOB even succeeded in blowing up a military vehicle outside the wall of the ghetto.

When the deadline had passed, the Germans tried to enter the ghetto again, with force. The partisans had planted mines, but the electricity supply had been cut off, so they could not detonate them. As a result, they began fighting house by house. Again, the Germans were forced to resort to arson. ZOB guided the inhabitants of the ghetto to underground shelters, where thousands sheltered for over a week.

When the burning was over, not a single building was left and the water supply was cut off. Still ZOB fought on – the Germans did not dare to enter the ghetto during the day. Ferocious fighting took place at night and there were heavy losses on both sides. Food and water were scarce, as was ammunition. ZOB knew that there were 20 rifles and more ammunition waiting for them on the 'Aryan side', but there was no way they could get them.

The Germans began looking for the shelters using police dogs and sensitive sound-detecting equipment. When they found them, battle raged. Although ultimately they could not resist the might of the Germans, ZOB fulfilled its aim – the Germans did not evacuate a single living person.

On 8 March, Germans and Ukrainians surrounded ZOB's headquarters. After two hours of ferocious fighting, they hurled in gas bomb. Seeing the position was hopeless, the partisans committed suicide rather than be taken by the Germans alive. Some shot their families, then themselves – 80 per cent of the partisans perished there.

The remnants banded together. Ten days earlier, two partisans had been sent out of the ghetto to contact their liaison men to arrange the withdrawal of the battle groups from the ghetto when it fell. Now the liaison men turned up. Those who remained were taken down into the sewers to make their way out. The Germans had anticipated this, so the sewers were full of obstacles and entanglements that were booby-trapped and would explode at a single touch. In some places the sewers were only 28 inches high and it was difficult for the escaping partisans to keep their mouths above the level of the sewage. Every so often, the Germans would pump gas into the drains. At one place, where the sewer was not big enough for them to stand, they had to wait for 48 hours. Partisans kept losing consciousness. For some, the lack of water was too much to bear. Driven mad by thirst they drank the foul sewer water.

On 10 May, a manhole cover was lifted in broad daylight. A number of Jewish partisans emerged and escaped in a truck. Others were left in the sewer. Those who got out were taken out to the woods where they fought with the Polish Home Army. Most died eventually. Those who survived took part in the Warsaw Uprising of 1944.

As the Soviet army approached the city in July 1944, the Polish Underground staged an uprising against the Germans. They were members of the Home Army who were run by the Polish Government in exile in London. However, they knew that in east Poland, which had already been liberated by the Red Army, the pro-communist Polish Committee of National Liberation was in charge. Hoping to gain control of Warsaw before the Red Army took it, the Home Army followed the suggestion of the Soviets and revolted.

The Home Army's Warsaw Corps numbered about 50,000 men. Against weakened German opposition, they had taken over most of the city by 1 August. However, the Germans counter-attacked, forcing the Polish Home Army into defensive positions which they bombed and shelled for the following 63 days. The Red Army occupied the suburb of Praga, across the Vistula River from the city and stopped there while the Germans bombed the city flat. The Soviets also prevented the British and Americans from supplying the rebels.

Out of food and ammunition, the beleaguered Poles had to surrender on 1 October. The remnants of the Home Army and the remaining Jews were taken prisoner and deported, and the rest of the city was destroyed. Only then did the Red Army move on.

This was an entirely cynical ploy by the Soviets: allowing the Germans to destroy the Home Army eliminated the main body of the military organisation that supported the Polish government in exile in London. So when the Soviets overran the whole of Poland there was little effective resistance to the communist-led puppet government they installed.

For the Jewish resistance fighters who had survived the Warsaw ghetto, this was the ultimate betrayal – many of them had been communists. On May Day 1943, a week before the ghetto was finally liquidated, they had held a communist-inspired celebration. There were speeches and the sound of the Internationale had rung out across the smouldering ruins of the ghetto. Of the 500,000 Jews that had passed through the Warsaw ghetto, only a handful had survived.

15 ❖ Babi Yar

There is a ravine outside Kiev, capital of the Ukraine, called Babi Yar. In 1941, the Nazis butchered 200,000 Jews there. If anyone had ever had any doubt as to Hitler's intentions towards the Jewish people, it was dispelled by the atrocity at Babi Yar.

When the Germans marched into Kiev on 19 September 1941, many Ukrainians rejoiced. It was the end of Soviet – Russian – rule. Since the Soviets took over in 1919, the Ukraine had been decimated by collectivisation, purges and famine. Even the Jews welcomed the Germans. The Soviet newspapers had carried not a word about Nazi atrocities. Right up until Hitler's sudden attack in June 1941, the Soviet press had heaped praise on Stalin's ally Hitler. Nothing was said of the treatment of Jews in Germany and Poland. Some Jews even praised Hitler for being an able statesman. The older people recalled that, when the Germans had been in the Ukraine in World War I, they had behaved very well – much better than the Russians. They had not been anti-Semitic then. The Germans were civilised Europeans with a respect for order. Most of all they were renowned for their consistency. Soon the Ukrainian Jews would discover, tragically, how wrong they were.

When the Germans entered the city, they headed straight for the Kreshchatik. This was the main street in Kiev where the party officials and secret policemen lived and worked. Naturally, these officials had already departed. The Germans set up their headquarters there, taking over the Continental Hotel and converting the Doctors' Club into a club for German officers. Germans filled the boulevard cafés. Two enterprising Jewish barbers set up shop and did a roaring trade, cutting German officers' hair.

The first ominous note was sounded when the Germans took over the radio station – all Jews working there were ordered out. On 24 September, the new boss of the radio station was just telling those remaining that he wanted the world to hear 'the voice of free Kiev' when there was a massive explosion: the German headquarters had blown up. Explosions continued for the next five days, setting alight the centre of Kiev. Nobody knows how many Germans were killed. Neither the Nazis nor the Soviets would say. Long after the war, the Soviets denied blowing up the Kreshchatik, blaming it on the Germans; however, it is clear now that the Soviet authorities mined the whole area before leaving. A few soldiers had been left behind to detonate the bombs, but word quickly spread that the Jews were to blame.

On the morning of 28 September, a notice went up. It said in Russian, Ukrainian and German, 'All Yids living in the city of Kiev and its vicinity are to report by eight o'clock on the morning of Monday, 29 September 1941, at the corner of Melnikovsky and Dokhturov Streets (near the cemetery). They are to take with them documents, money, valuables, as well as warm clothes, underwear etc.

'Any Yid not carrying out this instruction and who is found elsewhere will be shot.

'Any civilian entering flats evacuated by Yids and stealing property will be shot.'

Ukrainians assumed that the Jews were being deported to Palestine, possibly as a reprisal for the Kreshchatik. Most Jews thought so too and did what they were told. The following morning the streets near the cemetery were full of women and children, the sick and the elderly; all able-bodied young men had already been conscripted into the Red Army. These were poor people too – anyone with enough money to leave Kiev was long gone. Some had even managed to bribe their way out of the city after it had been occupied.

Many Ukrainians had no great love for the Jews: some hurled insults at them; others called for them to be confined in a ghetto. Some Jews already feared that they were going to their deaths. One woman had poisoned herself and her children; a young girl had thrown herself from an upper storey window. Her body lay in the street covered by a sheet – nobody bothered to remove it.

The crowd was moved off, a rumour having circulated that they were heading for the railway station. People carried suitcases; some seemed to have the entire contents of their houses strapped to their backs. Others had

President George Bush speaking in front of the Babi Yar Holocaust Memorial in Kiev.

clubbed together to hire a lorry to carry their possessions.

The Russians and Ukrainians were not universally hostile to the Jews. Some had come to see old friends off while others helped them with their bags. German soldiers looked on, keeping an eye out for pretty Jewish girls.

The dense crowd edged along until they got to the Jewish cemetery. The entrance was guarded by German soldiers and Ukrainian policemen who told the crowd that anyone who entered would not be allowed back – with the exception of cabbies who could drop their fare and go back for another one. Jews were separated from non-Jews, husbands from wives.

Still, most people assumed that they were being taken to a train – there was a war on and they were being evacuated to somewhere safer. The Jews were going first, they reasoned, because they were more closely related ethnically to the Germans than the Russians or Ukrainians.

Once inside the cemetery everyone was told to drop what they were carrying – foodstuffs on the right, baggage on the left; they would have to sort things out when they got to their destination. By now they could hear the occasional burst of machine-gun fire nearby, but could not admit to themselves that they were going to be shot. For one thing, there was such an enormous mass of people. Such things did not happen, they told themselves.

By the time they realised what was happening, it was too late. They found themselves walking through a narrow corridor lined by soldiers and dogs. The soldiers stood shoulder to shoulder, had their sleeves rolled up and were armed with clubs and sticks. As the crowd passed through, the soldiers beat them savagely, aiming for the ribs, the stomach and the groin, drawing blood. Those who fell to the ground were set upon by the dogs and trampled by those coming from behind.

Young women were propositioned by German soldiers who said that they could save them if they slept with them. Ukrainian policemen then ordered everyone to strip; those who hesitated had their clothes ripped off them. They were still being kicked and hit with knuckledusters and clubs by Germans who seemed to be in a sadistic frenzy. This was being done to keep the huge mass of people disorientated.

Bleeding, naked people formed lines at a gap that had been dug in the steep wall of sand. Some Ukrainians who had got mixed up with the Jews stood to one side there, but an officer ordered that they be shot anyway. He was afraid that if word got out of what was happening, no Jews would turn up the next day.

The lines of naked people were marched through into the ravine, and lined up on a narrow ledge in the quarry. It had been cut especially for the executions and was so narrow that victims automatically leant back against the sandstone. Below them was a sea of bodies covered in blood. On the other side, the machine-gun crews had built a fire, where they brewed coffee. When the ledge was full, they left the fire and returned to their guns. Then they loosed off a burst along the line. As each person was hit, they fell into the sea of bodies below. Around 34,000 people were killed that day.

One woman escaped, though. Her name was Dina Mironovna Pronichev. She was an actress and mother of two. Her husband was

Russian; she did not look Jewish, spoke Ukrainian and could have passed as one. When she read the notice, she decided not to go. However, she would see her parents to the train, then return home to look after the children. When she realised what was happening, her parents told her she should save herself. She approached one of the Ukrainian policemen and showed him her union card, which did not mention her ethnic group. He set her to one side with the Ukrainians who had got mixed in with the Jews.

'We'll shoot the Jews first, then let you out,' he said.

But when a German officer turned up, he ordered that she should be shot anyway. They were the last batch that day.

When she stood on the ledge, she heard the bullets coming towards her. Before they reached her, she jumped. It was a long drop, but she landed softly on the bodies below and was splattered with blood. Beneath her, she could feel people moving. The Germans climbed down and walked over the corpses, shooting anyone still alive. One SS man caught his foot on Dina. He shone a torch in her face, then picked her up and punched her, but she hung limp and lifeless. He kicked her in the chest and trod on her hand so the bones cracked. Then he walked away.

Earth was piled on top of the bodies. Sand went in Dina's mouth and she realised that she would rather be shot than buried alive. She held her breath to stop herself coughing and wriggled free. It had been a long day for the Ukrainian policemen and they only covered the corpses with a light sprinkling of sand. In the dark, she crawled to the edge of the pit.

She dug handholds in the sandy sides and hauled herself out. Hearing a whisper, she nearly jumped back into the pit. It was a young boy who had somehow escaped too. Together, they crawled off into the night.

They made little progress. When it grew light they hid in some bushes on the edge of another ravine. From there, they watched the Germans sorting out people's belongings. An old woman and her six-year-old grandson came by; the Germans shot them. Six or seven Germans led two young women out on to a ledge on the other side of the ravine and gang raped them. When they had finished, they bayoneted them, leaving their bodies there naked with their legs spread. All the time, in the background, was the sound of shooting.

Dina fell into a trance and saw her mother, father and sister in long white robes. She was awoken by the boy who said plaintively, 'Don't die, lady, don't leave me.'

When it grew dark again, they crawled on. Towards dawn, the boy crawled ahead as a lookout. She heard him shout, 'Don't move, lady, there are Germans here.'

Then she heard them shoot him. Luckily, they had not understood what he had said and they did not come looking for her. She was so distraught that she temporarily lost her mind, digging a small hole, then filling it up with sand, as if she was burying the boy who had saved her.

The next day she took refuge in a rubbish tip, covering herself with rags and boxes. Occasionally, she heard Germans passing by. Across the road, she saw tomatoes growing in a garden, so when it was dark, she crawled over and ate them. Still she dragged herself on. At around dawn she saw a barn behind a cottage and slipped inside. Hearing a dog barking, a woman came out of the cottage and sent her son to fetch the Germans. They took Dina to a guardhouse where soldiers were drinking coffee. She went to sit on a chair, but they shouted at her and made her sit on the floor.

When the soldiers went, they left one behind on duty. He was sympathetic and let Dina sit on the chair. Later he gave her a rag and indicated that she should clean the window. He told her to look out of the window and pick out the way she had to run. But before she could escape, an officer turned up with two 15-year-old girls. They were sobbing, kissing his boots and telling him he could do anything he liked with them – including have sex with them – if he did not shoot them. The officer took them and Dina back to the place where the victims had been stripped. Around 40 old men and women were sitting among the clothes; one was lying paralysed. They were guarded by a single sentry.

'Don't look at me,' he shouted at Dina. 'I can't do anything for you. I have children too.'

A girl in a soldier's tunic and greatcoat approached, putting the coat around Dina, who was shivering in the cold. She was a 19-year-old Russian nurse who had been left behind in the Soviet retreat.

A lorry arrived and they climbed aboard. It took them to a garage that was being used as a temporary prison. When they arrived, an old woman got off and squatted down to relieve herself. In response, a German soldier shot her in the head. The garage was already full of people rounded up on the streets, waiting to be shot, so the lorry pulled off again, seemingly heading for the Brest-Litovsk highway. It was going full tilt when Dina threw herself off. Either the guards did not see her, or did not care, because the lorry did not stop.

A group of people gathered around her. She explained that she had meant to go to the market, but had missed her stop and jumped off. They did not believe her, but took her into a nearby farmhouse anyway. Half an hour later she found refuge with her brother's wife, who was Polish.

Over the next two years, the slaughter continued. Between 100,000 and 200,000 Jews, communist officials and Russian prisoners of war were killed at Babi Yar. When the Germans retreated in August 1943, they had bodies exhumed by slave labour and burnt in huge pyres in an attempt to conceal what they had done. Dina survived the war and was the only eyewitness to what had happened at Babi Yar on 29 September 1941.

16 ❖ The Bombing of Dresden

After the Allies had successfully overcome the last serious German offensive in World War II, the Battle of the Bulge in the winter of 1944–45, the British and US to the west and the Soviets to the east were involved in a free-for-all, with each side seeing how much German territory it could seize.

However, Britain, the US and the Soviet Union were still ostensibly allies. So on the night of 13 February 1945, a matter of months before the end of the war in Europe, the Anglo-American air force made a show of helping the invading Red Army. They ordered some 1300 bombers to fire-bomb the medieval city of Dresden that stood in the path of the Russian invaders, reasoning that Dresden was a major communications centre. In reality, it had no strategic significance at all apart from a railway marshalling yard that was not targeted. There were no factories there either. However, the city was completely destroyed and as many 135,000 people were killed –almost twice as many as were killed by the atomic bomb dropped on Hiroshima. It was the biggest single raid of the war in Europe.

The people of Dresden could not be considered combatants. Most able-bodied men were away at the front. The women, children and the elderly left behind had been joined by refugees, again the young, the old and the female, from Silesia and Wargau. The peacetime population of 600,000 had swollen to one million. Before the bombing started one could hardly move in the station. Children were dying of hunger and cold; old people collapsed and died from the stress. Ironically, the only significant body of men

The destroyed city of Dresden. As many as 135,000 people were killed.

in the city was Allied prisoners of war who had been drafted in as forced labour to help feed the population.

The idea of bombing Dresden was first floated at the conference at Yalta in early February 1945. The three great war leaders, Churchill, Roosevelt and Stalin, met in the Crimean resort to discuss how to finish off Hitler. In return for the Anglo-American bombing of targets in the path of the Red Army, Stalin promised to declare war on the Japanese once the war in Europe was won.

Although the Germans had come up with the idea of carpet bombing during the Spanish Civil War, it had been perfected by Air Marshal Sir Arthur 'Bomber' Harris, who had taken command of the RAF's Bomber Command in 1942. He believed that the war could be won by turning every German city into a pile of rubble. His reasoning was that, if one destroyed all of the enemy's industry and killed its workforce, the front-line troops would have no weapons to fight with. They could then be easily overcome by Allied troops equipped with weapons made in the United States, Canada and the far-flung regions of Siberia, which were beyond the range of German planes. Churchill was uneasy about the morality of such a wholesale onslaught on civilians but, in 1942, there was no other strategy.

The operation that had been decided on had to be undertaken immediately, in February. The return trip to Dresden was a nine-hour flight from England, much of it across hostile territory. Even though the nights were still long, some of the journey across Germany would inevitably take place during daylight and the hope was that the bad weather usually experienced at that time of year would keep German fighters on the ground.

Bomber Command would attack on the night of the 13th in two waves separated by three hours. The Americans, whose Flying Fortresses were better suited to daytime missions, would attack on the morning of the 14th. The RAF's first wave would consist of 245 four-engined Lancaster bombers with nine Mosquitoes to mark the target. The Lancasters would take ten to 15 minutes to pass over the target. The second wave would be 529 Lancasters, which would take 20–30 minutes to pass over the target. Each Lancaster would carry 1,447.7 tons of high explosive and 1,181.6 tons of incendiaries, along with 2,154 gallons of fuel for the long flight. The bombing would be concentrated by using a broad formation with planes at different heights.

That night, numerous other planes would be in the air to confuse the German defences and make dummy attacks on other targets. The following two days, 527 B-17 Flying Fortresses carrying 953.3 tons of high explosives and 294.3 tons of incendiaries would again attack the target. They would be escorted by hundreds of fighters who, when not defending the bombers, would fly low and strafe trains and trucks.

The plan was to burn the centre out of the city. The lead plane would mark the sports ground in the centre of Dresden with red target indicators. Then the rest of the formation would move in.

It was known that there were light air defences around the railway yards. One interesting piece of intelligence came from Colditz Castle, which was used to hold British officers who had made a habit of escaping from other prison camps. One of the inmates had asked a guard whether there were any barrage balloons over Dresden. He was told there were none. Otherwise, little was known about the city and the aircrew were not supplied with maps, so it is plain that the bombers were not aiming to take out specific military targets – their target was the city itself.

During the briefing, the aircrew was told that Dresden was one of the few centres of communication between Berlin and the Russian Front. The men were informed that the city was full of men and material on their way to the Russian Front, which was not true. Many trains were due, filled with refugees fleeing the air raids on Berlin. The bombing of Dresden was designed to cause maximum havoc and intended to break the morale of those left defending Berlin. It would give Berliners the idea that there was nowhere safe to run to. Even so, some of the aircrew questioned their orders. They could not see the justification for firebombing a city like Dresden. It was not a military target; rather it was a famous centre of art. Some asked why they could not concentrate on industrial targets like Cologne or the Ruhr. However, their commanders intimated that the order had come from Churchill himself. Many got the impression that the raid was being staged to impress the Russians with the power of Bomber Command. Although this left them uneasy, in modern war terrible things do happen to civilians. And British cities had taken their share of punishment.

The fliers were ordered that if they were hit they should fly as far as possible westwards before ditching their planes. They should not try and fly eastwards to safety behind Russians lines; tension between the Allies was already showing and downed British and American airmen had already been maltreated by the Soviets.

The Lancasters began taking off at 6 p.m. on the evening of 13 February. The outward journey would take five hours, as the planes would zigzag to avoid flak and keep the Germans guessing about their destination. They had been told to expect harassment from enemy fighters. With such a long journey across enemy territory, almost to the point of no return, many of the airmen expected to be killed.

The Mosquitos left later and took a more direct route. Their flight time was two and a half hours. They were expected over the target at 10 p.m. It would then take them ten to 15 minutes to locate and illuminate the aiming points.

The attackers were lucky with the weather. Cloud cover was total over the continent, which meant they had little trouble with night-fighters. However, the weather forecasters in England had predicted that the skies over Dresden would clear at about 10 p.m. and stay clear for only a short while: timing was of the essence.

The Mosquitos found the target using radio beams but, due to the curvature of the earth, they had to be high to detect them; even then, they were faint. When they picked them up, they found that they were 15 miles south of Dresden, so turned back towards the city.

Using radar they located the sports stadium and dropped a green flare on it. The cloud over Dresden was solid, almost down to the ground, meaning that any sort of precision bombing would be out of the question.

Suddenly it cleared below 3,000 feet. The Mosquitos went down and marked targets with red flares, going so low that they could see cars and people on the ground. The main marker had missed the sports ground by about 300 feet, but was, effectively spot on. When dropping bombs from the height the Lancasters were operating at, anywhere within a couple of miles was considered a direct hit.

The Lancasters could see the flares through the clouds, though they could not see the city itself. The Mosquitos dived again, planting more flares so that there could be no mistaking the target. Then the order was given for the Lancasters to start their bombing run.

Over the target there was no fighter cover. A petrol shortage kept the *Luftwaffe* on the ground. There was some light flak from a battery of 20 millimetre guns manned by schoolboys, but there were no serious defences, so the master bomber ordered the Lancasters to come in low. The heavy guns had been taken away to the Russian front. Dresden was, essentially, undefended.

The people were unprepared. Dresden had only suffered two small daylight raids. When the green flare was dropped over the sports stadium, illuminating the city with an eerie glow, some people went outside to see what was happening. When the sirens began, many people assumed that the raid was not on Dresden but on some other city in the area.

The ten o'clock train had been stopped in the station when someone accidentally pulled the communication cord. Police directed people to the air-raid shelter under the station. Some stubbornly stayed on the train; others, who had been in air raids in other German cities, knew that it was better to be anywhere else other than a railway station during an air raid. They were right: 3000 dead were found in the shelter and another 300 were found on the train – all of them burnt to death.

As the Lancasters began unloading their bombs, people took shelter wherever they could. The famous Dresden choir was singing when the Lancasters came. Bombs fell among the choirboys, killing them. The blasts of the four- or sometimes eight-ton bombs had a terrible effect. Later, numerous pregnant women were found with their bellies open and their mutilated babies literally blown out of them.

The focus of the attack was not the sports stadium, or the station, but the old town to the east with its timber-framed houses. However, bombs were falling miles from there. Some of the RAF's incendiaries had poor ballistic qualities and, once dropped, spread out over an extensive area.

The houses in Dresden's old town were butted up against each other to save space. Inevitably, once one caught fire the whole street would burn. The houses were built with a cellar underneath for storage, in which most people took cover. Although these cellars afforded some protection against blast, they were no help against incendiaries. Once they hit, people had to come out of the cellar and try to smother the incendiary bombs with sand or water before they burst into flames. This was a hazardous business. By 1945, some incendiaries were fitted with a small explosive booby trap to kill, maim, or at least discourage anyone from smothering them.

After the first couple of casualties, people gave up trying to extinguish the incendiaries and fled, leaving the houses to burn. Soon the old town was a raging inferno: dust and smoke made it impossible to see; survivors covered with wet blankets tried to find their way out, while they continued to be blasted from above. A boys' school that had been turned into a military hospital – with a red cross on the roof – was hit; 300 wounded men were killed when the building collapsed.

Soon the fire had taken such a hold that the fire brigade could do nothing to halt the conflagration. The air above the target became superheated, making it difficult for the oncoming stream of bombers to identify any target other than the enormous fires. The markers were obscured by smoke and the violent winds caused by the updraft made it difficult to manoeuvre the Lancasters as they came in. As a result, the remaining aircraft simply dumped the rest of their bombs on the blazing city and turned for home. The final wave of high explosives blasted the fires horizontally a considerable distance.

Despite the horrific speed of the attack, Dresden had suffered no worse than hundreds of other town and cities across Germany – up to this point. No one on the ground realised that at the same moment the first flares were dropping, a second wave of planes – twice as big as the first – was taking off in England.

In all, the second wave of 529 Lancasters carried 650,000 tons of explosives in their dark bellies. Each plane also carried one 4,000-pound thin-walled blast bomb.

Again, the planes took a zigzag path across Germany. They needed no markers – the burning centre of Dresden was a beacon they could home in on from 50 miles away. When the master bomber got there, the city was lit up; he could not see the aiming point. There was no opposition so he flew in low. Being able to see people on the ground brought home to him the horror of what he was about to do.

When the sirens sounded again, the people of Dresden could not believe it. They could not believe that the British intended to raze their beautiful city the way they had the industrial cities to the west. Again, people took refuge in the cellars. When they emerged, they found the fire had turned into a firestorm. Those stuck in the cellars suffocated; many who braved the streets were burnt alive. As they tried to shed their burning clothing, people passed out from oxygen deficiency. Every last molecule of oxygen was being consumed by the burning buildings. People crawled on the ground to gasp what air they could; those who fainted in the streets were quickly charred.

Those who survived looked frantically for friends and loved ones. They searched among the dead, who littered the ground: some were black like charcoal and shrunk to half their size; others lay peacefully unmarked, as if sleeping, their lungs burst by the blast. Women and children sat on the trams as if they had nodded off, or lay around naked, their clothes blasted off them. Soldiers were only identifiable by their belt buckles. Some corpses lay in groups as if clawing at each other; arms, legs and heads poked out of the rubble. Static water tanks were full to the brim with corpses.

Temperatures at the centre of the fire reached 3,000 degrees – 1,200 degrees is the maximum sandstone can withstand so numerous buildings collapsed. Other structures were blown down by the winds the fire drew. Some people were literally blown off their feet and sucked into the flames.

Even at 20,000 feet, the crews in the Lancasters could see a rosy glow in the sky above them. The light was as bright inside the planes as if the aircrew had walked on stage as the heavy aircraft heaved and buckled in the enormous columns of heated air.

The people on the ground began to believe that Churchill had ordered the firebombing of Dresden personally, and cursed the airmen for blindly following his orders. Some believed that the aircrew listened into German radio to hear which shelters people were being instructed to go to. The large bombs, they believed, were then used to pound the shelters, and when people ran out on to the streets smaller bombs were dropped to kill them. The truth was that there was so much smoke and the air was so turbulent that it was impossible for the aircrew to tell where the bombs were going.

A rumour spread that an English spy with a torch was guiding the planes in. The British SS men stationed nearby were blamed. They had betrayed England by backing Germany, and now the Germans were losing the war they were betraying Germany to the RAF; to escape the wrath of the populace they deserted.

No one knew how many dead there were. Figures circulated: 250,000, 300,000, 400,000. There was no possibility of fighting the fires – even when it had been attempted it had been counterproductive. People sheltering in the cellars were drowned.

The famous Zwinger museum went up in flames. Even though its art treasures were to be moved before the Soviets arrived, they sat in a lorry outside, where they were burnt.

When the castle caught on fire, people were trapped in the cellars. Young men, trying unsuccessfully to break though the walls with axes, perished in the flames. Others who escaped the cellars found that the castle's roof hand melted, raining down molten copper on them.

Incendiaries lodged in the dome of the Sarrasani Circus building. The horses and 16 boys and girls who were acrobat riders were killed by a blast bomb. Although the circus people managed to get some of the animals out, the tigers suffocated in their cages. Despite the burning building collapsing on Wally the hippopotamus, he survived because he was half submerged in a tank of water.

The hippopotami at the zoo were not so lucky – when their house collapsed, they were pinned underwater and drowned. Two dwarf hippos took refuge in a bomb crater. A keeper threw hay down to them; but later on they were blown to bits by a time bomb. A gibbon was destroyed after losing its hands; chimps suffocated; some apes escaped and were seen in the forest later. The yaks were burnt and died from their wounds. A mother bear was blinded, but her cubs survived to be suckled by another bitch. The polar bear cubs were not so lucky, though. Their badly burnt mother, who had saved them, had to be put down. They could have been reared by bottle, but there was no milk in the ruins of Dresden and they died of hunger soon after.

Some bison and red buffalo escaped and menaced the people fleeing the city. The vultures escaped too but despite the rich pickings offered by the ruined city, returned to the zoo promptly at feeding time.

As the firestorm raged, it could be seen up to 50 miles away from the ground. Allied prisoners of war who saw the devastation were appalled. Even German soldiers who had suffered the horrors of the Eastern Front said they had never seen anything like it.

The retreating Lancasters could see the firestorm they had left behind for 100 miles. For most, this had been the first raid they had been on where there had been no opposition – no night fighters, no flak to speak of. They felt like murderers: the people they had bombed had been defenceless. For many, the bombing of Dresden seemed like a cowardly act. They felt sorry for the people who had been blasted on the ground four miles beneath them.

One night fighter, a JU 88, did eventually tail the Allied planes, but it quickly turned away, realising that with the light of Dresden behind him he made a perfect target for the Lancaster's tail gunners.

On the ground, the sirens could not sound their all clear – the air-raid warning system had been destroyed. Buildings that had been spared by the bombing caught on fire as the flames spread and a column of people, some in night clothes, some with the hair burnt off their heads, began to make their way out of the city.

The following day, at their brief, some of the American airmen expressed misgivings about attacking Dresden. The city, they knew, was full of refugees fleeing the Russians. Nevertheless, following orders was now routine to them; some of the fighter escort even strafed the trails of people fleeing the burning city.

On the morning of the 14th, there was cloud cover over the city. The American bombers did not even see their target. They simply dropped their bombs where they were told. But survivors said that low-flying aircraft attacked the civilians who were huddling down by the River Elbe. While the zookeepers tried to erect a special tent to protect the giraffe from the freezing weather, an American fighter flew low, killing a number of the animals the keepers had saved the night before. He also killed some of the animal keepers of the Sarrasani Circus.

The writer Kurt Vonnegut was with a working party of 100 American POWs who took shelter with their guards in the huge underground meat safes of the Dresden slaughterhouse. Ironically, they survived, but emerged the following morning to be bombarded by American Mustangs. They took cover in the rubble and watched as the Mustangs went on to shoot German civilians.

On the ground, people were desperately trying to tend the wounded or search for relatives when the bombs started falling again. There were no warning sirens this time. The raid lasted for ten minutes. A total of 487.7 tons of high explosives and 294.3 tons of incendiaries were dropped – small beer compared to the raid the night before. It did little more than disturb the rubble. However, many of the bombs had delayed-action fuses, which made trying to rescue people trapped in cellars a dangerous business.

That night the RAF sent Lancasters to bomb Chemnitz, which was crammed with refugees who had fled Dresden. Dresden was targeted again that night, maybe by the RAF mistaking it for Chemnitz, or maybe by the Russians.

As the Lancasters were returning home in the morning, 211 Flying Fortresses carrying 456.6 tons of high explosives and no incendiaries were taking off to give the ruins of Dresden another pounding. That day it rained, turning the city into a sea of mud, wreckage and half-exposed corpses. Even so, the city burnt for four days. As it was overcast, the Americans simply dumped their loads on the city without any pretence of strategic bombing. The devices must have just churned the rubble once more. Neither German records nor later aerial reconnaissance showed they had any effect whatsoever but this didn't prevent low-flying fighters from continuing to strafe the ruins for another eight days.

As a communications centre Dresden had three distinctive features. One was the railway bridge over the Elbe. It was left intact; indeed, it had never been a designated target. The second was the railway yard and its rolling stock. It too survived, being outside the RAF's target area. The third was the Autobahn bridge outside the city to the west. It was never attacked. Though the city was destroyed and over 100,000 people killed, as a communication centre Dresden was virtually unimpaired.

As the Air Raid Patrolmen, Red Cross and Fire Brigade had been decimated by the air raid, detachments of SS Pioneers worked alongside slave labourers doing rescue work. It was an impossible task. Corpses lay in the streets for days, those that could be collected were buried in mass graves. The centre of the city was cordoned off and the army went in with flamethrowers to cremate the bodies on huge grids. Piles of body parts were heaped together, dowsed with petrol and burnt. No one realised that beneath the rubble there were still people alive, trapped in the cellars. Later, when they opened the cellars, everyone was dead.

At first, they tried lifting out the corpses. 'Thus began the first corpse mine in Dresden,' said Vonnegut, who had helped dig it. But later the stench became too overpowering. The cellars became awash with a green liquid that dripped from the corpses. The SS Pioneers came in with flame-throwers and cremated the bodies where they sat.

For weeks, men carried remains in wooden boxes, cardboard boxes, anything they could find, to the crematorium. But no matter what they did, they could not cope with the scale of the problem. Soon the weather warmed, the unburied corpses became a writhing sea of maggots and the city a cloud of flies.

Survivors found what shelter they could. Wounds were covered with paper as the city had run out of bandages. As well as the cold weather, people were menaced by wild animals that had escaped from the zoo. An ostrich was found 50 miles away, dead in the snow, the remains of a fox in its mouth.

Although many people cursed the British after the bombing of Dresden, many of the survivors also cursed Hitler. After all, it was he who had brought this holocaust on them. Some critics earned themselves a bullet in the back of the head for their pains.

Although the German papers described the British as 'terror-fliers', 'air-gangsters' and 'child-murderers' after the raid on Dresden, British prisoners of war did not find this attitude reflected in their guards, even among those who had lost relatives or entire families in Dresden. The war was nearly over and the guards would far rather be captured by the British or Americans than by the Russians.

Some of the people took out their frustration on the American POWs who were helping to clear the rubble, though. They were cursed and spat on. There were rumours that Americans had been shot for looting; there was one such case, but he was not a POW. He was a 45-year-old school-teacher and former recruiter for the Free America Corps, who was then an infantryman in the SS. He had found a battered teapot in the rubble, and was court-martialled for looting and executed by a firing squad. At the time, his son was on the other side, serving in the US Marine Corps.

A massive 15 square kilometres of Dresden were destroyed completely. After the war, the authorities considered bulldozing the remains of the city and rebuilding the place from scratched. Instead, the castle and the Zwinger museum were restored, while the rest of the city was rebuilt in an undistinguished eastern European style. One of the loveliest cities of Europe had been lost forever.

17❖Sharpeville

South Africa has had a troubled history since the white settlers arrived. First the British fought the Zulus, then they fought the Boers. However, in the 1948 election, the Boers of the Nationalist Party took power. They stopped immigration from England and introduced the policy of apartheid, or separate development.

One major tool in ensuring the separation of the races were the pass book laws. Every black person who lived outside the *bantustans* – special areas set aside for African habitation – was to carry a pass book. This contained the bearer's name and address, sex, ethnic classification, the labour officer they were registered to, details of their offences against the pass laws, their employer's name and address (which had to be signed each week), tax receipts, drivers and weapons licenses, and a photograph. The system had been introduced by the British in the Cape in 1809. The African National Congress was formed in 1912 and held their first protest against the pass laws in 1919.

When the Nationalists took power they drastically tightened the pass-book laws. Pass books had to be produced on demand; those who did not have one or whose pass book was not in order were fined heavily, jailed, forced into low-paid work or confined to the *bantustans*. During the 1950s, 1_ million black people were moved out of the cities – which were designated white areas – and returned to the over-crowded, poverty-stricken parcels of land reserved for Africans.

In 1958, opposition to apartheid split and the Pan-African Congress was formed by 'Africanists' who demanded 'Africa for the African'. The ANC was a broader church: it was a coalition of Africans, largely English-speaking white liberals, communists, those of mixed race and Indians, and anyone else opposed to apartheid.

In 1959, both the ANC and PAC called for non-violent protests against the pass-book laws. The ANC's campaign was to start on 31 March 1960; the PAC began theirs on 18 March, and called for nationwide demonstrations on the 21st. Thousands responded in a small township in the Transvaal called Sharpeville.

Sharpeville had some 36,000 residents in 1960. At one o'clock around 10,000 of them turned up at the police station. This was not a single building but a compound, with a number of buildings and a big yard, surrounded by a wire fence. There were about 200 policemen – both white and African – inside. To the north was a large field; to the west was a square; and to the south a row of houses.

The protesters completely surrounded the police station. The commanding officer, Lieutenant Colonel Pienaar, turned up at around one o'clock with some reinforcements. A protester threw a rock at his car, which put him in a bad mood. Although there were batons and tear-gas canisters in the compound, his deputy, Major Van Zyl, had not tried to disperse the mob. By one o'clock, the crowd was too big and pressed too close to the fence to try that.

Pienaar had been expecting trouble. Nine policemen – four white, five black – had been killed when trying to close a beer hall in a township outside Durban a couple of months before. His men were heavily armed with Sten guns, rifles and revolvers, and there were six Saracen armoured cars in the compound.

The crowd outside was generally good tempered, but as more and more people turned up, they began shouting, 'Our land! Our Land!'

The rock that had hit Pienaar's car gave him the impression that the crowd had already been violent. Some of his officers were feeling tense; Pienaar himself was unnerved. Though peaceful, the demonstration was illegal – all protests by Africans were. It was his duty to break it up. At 1.30, Pienaar decided that what was needed was a show of force. He stationed the armoured cars along the north side of the compound, with their crews standing on the car roofs. Around 70 officers were positioned along the south and west, with rifles and machine-guns. Although most of them had already loaded their guns, Pienaar gave the order to load just five rounds – the idea was to intimidate the crowd. It was not clear what he intended to do next and he was under the impression that Major Van Zyl had tried threatening the crowd and firing over their heads – it had not worked.

Outside the compound were men from the South African Special Branch. A Colonel Spengler moved in to arrest the organisers of the demonstration and brought them into the compound. Although the gates had to be opened to do this, the crowd did not try to force their way in. According to Joshua Motha, who was standing in the crowd near the main entrance, the crowd was good humoured. They thought the police would

Over 50 people were killed when South African police opened fire on crowds of demonstrators in Sharpeville, 16th May, 1964.

make an announcement, addressing their grievances, then they would all go home.

A little later, a large grey police car, escorted by three Saracen armoured cars, arrived. The crowd let them into the compound and, again, did not try to rush in. Joshua Motha and the people around him thought that the man in the car was a spokesman for the government come to make the announcement. The car even bumped into one of the protesters, slightly injuring them, but the crowd did not react.

The armed policemen looked as though they were lined up as an honour guard for the man the protesters thought had come to make the announcement. The crowd pressed forward to hear what he had to say; two or three people at the front were arrested. Children began to shout slogans and throw stones. Lieutenant Colonel Pienaar said he thought they were in a state of frenzy; pictures taken by press photographers show that they were not.

No one is very sure what happened next. Some people close to the police station heard a loud noise. A newspaper photographer thought it was a shot, but no one was really sure. Others heard a voice saying, 'Fire!'

Most heard neither. But for whatever reason, the police opened up with everything they had. Within seconds, 69 people were dead or dying and 180 wounded.

When Joshua Motha heard the shooting, he thought the police were firing blanks, until he saw a man lying on the ground. A bullet grazed his trousers, and as he turned to run, another caught him in the hip.

The shooting had not stopped when the crowd turned and ran. The policemen continued shooting protesters in the back. One young woman fell and her boyfriend went back to help her. When he turned her over, he saw that she was dead. The bullet had blown away her chest. One small boy put his coat over his head, as if it would protect him.

It was not just the policemen at the fence who shot – the men standing on the roofs of the Saracens blazed away from the hip. They sprayed bullets indiscriminately in broad arcs, stopping only to reload. In the 40 seconds or so that the shooting lasted for, 705 rounds were fired.

When the shooting stopped, nothing was moving – the crowd had gone. Bodies lay scattered across the field and square. A young mother rushing to the square to find her husband mistook the bodies for sheep that had been mysteriously slaughtered there. Only when she drew nearer did she realised that they were people.

Not all the victims had been protesters. Lechael Musibi was just an innocent passer-by, a teacher at a local school. None of his pupils had turned up that morning, so he left his keys with one of his students and set off on his bicycle to get them. His route took him past the police station. Suddenly the crowd was running at him; he fell off his bike. As he tried to get up, the shooting started again. He lay flat on the ground and watched as people fell. As soon as the shooting stopped, he picked himself up and made his way to the library nearby. When he arrived, a little girl said, 'Look, he's been shot.' Before that, he had not realised that he had been hit.

One man who had been delivering invoices for his company some way away died – a stray bullet had hit him and his head had been blown off.

The police came out of the compound to inspect their handy work, but did nothing to help the wounded. Trucks were brought to cart away the dead. Joshua Motha was ordered to get up and get out of the way; nothing was wrong with him, he was told. He tried to move but could not, so the police dragged him out of the way. It was only then that someone thought about calling an ambulance.

Reverend Robert Maja, the local Presbyterian minister, turned up. He brought water for the wounded and tried to cover them with clothing to protect them from the heat.

Demonstrations in South Africa back then were not often covered by the white-run press. However, Humphrey Taylor from the magazine *The Drum* happened to be there that day. He searched the bodies to see if anyone was carrying weapons. There were none. All he found abandoned among the bodies were shoes, hats and bicycles.

Two truckloads of bodies were taken to the mortuary and 11 ambulances ferried the wounded to hospital. The living and the dead were all gone by 2.30 p.m. The rains came at four and washed the blood away.

Taylor found that he could not get the story of the atrocity published in the newspapers in South Africa, so he sent it to England. The next day, the British papers were full of the massacre at Sharpeville. The leading British television commentator, Richard Dimbleby, compared it to Guernica. The Daily Herald called for a boycott of South African goods and by lunchtime over 600 people had gathered outside South Africa House in Trafalgar Square to protest. In the evening, a long protest march wound its way through the streets of London, as the massacre was condemned in parliament and around the world. The UN passed a resolution of condemnation. Even investors protested: within three days, £90 million was wiped off the Johannesburg stock market. The slide continued – with the beginning of the ANC campaign on 31 March, £70 million were wiped off share values in a single day.

The South African government was unrepentant, though. A few days later the South African police tried to stop a PAC protest meeting in the Western Cape. They charged the crowd and were met with a hail of stones, so they opened fire. Two Africans were killed and 49 injured.

Over the next few days, the South African government gave their account of what had happened at Sharpeville. On 22 March, the Prime Minister, Dr Verwoerd, said that the riots had nothing to do with pass books or apartheid. They were periodic outbursts that might happen anywhere. He praised the police for their courage; the government claimed that they had been attacked by 20,000 demonstrators, many of whom were armed. The *Johannesburg Star* reported that 80 per cent of the injured and been wounded below the belt, and that the police had merely been trying to wound the demonstrators, not kill them. The South African papers also reported that the demonstrators had been armed.

The Bishop of Johannesburg and white liberal organisations challenged this, raising money for lawyers to take statements from the injured and defend the protesters the police had arrested and charged with public order offences. An independent doctor was found to attend the post-mortem examinations. He established that many of the dead had been shot in the back. Soon they had overwhelming evidence that the demonstrators had not been armed.

Lieutenant Colonel Pienaar said that this was beside the point. 'The native mentality does not allow them to gather for peaceful demonstration,' he said. 'For them, to gather means violence.'

On 26 March, ANC leader Chief Albert Luthuli publicly burnt his pass book and urged everyone to do the same. The ANC designated 28 March a day of mourning and many Africans stayed at home. Pass-book laws were suspended – briefly. The PAC and ANC thought they had won, but on 30 March the South African government declared a state of emergency. Another 30 years passed before the pass-book laws and apartheid were finally laid to rest.

However, Sharpeville was the beginning of the end. After the massacre, South Africa was no longer viewed as a civilised nation. Eventually, the South African government was forced to set up a Commission of Enquiry. It found that:

'The officers made no attempt to persuade the crowd to disperse by non-violent means.

'The officers failed to order the crowd to disperse.

'The officers failed to warn the crowd that if they did not disperse force would be used.

'The officers made no attempt to use any form of force less drastic than firearms.

'The officers failed to supervise and control the men under their command.

'The officers took no steps to ensure that if shooting started it would be limited and controlled and could be stopped.

'The constables started shooting without receiving an order to do so.

'Many of the constables shot to kill, not merely to wound.

'They did kill 69 people including eight women and ten children.

'The shooting was indiscriminate and continued long after the crowd had turned and fled.

'The 180 wounded included 31 women and 19 children.

'There was no justification for the police to open fire on the crowd and therefore no justification for the conduct of the police.'

The Commission of Enquiry failed to conclude that the system of apartheid was to blame for the atrocity. But the rest of the world knew.

18 ❖ My Lai

By 1968, the Vietnam war had been underway for three years and the Americans already knew they were losing. The war was the last act in a liberation struggle that had begun when Vietnamese leader Ho Chi Minh gatecrashed the Versailles Peace Conference in 1918, after the end of the World War I. He asked when the French, the colonial power occupying Indo-China, were going to leave his country. He was thrown out.

As part of the liberation struggle, Ho Chi Minh and his fellow Vietnamese nationalists became communists. They began an armed struggle against the French in the 1930s, then took up arms against the Japanese when they invaded during World War II. After the Japanese were defeated, the Viet Minh resumed the fight against the French, which they won in 1954. At a peace conference in Geneva, the country was temporarily divided in two for administrative purposes, with Ho Chin Minh's communists holding the North – the country would be reunited after a general election. That election never came.

As the Cold War grew colder, America saw Vietnam as a place in which they could stop the spread of communism. They were wrong; the Vietnamese had an entrenched military culture. They had been fighting the Chinese for centuries and knew the Americans did not have the stomach for a long war.

As guarantors of the Geneva Peace Agreement, America needed an excuse to go to war. In 1965, they pretended that one of their warships had been attacked by two North Vietnamese gunboats in the Gulf of Tonkin. Congress approved the money for the war and American troops went in. The alleged attack was a fabrication.

By 1968 the Americans knew they were out of their depth. Not only were they fighting a disciplined army from the North, but they also faced a guerrilla army, called the Viet Cong, in the South. Given that a Viet Cong guerrilla looked just like any other Vietnamese person, they were as hard for the Americans to find as a drop of water in a bucket of tears.

Worse was to come. The Americans realised that, as the Viet Cong could simply attack at will and run away, they could control their rate of casualties. Analysts in the Pentagon worked out that the Vietnamese were keeping the losses just below their birth rate. That meant that they could, essentially, fight forever.

Back home in the US, the American public saw the Vietnam as a small and backward place. They believed their massive military superiority should be able to crush any enemy on the planet. But even massive air strikes did no good. The Viet Cong simply crawled out of their shelters and began fighting again.

US ground troops were not highly motivated; many of them did not even know where Vietnam was, nor did they care. Poorly trained US conscripts were rotated home after a year. All most of them wanted was to get through that year in one piece, but these half-hearted soldiers were put up against a ruthless and dedicated enemy who were fighting for their country.

The Americans were consumed with paranoia. No one could be trusted: prostitutes who sleep with GIs left bombs under soldiers' beds after making love to them; toddlers were booby-trapped – if an unwary American picked up the child, both soldier and child would be blown to smithereens. It is little wonder that Americans came to see every Vietnamese person – even women and children – as their enemy. It seemed quite legitimate to kill children, as they would one day grow up to be Viet Cong. The random massacre of Vietnamese civilians became commonplace, but one atrocity in 1968 shocked the world. It helped weaken support for the war in the US and, although American involvement continued for another six years, eventually lost it for them.

On the morning of 16 March 1968, three companies of the American troops were sent on a search and destroy operation in the My Son area near Quang Ngai. Their job was to seek out the enemy and kill them.

The soldiers were from the 11th Infantry Brigade, American Division. Company C's target was the Viet Cong's 48th battalion which intelligence believed was operating out of a hamlet marked on American maps as My-Lai 4. Helicopters set troops down nearby. There was no resistance at the

Lieutenant William L Calley. His name was closely linked with atrocities that took place during the Vietnam War.

landing zone. The company commander Captain Ernest L. Medina sent the 1st and 2nd Platoons into the village. Seeing Americans coming, some villagers ran away and were gunned down. There was no resistance – the 2nd Platoon swept through the northern part of the village, hurling grenades into the huts and killing anyone who came out. They raped and murdered village girls, rounded up civilians and shot them. After half an hour, Medina order the 2nd Platoon on to the hamlet of Binh Tay, where they gang raped several more girls before rounding up some 20 women and children and killing them.

Appalling though these actions were, the name most closely associated with the massacre was that of Lieutenant William L. Calley, who commanded the 1st Platoon which swept through the south of the village, shooting anyone who tried to escape, bayoneting others, raping women, shooting livestock and destroying crops and houses. Survivors were rounded up and herded into a drainage ditch. Lieutenant Calley opened fire on the hapless villagers and ordered his men to join in. They emptied clip after clip into the tangled heap of human flesh until all the bodies lay motionless. When they stopped firing, miraculously, a two-year-old child crawled out of the carnage, crying. He tried to climb out of the ditch and run away. Calley grabbed him, pushed him back and shot him.

Half an hour later, the 3rd Platoon moved in to mop up. They shot wounded villagers to 'put them out of their misery', burnt houses, killed the remaining livestock, shot anyone trying to escape and rounded up a group of women and children and sprayed them with bullets.

No one is sure how many died. Estimates put the death toll at anywhere between 172 and 347 people. They were unarmed old men, women or children – only three of them were known members of the Viet Cong. Captain Medina reported a body count of 90 Viet Cong, no civilians; the divisional press officer announced 128 enemy dead. The war that had begun with a lie continued with lies, until no one in the Pentagon or in the US government knew what was going on. There was just one American casualty, and the wound had been self-inflicted. The press officer said 13 Viet Cong suspects had been captured and three weapons taken. That just three weapons were being shared among 141 enemy soldiers should have alerted someone that something was wrong, but it was just another day in Vietnam.

The reason that, on this occasion, the truth was unravelled was that two pressmen – combat photographer Ronald Haeberle and army reporter Jay Roberts – had been assigned to Calley's platoon. They had witnessed the appalling carnage. One woman had been hit by such ferocious, continuous fire that bone flew off chip by chip; another woman was shot and her baby opened up with an assault rifle; a baby was slashed with a bayonet. One GI, who had just finished raping a girl, put his rifle into her vagina and pulled the trigger; an old man was thrown down a well and tossed a grenade – he had to choose to drown or blow himself up; and a child escaping from the carnage was brought down with a single shot.

There was another appalled witness. Warrant Officer Hugh C. Thompson, the pilot of a small observation helicopter circling the village, had begun dropping smoke flares to mark the position of wounded civilians so they could be medevaced out. He was horrified to see American foot soldiers following the smoke and shooting the casualties.

Gradually, the news leaked out. The men of Company C were not shy about boasting of their great victory at My Lai. Meanwhile, the Viet Cong distributed pamphlets denouncing it as an atrocity. The US Army halfheartedly investigated the rumours of a massacre that had eventually spread up the chain of command, but decided there was no basis for an official enquiry.

However, another soldier, named Ronald Ridenhour, who had ambitions to be a journalist heard about the massacre and took an interest. He made it his business to meet the men from Company C, especially Michael Bernhardt, who had refused to participate in the killing. The other members of Company C were beginning to get uneasy about what they had done, too. They were about to be rotated back to the US and realised that the rest of the world did not operate in the same moral vacuum as Vietnam. They knew that there was nothing they could do without inviting murder charges, but they were happy to unburden themselves to Ridenhour.

Ridenhour compiled what they told him, but realised that if he took his evidence to the army they would stage a summary investigation, which would result in another whitewash. When he returned to the US he could not forget what he had been told, so he drew up a letter outlining his evidence and dispatched 30 copies to prominent politicians.

One of the recipients was Congressman Morris Udall of Arizona. He pressed the Pentagon to interview Ridenhour. Six months later, and nearly 18 months after the atrocity, Lieutenant Calley was charged with murder.

This posed a problem for the US military. What they needed was a scapegoat who could be branded a madman or psychopath – that way they could assure the world that the My Lai massacre was a one-off. But Calley was just a regular guy. He had been working as an insurance appraiser in San Francisco, when he had been called up in his native Miami. He started to drive home, but ran out of money just outside Albuquerque, so he enlisted right there.

Calley was sent to Fort Bliss, Texas, for basic training and went on to clerical school at Fort Lewis, Washington. By this time, the US Army had a severe shortage of officers. After introduction of the draft, the army did not have enough West Point graduates to command the rapidly swelling ranks. As the war grew unpopular the numbers joining the Reserve Officer Training Corps at universities and colleges declined rapidly. Consequently, poorly educated men such as Calley were picked for officer training.

After a so-called 'Shake 'n' Bake' course at the Officer Candidate School at Fort Benning, Georgia, Calley graduated without even being able to read a map properly. Undoubtedly, the course did not dwell on such complexities as the ethics of war. Before graduating, Calley was asked to deliver a speech on 'Vietnam Our Host'. At his trial, he recalled saying that

American troops should not insult or assault Vietnamese women – the rest he was foggy on.

Nothing could have prepared Calley for the moral morass that was Vietnam, and certainly not his sketchy training. He found himself unable to control his own men and incapable of resisting the mounting pressure from his superiors for a 'body count'. As the war in Vietnam had no clear military objectives, the body count had become all-important.

The problem was that Calley and his men could not find any Viet Cong. In his own book on the My Lai massacre Calley described how, when he went with a prostitute who showed communist leanings, he wondered whether he should have shot her. She was the only 'enemy' he had come close to. Out in the paddy field, he could find no one. His inept attempts at ambush were noisy enough to alert the enemy miles away, and the enemy were out there all right; although invisible, they kept taking pot-shots at Calley and his men.

Patrolling near My Son in the My Lai area in February 1969, Calley's radioman was shot. For three days the company tried to penetrate My Son but were driven back. Two men were killed by booby traps; another was hit by sniper fire. The patrol then blundered into a nest of booby traps, but when they extricated themselves unscathed, two more men were cut down by snipers.

On their next assignment, they were heading for the rendezvous point when an explosion tore through the early morning stillness and a man screamed. There followed another explosion and another scream. Each explosion was followed by another – they had stumbled into a minefield and, as men rushed forward to aid their wounded comrades, they detonated more mines. Severed limbs flew through the air, medics crawled from body to body and the explosions continued. The episode lasted for almost two hours, leaving 32 men killed or wounded.

On 4 March, the company was mortared and most of the men's personal possessions were destroyed. Ten days later, two days before the assault on My Lai, four men – including the last of the company's experienced NCOs – were blown to bits by a booby trap. In 32 days, Company C – whose field strength was 90 to 100 – suffered 42 casualties, and they had hardly glimpsed the enemy.

Calley had seen atrocities committed by the Viet Cong too. One night, the VC had captured one of his men and they heard him screaming all night. He was seven kilometres away. Calley thought the Viet Cong had a

PA system and amplifiers. They didn't: they had skinned the GI alive, leaving only the skin on his face. They then bathed his raw flesh with salty water; his penis was torn off. Calley's company recovered the body the next morning.

Calley had also seen a village elder broken in spirit when the VC delivered an earthenware jar containing what looked like stewed tomatoes to his door one morning. There were fragments of bone in it, and hair, and lumps of floating flesh. It was what remained of his son.

He had seen GIs shooting down civilians for fun or target practice. He had heard of helicopter gunships hired out for human turkey shoots and bored GIs going 'squirrel hunting' in civilian areas. He had seen US soldiers casually fire on each other for no reason at all, and he had heard of fragmentation grenades being tossed into officers' quarters when their men did not want to go out on patrol.

'I look at communism the same way a southern looks at a Negro,' he said in an interview. 'As for me, killing those men in My Lai didn't haunt me. I didn't – I couldn't kill for the pleasure of it. We weren't in My Lai to kill human beings, really. We were there to kill ideology that is carried by – I don't know – pawns, blobs, pieces of flesh. And I wasn't in My Lai to destroy intelligent men. I was there to destroy an intangible idea.'

He even wished, humanely, that he could shoot the philosophy part out of people's heads. Besides, he reasoned, it wasn't even really him doing it.

'Personally, I didn't kill any Vietnamese that day, I mean personally. I represented the United States of America. My country.'

Calley believed that he should put his duty to his country above his own conscience. He was not even worried about killing the aged, the women and the children. He had heard of mamasans throwing grenades, children laying mines, girls carrying AK-47s. Besides, when the children grew up they would be VC, like their fathers and mothers. Where were all the men? My Lai was full of women, and children whose fathers must be VC.

As far as Calley was concerned, was what he had done any worse than dropping 500-pound bombs on them or frying them with napalm? The atomic bomb had killed women and children in Hiroshima, hadn't it? And what were these damn Yankees getting so worked about? He had done nothing worse than General Sherman had done in his march to the sea during the American Civil War. The wisdom of the time was, he noted, that

'The only way to end the war in Vietnam was to put all the dinks [South Vietnamese] in boats and take them out to sea, kill all the North Vietnamese . . . then sink the boats.'

Like many American servicemen, Calley eventually stopped believing in the war. He came round to thinking that to argue that communism had to be stopped in Vietnam, before it spread to Thailand, Indonesia, Australia and finally the US – the then fashionable 'Domino Theory' which was the nearest thing the US had to a strategic aim – was like a man coming around to your house to murder his wife because he did not want blood on his carpets, then murdering your wife for good measure.

He knew that it was the Viet Cong who were winning the hearts and minds of the Vietnamese people, not the Americans. After My Lai, Calley became a welfare officer who bought pigs for peasant farmers, arranged sewing lessons for prostitutes and took sick children to hospital. But he began to realise that even his best efforts were wasted. The Vietnamese people did not want his help. They did not care about democracy or totalitarianism, capitalism or communism. They just wanted to be left alone.

When Calley was eventually called to Washington, he thought he was going to be given a medal. He was shocked when he was arrested and charged.

Calley's trial split the US. Those for the war protested that he was only doing his duty. Those against the war said that Calley was a scapegoat. Massacres like that at My Lai were happening every day and it was President Johnson, Defense Secretary Robert McNamara and the army commander General Westmoreland who should be in the dock: but 80 per cent of those polled were against his conviction.

In all, 16 were charged with the massacre at My Lai. Calley went on trial at Fort Benning with six other defendants, including his commanding officer, Captain Ernest Medina. The jury went out on 16 March 1971, the third anniversary of the massacre at My Lai. They deliberated for two weeks. In the end, they found Lieutenant William L. Calley guilty of murdering at least 22 civilians. He was sentenced to life imprisonment with hard labour. On review, this was reduced to 20, then ten years. He was finally paroled on 19 November 1974, after serving three and a half years under house arrest – less than two months for each murder he was found guilty of and less than four days for each of the civilians killed at My Lai.

Charges of premeditated murder and ordering an unlawful act – homicide – against Captain Medina were reduced to involuntary manslaughter for failing to exercise proper control over his men. Not convinced that Captain Medina actually knew what his men were doing in My Lai-4, the jury acquitted him.

Charges – including one of the Nuremberg charges of violating the laws and customs of war – were brought against 12 other officers and men. Only five of the accused were tried; none was found guilty.

A dozen officers – including Calley's divisional commander, Major-General Samuel W. Koster – were charged with participation in the cover-up. None was convicted.

Calley himself believed that he was no worse than most, and better than many, of the officers and men who served in Vietnam. 'I was like a boy scout,' he said, 'and I went by *The Boy Scout Handbook*.'

He believed that he did his duty to God and country, that he was trustworthy, loyal, helpful, friendly, courteous, kind, obedient, cheerful, thrifty, brave, clean and reverent. Yet there were 347 civilians killed in the atrocity at My Lai: 100 were slaughtered in a ditch, one of them a two-year-old child.

19 ❖ Cambodia Year Zero

The war in Vietnam destabilised the whole of South-East Asia and in 1975 Phnom Penh, the capital of Cambodia, fell to the fanatical communist guerrillas, the Khmer Rouge. On 17 April, their peasant army marched down the once smart boulevards. The expressionless teenagers of this austere fighting force struck a note of terror in the hearts of the inhabitants.

It was well known that this guerrilla army was extraordinarily well disciplined. They were impervious to argument, bribery or sentiment. These young troops had not come to loot or rape; they would have no drunken victory celebration. The fate that awaited the inhabitants of Phnom Penh would be much worse. The city was to be evacuated.

The leaders of the Khmer Rouge were Paris-educated communist zealots. They had adapted Marxism for the Third World. Instead of putting the urban proletariat on a pedestal, as Karl Marx had, they believed that all goodness stemmed from the rural peasantry. Consequently the city dwellers were going to be turned into peasants – or would die in the process.

On the afternoon of the 17th, the whole population of Phnom Penh was ordered to leave for the countryside. There was no transport so they would have to go on foot, and there would be no exceptions – even the hospitals were emptied. The country had been at war for eight years and Phnom Penh had been under siege for fifteen months. Many people had been wounded by shelling fire or were suffering from disease and malnutrition. For them, it was a death march: as the great exodus stumbled out of the city into the unknown, under the watchful eyes of the impassive Khmer Rouge, the weak fell by the roadside and were left to die where they lay.

Meanwhile, the teenage soldiers looked for anyone appearing to be well-educated or enjoying wealth and power. They looked for people with soft hands, those who looked well fed or well dressed. They were pulled out of the human stream and interrogated. Anyone who admitted to being one of the urban elite – a bureaucrat, a businessman, a doctor, a teacher, a lawyer or an engineer – was taken away and shot. This was known as 'class vengeance', a favourite slogan of the Khmer Rouge.

The officials of the previous government and army officers were treated separately. A Khmer Rouge broadcast ordered them to present themselves at the Ministry of Information. Fearing that worse might happen to them if they did not, most turned up as ordered; all were killed.

By the evening of the 17th, the tree-lined avenues, the pavement cafés, the chic haute cuisine restaurants, the opium dens and the brothels of Cambodia's capital were empty. The city was silent, deserted. Only a handful of journalists remained behind, huddled in the French embassy. They were evacuated three weeks later.

The evacuation of Phnom Penh was not done on a whim. The decision had been made three months earlier. The leadership of the Khmer Rouge realised that they were not strong enough to run the country in a conventional sense. The communist cadres responsible for building the new society numbered only 14,000. Even their young peasant army was not big enough to control the population of the city, which numbered over one million. The reasoning behind the evacuation was that if one took those city dwellers and dispersed them across the countryside, they would be too disorganised and disorientated to offer resistance – leaving the Khmer Rouge with undisputed power.

Manpower was certainly needed in the countryside. The guerrilla war and American bombing had laid waste to much of the land. Rice stocks were perilously low but, being fanatically anti-colonialist, the Khmer

Saukam Koy, assisted by US Marines, leaves Phnom Penh before the fall of the city to the Khmer Rouge.

Rouge would not accept any aid from abroad, as an article of faith. The economy would be rebuilt by Cambodians themselves. This would be done by turning Cambodia into one huge labour camp.

Fundamentally, the evacuation of Phnom Penh was seen as a great leap forward towards the ideal communist society. In one stroke the urban rich lost all their property and became peasants. Those who could not adapt or accept the change were not worthy of the communist paradise and would be killed. With urban corruption eradicated, a new – utopian – society could flourish. 1975 was to be Year Zero: Cambodia was to be built again on totally new foundations.

The seeds of this new society already existed in the 'liberated' areas that had been under Khmer Rouge control during the war. There, money and private property had already been abolished; the peasants had been organised in collective farms. For the meagre rations doled out by the Khmer Rouge leadership, they had worked from dawn to dusk to support the war effort.

These collectivised peasants were the communists' 'old people' and they would instruct the 'new people' from the cities on how to be good peasants and good communists. However, those who survived the forced march from the city arrived at the collectives to find that they did not receive a warm welcome. The peasants resented the easy life city folk had lived while they tolled in the paddy fields.

Once they got to work, the city people's incompetence in the fields earned them the contempt of the 'old people'. Those who were completely useless were 'eliminated' for 'economic sabotage'. Most just perished from 'natural causes', being unused to the privations the peasants suffered – backbreaking labour, starvation, disease and lack of medical care. The attitude of the Khmer Rouge was summed up in the slogan, 'If this man lives there is no profit. If he dies there is no great loss.'

The identity of the leaders behind the murderous policy remained a mystery for a long time. They were a small group of Paris-educated intellectuals that included the infamous Pol Pot, Ieng Sar, Ieng Thirith and Khieu Samphan. They had set up headquarters in the ghost city of Phnom Penh and ruled the country with a rod of iron. Cambodia was divided into zones, each of which had a party secretary directly answerable to the central authority in Phnom Penh. Below each party secretary was a central committee and, beyond the committee, no one had ever heard of Pol Pot and his merry men. Orders were issued simply in the name of Angka, the Organisation.

In March 1976, Cambodia was renamed the Democratic Republic of Kampuchea and Pol Pot and his henchmen pushed forward towards the establishment of their ideal society. Solitary eating was abolished – all food had to be consumed in communal canteens and came from stocks controlled by the Khmer Rouge. Any private enterprise such as picking wild fruit or vegetables to supplement the diet was punishable by death; even the consumption of lizards, toads and earthworms was outlawed.

Family ties were discouraged. Children in the co-operatives slept in dormitories away from their parents; youngsters were encouraged to spy on their parents and denounce them if their behaviour fell short of what was demanded by the Angka. Members of families were assigned to different work parties and sent to opposite ends of the country. With no telephones and no postal system, once contact had been broken between family members and friends they were unlikely ever to come across each other again.

The teachers and intellectuals had already been exterminated. Instead of education there was a brutal process of indoctrination. Executions were carried out either on the orders of the secret police or of the co-operative ruling committee and they were a discrete and mysterious as the Angka itself. People disappeared in the night; it was not advisable to ask where they had gone. Some were killed on pure whim. To possess thick-lensed glasses, for example, meant you had read too much, so you were the target of Pol Pot's butchers.

The favourite method of execution was a blow to the back of the head or neck with the base of an axe-head: bullets were in short supply. Disembowelling and burying alive were also popular – victims were usually required to dig their own grave first. Whole truckloads of people would suddenly disappear. Curiously, Khmer literature did not use the figurative struggle between good and evil that is the staple of Western stories. Rather, it stressed harmony and beauty. Cambodians were therefore completely unprepared for the mindless violence that their leaders had brought back with them from France. Many Cambodians would stand in line, awaiting their turn to be struck on the back of the head. A traditionally peaceful people, they had no intellectual defence against the Khmer Rouge's murderous strategy.

Keeping a firm grip on the reign of terror in the village was easy for the communists. Rotting human remains, scattered along the trails into the village, did the job. Rumours of grotesque tortures were spread – victims were said to have had their throats cut open by razor-sharp reeds or serrated palm fronds. These accounts had a chilling effect.

After the 'class enemies' – anyone who had an education, anyone who had not been born a worker or a peasant – were eliminated, the Khmer Rouge targeted the ethnic minorities. The Chinese, the Vietnamese and Cham Muslims were 'liquidated'. Pol Pot believed in ethnic cleansing and racial purity, along the lines of Hitler and his 'final solution'; minorities were systematically exterminated.

From the beginning of 1977, the Khmer Rouge executioners turned in on themselves. Those in the party from a 'bourgeois' background were the first to be picked out. They were blamed for the continuing failure of the economy – though everyone else saw that the real blame lay with the murderous system itself; they paid with their lives.

Food shortages continued, because agriculture was now in the hands of people who knew nothing about it. Irrigation projects and dams were build by hand without engineers and experts supervising the work. They were dead. When the first rain came, these massive civil-engineering projects that had cost thousands of lives in their construction were simply swept away.

As far as the party was concerned, these failures could not be the fault of the system – they were being sabotaged by enemies of the state. The Khmer Rouge became consumed by paranoia: torture centres were set up. The most notorious was Tuol Seng in Phnom Penh, where expert Khmer Rouge torturers 'uncovered' conspiracies that usually implicated more people who were about to suffer their tender mercies. Tens of thousands died a horrible death.

The killings became so indiscriminate and widespread that, by mid-1977, Pol Pot himself tried to call a halt. In September 1977, he went public for the first time, making clear his own dominant role in the Communist Party that was now running Kampuchea. In an address to the people, he claimed to have liberated them from 2000 years of 'despair and hopelessness'. However, most of his speech was devoted to the need to defend Kampuchea against foreign aggression.

The Khmer Rouge had always distrusted the Vietnamese who, in pre-colonial times, had dominated the region. There had been border clashes immediately after the fall of Phnom Penh back in 1975. In the autumn of 1977, the border conflicts flared up again. The Khmer Rouge central committee sent out a new instruction: purge all those who had contact with Hanoi. More party members died.

The Eastern Zone committee came under suspicion. Their region bordered Vietnamese territory. They were not doing enough to resist the highly efficient Vietnamese Army who had, after all, ousted the Americans. At the beginning of 1978, the Eastern Zone leadership was purged, but some escaped the Khmer Rouge executioners by fleeing across the border into Vietnam. One of those who fled was the man who would eventually replace Pol Pot; his name was Heng Samrin. With credible Vietnamese leadership in their territory, the Vietnamese took a hand. The excesses of Pol Pot and the Khmer Rouge were undermining their victory in Vietnam and inviting renewed foreign intervention. On 21 December 1978, Kampuchea was 'liberated' once more – this time by a full-scale Vietnamese invasion that installed Heng Samrin as head of a puppet government. Pol Pot's first wife, the ideologue whose crazy ideas underpinned Year Zero, went mad.

No one knows how many people died in the killing fields of Pol Pot's

Year Zero Kampuchea, or what proportion of deaths were due to malnutrition and disease – much of which was cause by ideology-led dislocation – as against deliberate execution. The accepted figure is that two million people died at the hands of their own countrymen – making Cambodia's Year Zero a greater human catastrophe, per capita, than Hitler's Germany.

Vietnamese intervention in Cambodia did not mark an end to atrocities, though. For arcane political reasons, the world embargoed Vietnam until it withdrew its troops. The Khmer Rouge fought on, killing and maiming with the indiscriminate use of land mines. It was only in 1998 that Pol Pot was captured. He was tried, but died of natural causes before he could be punished for the atrocities he had committed.

20 ❖ The Gassing of the Kurds

The Kurdish people are the largest ethnic group in the world to have no homeland. They occupy eastern Turkey, northern Iraq and western Iran, and have been fighting for their independence for centuries. But they have no more bloodthirsty opponents than Saddam Hussein, so when the Iran–Iraq War broke out in 1980, the Kurds thought they could use it to their advantage.

By 1988, the Kurds had a guerrilla army of some 60,000 men and controlled some 4,000 square miles of territory. This was causing Saddam some headaches, as suppressing the Kurds diverted men from the battlefront. As early as 1983, Saddam had begun using chemical weapons – mustard gas, nerve gas and cyanide – against the Iranians. Then, in April 1987, he began to use them against the Kurds.

The first place to be hit was Balisan, a large village of around 250 households with a population of some 1,750 people. It had a primary school, a secondary school and four mosques.

It was drizzling in the late afternoon of 16 April, when the people of Balisan returned home from the fields. They were preparing dinner when they heard the drone of approaching aircraft. Some stayed in their houses; others dashed to makeshift air-raid shelters. Dozens of planes hove into view, wheeling overheard and dropping bombs on Balisan and Seikh

Wasan, a smaller settlement of about 150 households a little way to the north-east.

As the bombs hit, there was a muffled explosion. Until then, no government had ever used chemical weapons against its civilian population. Video footage the Iraqis shot shows towering columns and broad drifting clouds of white, grey and pinkish smoke. A cool breeze was blowing in off the mountains; it carried the gas into the village. Survivors have different memories of what the gas smelt like. Some said it seemed pleasant, reminding them of roses, apples and garlic; others say it was pungent, like insecticide.

One elderly woman from Balisan reported that everything went dark – the gas was like a fog. Everyone became blind; some vomited; faces turned black. Men experienced painful swellings under their arms, women under their breasts. Later, a yellow discharge oozed from their eyes – survivors lost their sight for up to a month.

In Sheikh Wasan, survivors watched a woman blindly staggering around with her baby, not realising that it was dead. Villagers close to the impact died immediately. Others ran into the mountains and died there. A second attack followed an hour later.

The following morning Iraqi troops entered Balisan, looted the villagers' deserted homes and razed them to the ground. Army engineers dynamited Sheikh Wasan and bulldozed it.

The survivors had already fled. The inhabitants of the nearby town of Beiro sent tractor-drawn carts to evacuate people to Raniya. At a resettlement camp there, they buried 50 or 60 people. A local doctor dressed wounds and administered eye drops, though these did little to help restore vision.

The next day the Iraqi security police turned up, ordering everyone out of the hospital and into vans waiting outside. These would take the survivors to the city of Erbil for medical attention – but they were told they would be treated only if they told the doctors at Erbil they had been attacked by Iranian planes. Of some 200 people taken, four died on the way.

By the time they had reached Erbil, the victims' eyes had dried out and were glued shut. Doctors applied eye drops, washed burns and gave everyone an injection of atropine, a powerful antidote for nerve gas. The origin of their injuries was not discussed. The doctors and nurses were afraid: the hospital knew of the reputation of the security police all to well. Their morgue held the bodies from the local branch headquarters. Some

Kurdish children gather together at a refugee camp in Diyarbakir, Turkey.

showed signs of having been beaten to death; others seemed to have been executed by firing squad. The bodies had been stripped of their wristwatches, identification papers and personal property.

The morgue staff were ordered, on threat of death, not to contact the dead people's families or reveal their names. They were forbidden to touch the bodies and merely had to supply a death certificate. Sometimes the morgue was full to overflowing and the staff had to borrow a bulldozer to dig a mass grave. The morgue staff were forbidden to wash the bodies or prepare them for burial facing Mecca as Muslim tradition demands.

'Dogs have no relation to Islam,' said one security police officer.

The security police turned up at the hospital and ordered the doctor, at gun point, to remove the dressings from the survivor's wounds. They were going to be transferred to the military hospital, the chief policeman said. Later, when the doctor called the military hospital to see that his patients were all right, he was told that they had not arrived there.

Instead, they had been taken to the local security police headquarters, which over the next three days provided the morgue with 64 more bodies. The morgue staff who went to pick them up saw the gas-attack survivors there; they were in a pitiable state. The men were later taken off in a sealed bus and, presumably, executed. The women and children were driven three hours out of the city at night and abandoned in a deserted area – many children died of exposure. It is estimated that around 400 people from Balisan and Sheikh Wasan died as a result of the gas attack.

Kamal, a Kurdish guerrilla, heard of the attack on Balisan and Sheikh Wasam and rushed home to his family, who lived in the nearby village of Upper Bileh. He found they had taken refuge in some caves in the mountains, but it was bitterly cold and he persuaded them to return home. At 6 a.m. on 27 May 1987, his wife woke him to warn him that the village was under attack.

'We knew it was chemicals,' said Kamal, 'because the sound of the explosions was not loud. There were many bombs. I told my family that it wasn't a chemical attack. I did not want to scare them, but they knew what it was. So we began burning the branches we had stored for animal feed, and they made a very strong fire. We also soaked cloths and headscarves at the spring. My aged father was there. The attack was so intense that we were unable to leave the village. That was why we lit the fires. There was a separate spring for the women and I told everyone, men and women, to jump into the water. The attack lasted until 10 a.m. I sent my brother to get medical help. By sunset, the situation was getting worse. Several people had gone blind.'

After sunset, they crossed the stream and moved into a rocky area outside the village. They had all been affected by the chemicals and their situation was going from bad to worse.

'We had trouble seeing, and we were short of breath. We had nosebleeds and fainting spells. We sent someone to the surrounding villages to fetch water. I offered to pay them whatever they asked for, but the villagers were afraid to come, thinking that the chemicals were contagious. But the people from the village of Kandour were brave. They came to bring us milk.'

By that time that Kamal's brother had reached the local guerrilla headquarters to get help, but on the way back they lost their sight and collapsed. People from other villages collected them on mules and brought them back to the survivors from Upper Bileh; they had with them eyedrops and medicine. A doctor arrived and the guerrillas sent money to buy horses to take the injured Kurds to Iran. By this time the women, particularly, were in a terrible condition, and had to be spoon-fed, while the small children were hardly breathing.

'We went to Malakan,' said Kamal, 'where it was colder. We thought the fresh air there would help. Then we reached the Sewaka area. There were people there who raised animals and they took pity on us. They wept a lot and gave us food. Next morning we left for Warta. We had to cover our faces because the bright light hurt our eyes. It was like needles were being stuck into them.'

Eventually, the survivors escaped to Iran where they were given medical treatment.

After the Balisan valley chemical attacks, Iraqi troops bulldozed at least 703 Kurdish villages. Over the next months there were a further 67 chemical attacks. The worst came on 16 March 1988, in Halabja, a bustling Kurdish town with a population of 40–60,000 or more. The town was full of refugees and Iraqi troops had already bulldozed two entire quarters of in May 1987. It lay on the very edge of the war zone. All the villages between Halabja and the Iranian border had been razed and their inhabitants had come to live in camps around the town.

On 13 March, the town came under three days of Iranian shelling. The Iraqi forces pulled back, leaving the town open on 15 March. The Baghdad regime could have reinforced the garrison, but it had other fish to fry. Iranian and Iraqi Kurds took over.

Reprisals began on the following morning. At first, the town was subject to conventional artillery and air strikes. Next came incendiaries – phosphorus and napalm. The planes flew so low that those on the ground could see their Iraqi markings. At around 2 p.m., a single bomber turned up. It dropped bombs that spread a yellow and white cloud through the town, which contained a mixture of mustard gas and cyanide.

Around 3 p.m., people in the makeshift air-raid shelters noticed an unusual smell. They compared it to sweet apples, perfume, cucumbers or, according to one witness, 'snake poison'. There was immediate panic. People tried to pack cracks around the entrances to the shelters with damp towels, while others pressed wet cloths to their faces or made fires.

When darkness fell, people came out of the shelters. There were no streetlights – power had been knocked out by artillery fire. In the dusk, those emerging from the shelters saw horrific scenes. There were dead bodies – human and animal – everywhere. They were huddled in doorways and slumped over the steering wheels of cars. Survivors stumbled around laughing hysterically, before collapsing. The only ones left alive on the streets of Halabja were Iranian troops in gas masks and full chemical suits.

Some victims made it out of the town. Their eyes felt like they were being jabbed by needles and their urine was streaked with blood. They headed for the Iranian border. Freezing rain had turned the path to mud. Many victims were barefoot; children who died along the way were abandoned. Thousands of refugees huddled in the ruins of villages on the Iraqi side of the border, while Iranian doctors came and gave shots of atropine, before ferrying them across the border.

At least 5,000 people died as a result of the gas attack on Halabja. When Iraqi forces retook the town, they dynamited what was left of it, along with the neighbouring town of Sayed Sadeq, and left the bodies of the people killed there to rot in the street.

21 ❖ Lockerbie

At 6.25 p.m. on 21 December 1988, Pan Am Flight 103 took off from London's Heathrow Airport 25 minutes behind schedule. The Boeing 747 was carrying 246 passengers and ten crew members.

The plane, which was heading for New York, had on board both Britons and Americans heading for the States for the Christmas holiday, among them 35 of a party of 38 students from Syracuse University who had been studying abroad and were going home to spend Christmas with their families. Others were on more serious business: Brent Carisson, a Swede and chief administrative officer for the United Nations' Council for Namibia, was flying to New York to sign an accord on Namibia's independence.

At 37 minutes after take off, Flight 103 was cruising at 31,000 feet – six miles high – over the Scottish border. The plane was flying at 434 knots – 500 miles an hour. James MacQuarrie, the 55-year-old American pilot, and his 52-year-old co-pilot, Raymond Wagner, switched on the autopilot and settled down for a routine transatlantic journey. As they gave their instruments one final check, the air traffic controller at Shanwick gave them final radio clearance for their flight out over the Atlantic.

Outside it was cold and dark. Intermittent rain splattered against the cockpit's reinforced windscreen. The 115-knot jet stream was creating light turbulence. Below them, clouds at around 16,000 feet covered the Scottish landscape.

A precisely 7.02 and 50 seconds p.m., over the tiny village of Castlemilk three miles south of Lockerbie, a terrorist bomb planted in a radio-recorder in the plane's baggage hold exploded. It weighed less than a pound.

The baggage hold was in front of the plane's left wing. The bomb went off just 25 inches from the skin of the fuselage. The shock wave punched a hole in the side of the plane, sending burning baggage out into the freezing air, and ripping through the jumbo's main electrical cables. MacQuarrie had no chance to make a Mayday call. The flight recorder only recorded the sound of the explosion before its power failed too.

Then came the blast itself. It stretched the fuselage skin. Within a second, it had blistered and busted. Around the five-foot hole, the edges 'petalled' outwards in a starburst. The blast was also channel upwards, causing the passenger compartment to buckle and break. Everyone on broad had heard the explosion; shock waves travelled down the air-conditioning, reverberating through the cabin; and those in the forward section and those on the left-hand-side of first class on the upper deck suffered minor injuries from the blast.

People sitting directly over the left wing felt the plane disintegrating beneath them. The starburst around the hole was rapidly unzipping. One petal tore back as far as the wing; a second ripped forward 43 feet and a third tore around under the belly of the plane almost up to the windows on the starboard side. A passenger plane is only held together by its thin skin – it does not have a metal chassis like a car. With such severe damage, the forces on it will rip it apart.

Amid the sound of tearing aluminium and popping rivets, the aircraft nose-dived. The flight control cables had been severed by the explosion and it rolled to the left. The left side of the forward fuselage ripped open and the entire nose section twisted upwards and to the right. The cockpit turned all the way around until it was facing the back of the plane, then broke away. It hit the right wing, knocking the inner engine off its stanchion. The nose hit the tailplane, causing extensive damage. From there, the body of the plane travelled in an increasingly steep flight path until, by 19,000 feet, it was travelling vertically downwards.

On the way down, both the nose and the fuselage spilled their contents. The aerodynamic effects of the plane's steep dive tore the remaining three engines off the wings. At around 9,000 feet, the rear of the cabin broke away and disintegrated, scattering bits of the cabin floor, the rear baggage hold and the landing gear across the fields and houses below.

The small Scottish town of Lockerbie is devastated by Pan Am flight 103 on 21st December, 1988.

It was a quiet Wednesday evening in the small Scottish village of Lockerbie when Myra Bell looked out of the window of her flat. As she looked out at the southern edge of the village, she saw a huge black object falling from the sky, realising that it was a passenger plane and all the people on board it were going to die.

A wing filled with more than 200,000 pounds of aviation fuel crashed into Sherwood Crescent at 200 miles an hour. It crashed into the houses at the end of the crescent, leaving a huge crater 100 feet long and 30 feet deep. The fireball could be seen six miles away, while those in the rest of the crescent felt the terrible heat and air being sucked out of their houses. The force of the blast sent Robert Jardine flying across his living room. When he looked out of the window he saw that the home of his neighbours, the Flannigan family, had disappeared completely. The body of ten-year-old Joanne Flannigan was found in the wreckage of their home, but those of her parents, 44-year-old Thomas and 41-year-old Kathleen, were never found. The home of John and Rosaleen Somerville and their children 13-year-old Paul and ten-year-old Lyndsey, had disappeared too; their bodies had been vaporised in the impact. In all, 11 residents of Lockerbie died in the disaster.

The main body of the fuselage landed 350 yards from the Townfoot service station, which went up in flames. The ball of fire that had been number three engine hit the town, while the nose section buried itself in a hilltop three miles from the east of the town. The other engines hit the Netherplace area; one hit the water main.

Nearby, the seismic station belonging to the British Geological Survey registered 1.6 on the Richter scale. The main impacts occurred at 19.03, 36.5 seconds and 46 seconds after the bomb had gone off. Some local residents believed that there had been an earthquake, others that two low-flying fighters had collided. Keith Paterson thought that the Chapelcross nuclear power station had exploded. He only discovered what had really happened when he grabbed a torch and went outside. In the dark, he saw two eyes looking up at him. They belonged to a dead body. All 257 people on board Flight 103 were dead – or soon would be. It was later discovered that some people had miraculously survived the crash and may have lived for some time after they hit the ground but, by the time they were found, it was too late.

The first fire engine arrived at 7.10 p.m., eight minutes after the bomb exploded. Rescuers were soon combing the area for survivors. It was an impossible task: wreckage from the plane was spread over an arc 80 miles long. All those they found were dead. Captain MacQuarrie's body was found on the grass outside the cockpit. Inside the nose section rescuers found another 15 bodies, nearly all of them cabin crew or first-class passengers.

Christine Copeland found the body of a young woman in her garden, which turned black before her eyes. The body of a young man landed on the front doorstep of Esther Galloway – for the next three days she had to step over it while the accident investigators went about their work. However, most of the bodies were not intact and the emergency forces had to set about the grim task of finding body parts.

Every body part had to be examined by a doctor, photographed, numbered and tagged before it could be removed. Some pieces had to be dug out of the rubble or cut out of the wreckage of the aircraft. This was a gruesome and laborious business – some bodies were not removed until five nights after the crash

The Lockerbie disaster was the worst air crash in British history, and the worst plane crash in the life of Pan Am. What made it an atrocity was that it was not an air accident at all – the bomb with a timing device had been planted deliberately. Furthermore, the authorities had been warned.

One week before Flight 103 was blown from the skies, the American Embassy in Finland received a message from an anonymous caller saying, 'There will be a bombing attempt against a Pan American aircraft flying from Frankfurt to the United States.'

Flight 103 had originated in Frankfurt. Passengers from Germany travelled on a 727 to London but the flight used the same number. At Heathrow, the passengers and luggage were transferred to the 747, along with more passengers from England and others on connecting flights from elsewhere.

This information was forwarded to the American embassy in Germany. Embassy staff cancelled their reservations on Flight 103, surveillance was stepped up, but no warning was given to the general public.

At first, two anti-Arafat Palestinian terrorist groups – the General Command of the Patriotic Front for the Liberation of Palestine and Abu Nidal's Fatah Revolutionary Council – were blamed. Later, Scotland Yard concluded that the bomb had been planted by Iranians or groups sympathetic to Iran.

In November 1990, it was discovered that the US Drug Enforcement Agency often used Flight 103 to fly informants and suitcases of heroin seized in the Middle East back to America. Pan Am staff were used to loading these cases without the usual security checks. One of the DEA men involved in this operation, Detroit-resident Nazir Khalid Jafaar, was on board the downed flight and it was thought that he might have unwittingly put the bomb on board the plane.

In the end this theory was rejected. Eventually, the world's biggest murder investigation concluded that Libya was to blame. The attack, investigators said, was done in retaliation for the 1986 bombing of Libya by US planes that had taken off from bases in Britain. The United States and Britain asked the government in Tripoli for the extradition of two Libyans – Lamen Khalifa Fhimah and Abdel Basset Ali al-Megrahi. Colonel Qaddafi refused to hand them over for trial.

In 1992, the UK and US went to the United Nations and asked for economic sanctions to be imposed on Libya, if Qaddafi did not hand over the two men. In late March, the United Nations Security Council gave the Colonel two weeks to hand over the suspects, or flights in and out of Libya would be banned and the country would be shunned as a diplomatic pariah. In response, Qaddafi threatened to cut off oil supplies to those countries supporting the resolution. There was a surplus of oil on the world market at the time and no one took any notice.

However, by 1998, Qaddafi was tired of being an international outcast. South Africa's President Nelson Mandela flew to Tripoli and brokered a deal. In 1999, the two men were sent to the Netherlands where, as this book goes to press, they are waiting in a special terrorist-proof military compound to be tried under Scottish law. *The Sunday Times* claims that it was Colonel Qaddafi who gave the order and the British government know all about it but are saying nothing because of lucrative contracts negotiated between the UK and Libya. *The Sunday Times* also says that Qaddafi should be on trial alongside his henchmen.

Until these men – or others – are convicted, it will be difficult for the families of the dead to forget what happened on that appalling night. The residents of the small Scottish town where it happened have another cross to bear. The name Lockerbie will forever be associated with an air atrocity and send a shiver down the spine of anyone who sets foot on a plane.

22 ❖ Tiananmen Square

Tiananmen Square in Beijing is one of the biggest squares in the world. It was frequently used for mass rallies during the long reign of Mao Tsetung. After his death China began changing: in the 1980s, under the leadership of the ageing revolutionary Deng Xiaoping, it was slowly being opened up to free market economics. However, some young men in the administration wanted the pace of change to quicken.

One of these was Hu Yaobang. As Secretary-General of the party, he was the first in the communist leadership to wear Western-style suits. He even suggested that the Chinese give up chopsticks and eat with a knife and fork. This was seen as a leap too far for the Mao-suited old guard and, in 1987, he was sacked. Hu was no democrat, but he was seen as young and honest while many of the old guard were known to be corrupt; and slowly, Hu came to be seen as a symbol of liberalisation and democracy.

When he died on 15 April 1989, he suddenly became a martyr. Under the pretext of mourning for Hu, students took to the streets several times, demonstrating in Tiananmen Square and bringing the traffic in the centre of the city to a standstill. These demonstrations were witnessed by the large corps of foreign journalists who were in town to report the forthcoming visit of Mikhail Gorbachev, another idol of China's growing democracy movement.

The great mausoleum of Mao Tsetung flanks Tiananmen Square, as does the Great Hall of the People. In the middle is the Monument to the People's Heroes. It was there in 1976 that people had risked their lives to mourn for Zhou Enlai and call for the arrest of the Gang of Four. The resulting coup may have put Deng Xiaoping in power, but the Monument seemed the appropriate place for the students of Beijing to mourn for Hu Yaobang and make their call for democracy.

On 26 April, an editorial in the Communist party newspaper, the *People's Daily*, warned that a 'handful of people' were planning a 'conspiracy and a disturbance'. In the communist world, these are serious charges. Incensed, the students demanded the paper withdraw the accusations. On 27 April, they occupied Tiananmen Square and demanded a dialogue with the government. Having brought sleeping bags and blankets with them, they stayed the night. When they awoke the next morning, the students were surprised that the authorities had not tried to evict them, and they gained confidence. That day the speeches were about democracy and freedom. One of their leaders, Chai Ling, claimed passionately that democracy was their 'natural right'.

Posters went out to other universities and colleges, and 100,000 people flocked to the square. The debate raged about how long they should stay. One problem was that, on 30 April, Gorbachev was scheduled to lay a wreath on the Monument to the People's Heroes. Some wanted to withdraw partially to allow Gorbachev's visit to go ahead as planned. Chai Ling wanted to remain in occupation for the entire four days of his visit. This was not meant as an insult to Gorbachev, who was seen as a hero – he had brought an openness to the Soviet Union that the students wanted in China – however, such a demonstration would damage two unpopular figures in the regime, the President Yang Shangkun and the Prime Minister Li Peng, both of whom were educated in the Soviet Union. Better still, it would upstage Deng Xiaoping. Gorbachev's visit marked an end of the Sino-Soviet split. This was to have been Deng's last great coup. After it, at the age of 85, he planned to retire in favour of Hu Yaobang's successor as party secretary Zhao Ziyang. Deng, they knew, would be angry at any demonstration.

Deng was a fearsome adversary and not to be underestimated. Although he ran the country, he had no constitutional or party position. The only official title he held was chairman of the Central Military Commission. He was in charge of the army and the students knew that he would have no qualms about causing bloodshed.

A faction of the students under Wuer Kaixi withdrew from the Monument, but the majority, under Chai Ling, stayed. Zhao Ziyang, who was embroiled in a leadership struggle with Li Peng at the time, turned up in the square and saw that no ceremonial wreath-laying could take place there. Effectively, Tiananmen Square was no longer under the control of the government. Furthermore, some of the students had started a hunger strike.

In many ways, Deng Xiaoping was a liberal. He even introduced limited free speech into China – though, in 1979, he ordered the clearing of Democracy Wall where people had been allowed to post anything they wrote when someone put up a poster critical of the Communist Party. However, he had been a victim of the Red Guards in Mao's Cultural

Students are kept back by soldiers during demonstrations in Beijing, China.

Revolution. He had been ousted and his son had been crippled when the Red Guards had thrown him out of an upstairs window. He was therefore deeply suspicious of young people with political ideas.

The Beijing government could have cleared the students out of the square before Gorbachev turned up, even though the world's press was there. That they didn't was due to the fact that the representatives of the Asian Development Bank were also in town at the time – China wanted a loan and the last thing the government needed was a bloody riot on its hands.

When Gorbachev arrived, he was greeted at the official reception at the Great Hall of the People. Normally, the route from the airport would have taken the motorcade across Tiananmen Square. Instead, it had to be directed down grubby backstreets.

In the square, demonstrators had banners proclaiming 'We are Fasting for the Liberty of this Nation' and T-shirts that proclaimed they would rather die than live without democracy. Portable radios were turned into the BBC Chinese Language Service, which was an offence. Although the secret policemen moved through the crowds taking photographs and jotting down names, they arrested no one.

The students made it clear that they were not demonstrating against Gorbachev or challenging the government. They made only limited political demands, largely to do with cleaning up corruption. All they wanted, they said, was to have a dialogue with the government. However, cleaning up corruption was not a simple matter. The leadership was steeped in it – the new free market economics encouraged foreign investment and no one was checking the books.

The ordinary people of Beijing supported the students, bringing food and water. Doctors set up a field hospital in the square to look after those suffering from heat exhaustion and the hunger-strikers, whose numbers had swelled from 400 to 3,140. Student marshals now controlled the square and checked people's passes. The police withdrew.

Gorbachev visited the square and wished the demonstrators luck. By this time the demonstration had grown so big that he was hardly noticed. The students gained some comfort from the fact that, at the televised banquet laid on for Gorbachev, Deng Xiaoping looked old and frail. It was rumoured that he was on heavy medication. However, Zhao Ziyang, whose liberal views were supported by the students, made a great show of backing Deng.

On 10 May, 10,000 cyclists took a 25-mile ride around the city, ending up outside the offices of the *People's Daily*, where they demanded the editorial of 26 April be withdrawn. This did not happen, but workers from the *People's Daily* turned up to lend their support in Tiananmen Square.

By mid-May, ordinary people outnumbered students. About 600 hunger strikers had ended up in hospital. The police appeared to support the demonstration and on a daily basis, criticism of Deng Xiaoping was growing. On 18 May, the rumour spread through the square that Deng would resign at 7 p.m. There was an outbreak of spontaneous clapping and singing. Even government officials seemed to believe this was true.

However, Deng did not resign. With Gorbachev gone, he began making plans to bring in the army. Li Peng backed him, Zhao Ziyang did not, but both of them made a televised appearance at Beijing hospital to show sympathy with the hunger-striking students who had ended up there. The reception was hostile. The students lectured them, one telling them that they should make the government popular 'like in the United

States'. Another said they should punish nepotism – it was well known that Deng's crippled son was milking the system.

Li Peng had a meeting with student leader Wuer Kaixi in the Great Hall of the People, which turned into a shouting match. In a country where deference is shown towards the aged, there was no precedence for this. Li Peng stormed out. Wuer Kaixi went back into the square and argued that the hunger strike should stop. Chai Ling opposed him and it continued.

That night, Deng Xiaoping called a meeting of the central standing committee of the politburo. They discussed declaring martial law. Zhao Ziyang found himself in a minority of one. Nevertheless, he and Li Peng went to Tiananmen Square and begged the hunger strikers to end their fast. The next day, martial law was declared and Zhao was arrested.

On 19 May, the army began to move into the city. With Zhao gone, it was clear that Deng Xiaoping was still very much in charge. The students grew wary and decided to give up their hunger strike, but they would not leave the square.

Li Peng and Yang Shangkun went on TV, promising action against the demonstrators. 'We've restrained ourselves for over a month now,' said Li. 'But a government which serves the people must take strong measures to deal with social unrest.'

Yang sought to draw a distinction between the mass of students, whom everyone supported, and a small bunch of troublemakers who egged them on. 'I would like to make it clear that by sending in the troops we are not intending to deal with students,' he said.

Those in Tiananmen Square heard the speeches on loudspeakers. They saw this as a declaration of war and more students and workers rallied to their cause. When the troops tried to drive into the centre of the city, the people of Beijing blocked their way. Their lorries were marooned in a sea of chanting people, many of them middle-aged. Nevertheless, it was quite good-natured – some people even brought food for the beleaguered soldiers. The people meant no harm to the troops; they just did not want them to attack their sons and daughters who were in the square. It was rumoured that one army commander had even refused to issue ammunition to his troops because his daughter was one of the protesters.

The following morning, the inhabitants of Tiananmen Square could not believe that they were still there. They had been expecting the army to come that night and drive them out. But things were indeed hotting up. At 9 a.m., a martial law order was issued prohibiting demonstrations and placing reporting restrictions on foreign journalists. Helicopters buzzed over the square, dropping leaflets supporting Li Peng. The students tore them up. That evening, they started building barricades.

The next day a troop train arrived in the central station. The students, however, had had advanced warning, and headed to the station to besiege the train. All the troops could do was sit there sullenly until the train pulled out again.

A newsreader named Xue Fei, who stumbled over his words when reading the martial law decree, was sacked when a banner saying 'Long Live Xue Fei' appeared in Tiananmen Square. The government ordered banners proclaiming the martial law orders to be displayed down Beijing's central avenue. Mysteriously, the letters peeled off after a couple of days. Even the sub-editors at the *People's Daily* joined in, running prominent headlines criticising the use of martial law and urging old men to retire from politics or stories that reported these things in other countries.

Despite these guerrilla actions, Deng knew all he had to do was wait. Although most people in the cities backed the students, 800,000 of China's population of a billion lived in the countryside. They supported Deng because his land reforms had transformed their lot.

By June, the students were drifting back to their studies. The square's makeshift latrines were overflowing and stinking, and the students' marshals had become officious – occupying Tiananmen Square was not exciting or fun any more. Though there were still speeches and slogans demanding democracy, troops now ringed the square.

Deng left Beijing and called his army commanders to a meeting at Wuhan. They offered him their support. The troops, who had been kept isolated from the news, were told to study the speeches of Li Peng and the *People's Daily* editorial of 26 April. Former supporters of Zhao Ziyang issued statements condemning the 'handful of people' who were controlling the students.

The government then worked on black propaganda. Three agent provocateurs went into the square and threw ink over a portrait of Mao Tsetung. The students handed them over to the police, but the damage was done. A lone soldier drove a truckload of guns and ammunition into the square and ran off; again, the students handed it over to the police, even helping to unload the truck. This was filmed by a Chinese camera crew and when the footage was shown on TV an entirely different construction was put on the event.

Then the weather turned against the demonstrators – a storm came and people left the square to take cover from the rain. Only a couple of dozen students braved it out. The protest in Tiananmen Square was now in trouble – half-a-dozen troops in sou'westers could have taken the square that night.

However, on 29 May, a small group of students from the Central Institute of Fine Art turned up, erecting a 30-foot high fibreglass and plaster-of-Paris model of a woman, like the Statue of Liberty, holding a torch. Chai Ling dubbed her the Goddess of Democracy and people came flooding back. She stood directly opposite Mao's portrait with her torch practically in his face: this was a deliberate insult to the government.

On the night of 2 June, the army moved in again. This time they had chosen their route carefully, and did not come in lorries but on foot, at the double. This tactic backfired; before they even reached the square, they were exhausted. Already confused and disheartened, they were easily disarmed. Their equipment was piled in the middle of the street; they sat on the ground, the officers lowering their eyes, while students shouted slogans at them. Eventually the students and the officers reached a deal and the soldiers returned to their barracks.

The following night, the army returned with tanks and armoured personnel carriers. Government loudspeakers boomed out a chilling message. 'Go home and save your lives,' it said. 'You will fail. You are not behaving in the correct Chinese manner. This is not the West. It is China. You should behave like good Chinese. Go home and save your lives. Go home and save your lives.'

No one moved.

People began shouting that the army was coming. Students began shoring up the barricades; young men were suddenly brandishing knives, clubs, bricks, coshes, spears; some even had Molotov cocktails. People were afraid, sure that they were going to die. Nevertheless, the speeches and the singing continued.

An APC came hurtling into the square, running people over and ripping their legs off with its metal tracks. It was pummelled with Molotov cocktails and sped away. A second APC arrived, killing more people. It rammed into a concrete barricade and got stuck. Petrol was poured over it and it was set alight. When three soldiers at the back emerged, their guns were grabbed from them. Two of them were beaten to death by the mob, the other one was saved by some students in a bus; the two men in the front seat were burned to death.

The students sang the Internationale. Some were crying and knew that they had just suffered their first defeat. So far the demonstration had been successful because it had been non violent. They now realised that the two APCs had been sent in to the square in the hope that one or both of them would get caught. Once some soldiers had been killed, the blood of their comrades would be up. Now there would be a massacre.

Troops began pouring in through the Gate of Heavenly Peace. They charged across the north end of the square, clearing it. Tanks rolled over the tents some students had taken refuge in. Those close by heard their screams. At least 200 died that way.

At 4 a.m., the lights went out in the square to prevent foreign TV crews filming what was going on. A pop singer named Hou Dejian, who had joined the demonstrators, negotiated a peaceful withdrawal for the students; by 4.40 a.m., they were starting to leave. Then all the lights suddenly came back on. A line of well-armed troops was approaching the students. The police began hitting the students with clubs studded with nails and cattle prods. Scores of bleeding youths retreated up the stairs of the monument. They held hands and sang the Internationale again, while completely surrounded by soldiers. The police rushed at them repeatedly until the crowd collapsed. The soldiers then shot over the heads of the students, and into the crowd itself. They also shot at the journalists watching from the Beijing Hotel and the secret police were sent to arrest them. Workers and ordinary citizens took up sticks and charged the soldiers. They were shot down.

The students tried to escape, but the only hole in the line of troops was quickly filled with tanks. They managed to force a way through between the tanks and some escaped.

Outside the square, the crowd remained defiant, shouting at the troops who answered with gunfire. It is estimated that between 1,500 and 3,000 lost their lives in Tiananmen Square. Their bodies were burnt and the Goddess of Democracy was smashed by the tanks. Next day, the leadership came to the square in a helicopter to see the ruins of the lady. Around the city, the shooting continued.

The student leaders were dispersed. Many of them escaped, via Hong Kong, to the United States. Those who remained were arrested. These days, the Chinese democracy movement exists only on the Internet. Unfortunately, not many people in China have personal computers – especially not the aged leadership.

23 ❖ Rwanda: Heart of Darkness

The twentieth century has been particularly cursed with abominable acts. Even in this last decade of the century, revolt in Chechnya, revolution in the Congo, civil war in Sierra Leone and 'ethnic cleansing' in the Balkans have provided ample material. But there is one name that chills the blood like no other, conjuring up images of bodies, flyblown, bloated, uncountable: that name is Rwanda.

Rwanda is a small country, not much bigger than Wales. However, while the Land of My Fathers has a population of three million, in 1990 there were nearly eight million souls crammed into Rwanda, making it the most densely populated country in Africa. The conflict in Rwanda was between the Tutsis, who make up 14 per cent of the population, and the Hutus, who make up 85 per cent. The other one per cent consists of Twa hunter-gatherers, who, in less politically correct times, were known as pygmies.

The Tutsis and Hutus are not distinct races. They do not have separate languages or cultures. However, the Tutsis are cattlemen while the Hutus are farmers, so their rivalry is akin to the range wars that broke out in America's Old West in the late nineteenth century, between the ranchers and the homesteaders.

In the nineteenth century, as cattle were a form of convertible currency in central Africa, the Tutsis became the wealthy elite and the division between Tutsis and Hutus became institutionalised in the caste system – rather like the division between Norman and Saxon in post-conquest England. Sadly, in Rwanda there was no Robin Hood.

In 1890 the Germans entered the equation, colonising Rwanda as part of German East Africa. They naturally co-opted the Tutsis, whose well-established administrative system would run the country for the colonial power. Race theory was all the rage at the time. The Tutsis were tall and slim, with straight noses and long fingers – more European-looking than the Hutus, who were stockier and had broad noses and shorter fingers. The Germans also seized on folklore that said that the Tutsis had originally come from Ethiopia and had taken over the country from the Hutus – in other words, they were colonisers themselves. Such a claim is almost certainly not true. No one knows who got there first – though it is known that the Twa were there before either the Tutsis or the Hutus.

If the Tutsis had once been Ethiopian, they had once been Christians. Or so the Catholic Church reasoned. Missionaries were dispatched to re-Christianise the Tutsis; saving the souls of the Hutus came later. Catholic schools dedicated themselves to educating Tutsi children, as they would become the administrators, while the poorer Protestant churches mopped up the Hutus. This religious dimension further entrenched the Tutsi–Hutu divide.

In 1916, the Belgians took over these religious and social dichotomies – and the country. The Hutus were then press-ganged into forced labour in a system of slavery only abolished in 1927. In the late 1950s, the wind of change started blowing through Africa. In Rwanda, the call for independence came from the Hutus. Seeing which way the wind was blowing, the Belgians quickly dropped the Tutsis from favour. The Tutsi king was assassinated while visiting Burundi; an uprising in the north left 15,000 Tutsis dead; and thousands more fled to neighbouring Uganda, Zaire, Tanzania and Burundi.

A Hutu named Gregoire Kayibanda became the first president of an independent Rwanda in 1962. His aim was to overturn the feudal system that favoured the Tutsis. Rather than abandon the old racial theories, he used them for his own ends. The identity cards that had been introduced by the Belgians in the 1930s were retained. These specified whether the holder was a Tutsi, Hutu or Twa. One's ethnic designation could only be changed on payment of a huge bribe.

Tutsis were dubbed *inyenzis* or 'cockroaches' and removed from all positions of authority, except in the Catholic Church. These Rwandan Tutsis looked to their exiled counterparts for their salvation. However, Kayibanda was maintained in power by Belgian paratroopers. In 1963, Hutu peasants turned on the Tutsis, massacring 20,000 and sending another 100,000 fleeing into Burundi.

Fresh attacks on the Tutsis destabilised the government and, in 1973, Major General Juvenal Habyarimana seized power with the promise that he would end ethnic strife. And so he did, in his own way. He soon declared that not only would Tutsis be excluded from power, but also any Hutus who had been 'infected' by Tutsis – in other words, anyone Habyarimana did not like. He and his cronies ruled the country with an iron hand – and with an army that he increased from 5,000 to 35,000 men.

Inevitably, under the surface, the conflict was simmering. Rwandan women have one of the highest fertility rates in the world and, despite massacres and the exile of hundreds of thousands of Tutsis, the population swelled from 2.8 million in 1962 to over 7.5 million in 1990. There was an acute shortage of land. Hutus, who had occupied the land of exiled Tutsis, feared the return of the *inyenzi*. Habyarimana argued that the Tutsi refugees in neighbouring countries would have to stay there because Rwanda was, in effect, full up.

However, the exiled Tutsis had not been sitting on their hands. In Uganda they had joined the National Resistance Army, which overthrew the regime of Tito Okello who, in turn, had ousted Milton Obote. They were battle-hardened and had seen how a well-organised army could seize political power. In 1986, Tutsi ex-NRA officers formed the Rwandan Patriotic Front, and in 1990, the 1,500-strong RPF invaded.

Habyarimana's army clearly outnumbered them by over 20 to one, but were inexperienced and poorly motivated. It was only the intervention of Zaire and then France that kept Habyarimana from being routed. A cease-fire was called and the two sides sat down to peace talks that dragged on for three years.

Meanwhile, other Rwandans, alienated by the corruption of the Habyarimana regime, seized the opportunity to form new political parties. Finding himself outmanoeuvred politically, Habyarimana began organising his own fiercely loyal militia. It was called the *interahamwe* – 'those who stand together'. Its men were well equipped, well trained and well paid.

Although Habyarimana distanced himself from the *interahamwe*, it could essentially do what it liked. What it liked was to bump off Habyarimana's political opponents. Over 2,000 dissidents were killed at his behest, but when the killers were caught, they were pardoned. This meant that Habyarimana could maintain the appearance of a democracy by allowing other parties into the government with no danger of losing power. He even promised a multi-party election, though he did not deliver it. In the meantime, he could fire opposition politicians from his administration at will. By this time Habyarimana's henchmen – known as the *Azaku* – ran everything in the country, including drugs, prostitution and protection rackets: not things they were going to give up without a fight.

The RPF began to see that the peace talks were getting them nowhere. They attacked the Rwandan capital Kigali. This time, Habyarimana was saved by the intervention of French troops. However, neighbouring countries were growing worried that Rwanda might destabilise the whole region. They forced Habyarimana and the RPF back to the negotiating table. A power-sharing deal was hammered out, which would station a 600-man RPF battalion in Kigali to protect Tutsi politicians, while the French-trained Presidential Guard – essentially Habyarimana's hit squad – was to be disbanded.

However, during the handover the World Bank blocked all funds. Bankrupt, the country was on the brink of anarchy. The *interahamwe* ruled the streets, setting up its own roadblocks in downtown Kigali to harass and rob Tutsis. The *Azaku* were desperate to hold on to their ill-gotten gains. Habyarimana's in-laws, who had grown wealthy under his rule, owned a radio station, which began pumping out anti-Tutsi propaganda. Meanwhile, Habyarimana stalled on implementing the power-sharing deal.

The Secretary-General of the Organisation of African Unity, along with the heads of state of Tanzania, Uganda, Kenya and Burundi, summoned Habyarimana to a meeting at the Hotel Kilimanjaro in Tanzania. They insisted that he implement the power-sharing deal. Under immense pressure, he gave in.

Habyarimana had flown to the Hotel Kilimanjaro meeting in a French Mystère Falcon given to him by President Mitterand. He was giving the president of Burundi a lift home when his sleek jet was blasted out of the sky by three hand-launched heat-seeking missiles. Habyarimana did not get home in one piece, but get home he did. His plane was just passing over the outskirts of Kigali when it was hit and Habyarimana's charred remains landed in the gardens of his splendid new presidential palace. Within 100 days, one million Rwandans would be dead and half the country's population displaced.

Bizarrely, the rockets that had brought down Habyarimana's French-made jet were also supplied by the French. In an effort to maintain its influence in francophone Africa, the French were playing a double game. As well as supplying the RPF, they also paid for all the latest military goodies that the Rwandan army was stockpiling. Previously, it had been equipped well enough only to carry out the occasional massacre. Now it was up to strength for full-blown genocide. There were more than enough small arms to equip the army and the *interahamwe*, who were taught to use their new toys by the French. Although the French paid for the arms, they actually came from Egypt and South Africa, and Hutu officers were trained in the US. But French military advisors were on hand to make sure the killing went smoothly.

Despite this high-tech hardware, the Rwandan murder weapon of choice was the *panga* – a small machete imported from China that Rwandan peasants used as an all-purpose farm implement and carried around like a third arm. Those who could not afford a *panga* and still wanted to join in the fun simply hammered nails into a piece of wood to make a club called a mazu. Ironically, it was with such simple instruments that the Rwandan people became the most efficient killing machine the world has ever seen.

The *interahamwe* was essentially a criminal organisation. Despite, the fact that the unemployed youths who joined it were paid much more than they could hope to receive in gainful employment, they supplemented their incomes by robbing and looting. Plainly, the more Tutsis that were killed the greater the spoils for the Hutus.

If any one party was truly to blame for the genocide in Rwanda, it was the family of Agathe Habyarimana, the president's widow. With the death of Habyarimana, they feared the end had come and they would be caught with their hands in the cookie jar. Having softened up the population with years of anti-Tutsi hate propaganda, they instructed their radio station to tell every able-bodied Hutu to go out and kill the 'enemies of democracy' – that is, the Tutsis. The station even broadcast tips on the best ways of killing the *inyenzi*.

The RPF were well aware of the threat the radio station posed and bombed its studios. But it continued broadcasting from an armoured car in a zone protected by the French and, later, by Zaire. Throughout the civil war that followed, the station consistently played down the gains of the RPF and urged all patriotic Hutus to kill every Tutsi they could find. Hutu propaganda said that the RPF was invading with the aim of restoring the Tutsi monarchy. If they succeeded, they would purge the Hutus. It was a case of kill or be killed.

The massacres that followed were not random acts of violence. They were designed to destroy the peace accords that the OAU and Rwanda's neighbours had foisted on the country. The Presidential Guards distributed weapons; death lists, already prepared, were circulated, and the killing began within an hour of Habyarimana's death.

The first to die were not Tutsis, but moderate Hutus who had opposed the extremists in Habyarimana's administration. Among them was Joseph Kavaruganda, president of the constitutional court.

Early on the morning of 7 April, the Presidential Guard came to the residence of Agathe Uwilingiyamana, Rwanda's attractive 41-year-old acting prime minister. She escaped and tried to climb over the wall into the home of a US consular official, but the wall was too high and no ladder could be found. Surrounded by 20 of the Presidential Guards, again she managed to escape, and found sanctuary at the United Nations Development Programme. Although ten Belgian soldiers were sent to protect her, they had no choice but to obey the Presidential Guard's orders to disarm; they had no mandate to resist.

Mrs Uwilingiyamana tried to flee again, but was gunned down. Her bloodstained body was left in the road. The Belgian soldiers sent to protect her were tortured mercilessly, then executed, by the Presidential Guard. Fearing another Somalia, the United Nations ordered its 2,500 troops in Rwanda to return to barracks. Even when they saw a young Rwandan woman being hacked to death by machete, they did not intervene. Their Canadian commander General Dallaire said that his men could have taken out the Presidential Guard, the gendarmerie and the worst of the *interahamwe* within 48 hours, saving hundreds of thousands of lives. But he was ordered by a UN general in New York not to do so. After all, Rwanda's murderous government still had a seat in the general assembly. Two weeks after the genocide began, the UN withdrew, leaving only a token force of 450 men. General Dallaire could not even prevent the slaughter of 250 Tutsis and six priests who were trapped in St Andrew's College in Kigali.

US Marines and French and Belgian paratroopers oversaw an airlift that took 5,000 foreigners out of the country. Others fled over the border to Burundi. Not a single Rwandan was allowed to escape – with the exception of Agathe Habyarimana and 15 members of her family. Within hours of her husband's death, they were on a flight to Paris, where they stayed as guest of President Mitterand.

The rump of Habyarimana's government cut telephone lines to prevent the world from hearing about what was going on; electricity and water supplies failed; drunken *interahamwe* youths rampaged around the streets tossing grenades; banks were looted, fire trucks vandalised, government offices and private businesses smashed up. Nowhere was safe – even in hospital the sick and wounded were murdered in their beds.

The international community's response was to wash its hands of the problem. All foreign embassies were closed and staff evacuated. The extremists now had a free hand and the killing of Tutsis started in earnest. In one day alone, 40,000 corpses floated down the Kagera River into Lake

Victoria and 250,000 Rwandese fled across the border into Tanzania. Many of the bloated bodies seen doing a macabre dance of death in the swirling waters of the Rusumo Falls were women and children. Some had been decapitated; others had drowned themselves, rather than face the raging *interahamwe*; while some who begged to be slaughtered were spared by *interahamwe* who complained that they had done so much killing that day that they were too tired to kill even one more.

A month after the beginning of the massacre, when it was clear that an organised campaign of genocide was underway, no one in the rest of the world had the faintest idea what to do. A spokesman for the US State Department said that they simply hoped that the Rwandans would stop killing each other. 'They cannot kill each other forever,' he said.

It is estimated that a total of one million died before the RPF finally achieved victory on 4 July. One third of them were children.

In the city of Cyangugu, fewer than 8,000 of the 55,000 Tutsi inhabitants survived. It was the Prefect of the district of Cyangugu who organised the slaughter. Tutsis were rounded up and herded into the stadium where fragmentation grenades were lobbed at them. There are eleven mass graves in the city, but in the rural area the slaughter was worse. Of the 450,000 Tutsis in country districts of the Prefecture of Cyangugu, only a handful remained.

One survivor reported that he was hiding in a church with his wife and five children when the *interahamwe* came. His wife and two children were butchered. He was told that the Hutus were going to cut the tall Tutsis 'down to size'. Then he was slashed across the face and had his Achilles' tendons severed. He can no longer walk without crutches.

Another survivor said that he was among a group of around 100 Tutsis that the *interahamwe* hacked their way through. This was such tiring work that the killers had to stop to rest a couple of times. Badly injured, he seized the opportunity to hide behind some bushes and, when it was dark, escape. But he had to leave his children behind and was sure they had been killed.

One Tutsi woman admitted killing her wounded stepmother and two of her friends with a nail-studded club. The *interahamwe* forced her to do it. If she did not, she knew her own life and those of her children would be forfeit. Some people went mad with guilt and grief.

One man killed his badly wounded brother to put him out of his misery. He then hid in the pit of a latrine, up to his neck in sewage, for three days. He would have drowned, but someone came to use the latrine and heard his feeble cries. Others hid in sewers and ceilings and had to watch helplessly as the rest of their family was killed. Babies survived under mounds of corpses, though some were spared for no apparent reason.

There was no sanctuary anywhere. More than 30,000 Tutsis crammed into the Roman Catholic centre at Kabgayi. Most were killed. Entire families – which are large in Rwanda – were wiped out in one fell swoop. The Eglise Sainte Family in Kigali became notorious. The priest there had offered sanctuary to 8,000 Tutsis. It was a deliberate ploy by the Hutu to round up the Tutsis, making it easier for the *interahamwe* butchers to slaughter them. From the church, the *interahamwe* could abduct people and hack them to death at will. Or they could pick out hundreds from the congregation to machine-gun. Those remaining were left to starve or die from the diseases that spread easily in the cramped conditions while they waited their turn.

Outside the city, one 12-year-old boy said that he and his mother and sister had gone into hiding at his grandmother's house after his father was killed in a school where he was hiding. But the *interahamwe* caught up with them there too. They shot his grandmother, badly wounding her, killed the boy's sister, and slashed him around the head. His mother ran to get help, but they caught her and cut her legs. Then they set the house on fire. His grandmother helped him escape, but his mother died in the blaze. The boy and his grandmother hid in the burnt-out house, until she died. He was there for a long time on his own with her corpse, until the RPF came along and took him to a hospital.

Girls as young as seven were raped and mutilated. The killers liked to lop off a hand or a foot. Some mothers killed their own children rather than let them suffer at the hands of the *interahamwe*. One mother was trying to flee from the killers with her baby tied to her back. Her pursuers beat the baby to a pulp but, cruelly, spared the mother.

Hutu politicians excused their actions, blaming it on the RPF's resumption of fighting after the death of President Habyarimana. The politicians claimed that government soldiers were so busy fighting the rebels that they could not prevent the atrocities. They justified the killing by comparing it to the fight against apartheid. The Tutsis, they said, wanted to control everything, like the whites in South Africa. However, when the RPF finally took control, they installed a provisional government consisting of two Hutus and one Tutsi.

The mass slaughter in Rwanda was not an accident of war; the dead were not civilians caught in the crossfire. It was a systematic attempt to exterminate the Tutsis: it was genocide. Even when the battle against the RPF was lost and the French managed to persuade the government, civil servants, army commanders, militia leaders and their families to leave – taking with them the entire contents of Rwanda's exchequer – the Hutu government saw this not as a defeat, but as a strategic withdrawal. They intended to return and finish the job.

There is no doubt that the RPF also committed atrocities. As they took over the country, it was the Hutus' turn to flee. Soon the Tutsis in Tanzania were sharing their refugee camps with the killers who had tried to exterminate them. Tanzanian soldiers confiscated machetes, but they could not stop the killers taking over the camps.

The situation in Zaire was worse. By systematically robbing the exchequer, President Mobutu had let the infrastructure of the country collapse to such a point that it was impossible to feed or care for the refugees who fled there. Malnutrition and cholera were rife. However, 40,000 Rwandan government troops also withdrew to Zaire. Mobutu was a friend of the old regime and allowed them to regroup there and train, ready to restart the war. Fortunately, this strategy backfired – it destabilised Zaire and in 1997 Mobutu was forced out. Many of those responsible for the massacres have gone on trial. However, the senior officials responsible have largely found safe havens in Europe and the US. It was always the way.

BENEATH THE SKIN

Born a Yorkshire lass, Caroline Engla... Law at
Manchester University and stayed over ... She deserted
the law to bring up her three lovel... and discovered
writing was far preferable to dusting, ... and vacuuming.
Her short story collection *Watching Horsepats Feed the Roses*
was published by ACHUKA Books in 2012. *Beneath the Skin*
is her first novel.

CAROLINE ENGLAND

Beneath the Skin

avon.

HarperCollins
PUBLISHERS
Since 1817

AVON

A division of HarperCollins*Publishers*
1 London Bridge Street,
London SE1 9GF

www.harpercollins.co.uk

A Paperback Original 2017

1

A catalogue record for this book is
available from the British Library

ISBN-13: 978-0-00-823752-3

Set in Minion by Palimpsest Book Production Limited,
Falkirk, Stirlingshire

Printed and bound in Great Britain by
CPI Group (UK) Ltd, Croydon CR0 4YY

MIX
Paper from
responsible sources
FSC™ C007454
www.fsc.org

This book is produced from independently certified FSC paper
to ensure responsible forest management.

For more information visit: www.harpercollins.co.uk/green

For my three gorgeous girls, Liz, Charl and Emily.
And, of course, Jonathan. Love you all.

PART ONE

CHAPTER ONE

'Antonia, Antonia. My name is Antonia.'

It's been her name for many years. But sometimes, like tonight, she forgets.

Lying in the bath, she stares at the naked razor blade. The tiny distorted reflection of a girl gazes back. If she was brave, if she was very brave, she'd use it on her wrists, two deep final lines. Then she'd close her eyes and let this masquerade slip away.

She removes a curl of damp hair stuck to her cheek. The thought of all the fuss her death would create is unbearable. Even in death, the notion of being the centre of attention, the talk of the town, even for fifteen minutes, is excruciating.

And she knows the pull is there. She can feel it inside, somewhere deep and hidden. That tiny pulse of life, drawing her back from the overwhelming desire to disappear, to become something, somebody. To live, to really live, instead of hiding in this bathroom, this house.

Rocking her head from side to side, she tries to expel the memory of the unexpected telephone call this afternoon. She doesn't want to think of it now. She doesn't want to think about it ever.

She adjusts the position of the razor blade, watches the imprint of her fingers disappear and takes a deep breath before slowly slicing into the soft flesh of her arm. Closing her eyes, she smiles, a small sigh escaping her lips. There's always a moment, a throb of expectation, then the sharp pain sets in, taking her back to a moment of acute pleasure. Crisp and clear: the still of a film. Antonia and Sophie, Sophie and Antonia, smiling, naked and drunk. But today it's of a girl on a swing, laughing with sheer happiness, her daddy pushing her high into the clouds.

But of course that wasn't her.

Seconds pass and the intensity of the moment ebbs away to a moderate stinging sensation. She opens her eyes, shame and disgust replacing the delirium. The bath water has cooled, the mirrors weep with condensation. Her dark nipples skim her legs as she leans forward to drain the tepid water, now tinted salmon by blood. She covers the wound with a flannel, then steps on to the bathmat and into the chill of the newly tiled bathroom.

A cutter, she thinks, remembering the pretty girl in the razor blade. Cutting to cope. To forget the past. To replace the pain inside her head with one she could see. To watch it seep away. But what of the woman? The one called Antonia? Cutting to feel. To stop the numbness, the isolation. To scar the perfection. She is addicted to the high.

Or perhaps she just wants to see what's beneath her skin.

'My Friday night treat,' she mutters. She glances at the woman in the mirror, flawless and perfect, no history, no past. With a small sigh, she peels away the crimson-stained flannel to study her artwork, then she blows out the candles and reaches for a towel.

'Where's bloody Sami?' David Stafford asks, looking at his watch. 'With his flunkeys, do you think? Mo and Salim and the rest of his ever-changing entourage?' He scrapes back his chair across the slate floor as he stands. 'Same again?'

Mike Turner glances down at his third pint: it's hardly been touched and he already feels pissed. Bloody hell, David's going for it tonight, he thinks. David's breath has the acrid smell of an all-day session. But that isn't particularly unusual.

He looks up and smiles. David appears as he always does. Tall, slightly overweight, tanned. Jeans with a stripy shirt tucked in. But something's not quite right. His eyes, he decides. David's eyes seem lifeless.

'No, you go ahead,' Mike replies. 'I'm pacing myself. You're a thirsty man tonight. Everything all right?'

'It's nothing that another pint won't cure. Come on, Mikey, it's the start of the weekend. I'll get you one in.'

A busy September Friday night at the Royal Oak pub, composed of the usual mix of students and the long-standing faithful. Not a convenient venue for any of them now, but David, Mike and Sami have all lived in the leafy Withington area of South Manchester at some point in their lives. 'Probably the only thing we have in common,' Sami once joked, which wasn't entirely true.

David walks away, slightly unsteady, and dips his head to evade a low oak beam. He lifts his arm and wafts his empty pint glass above the heads of several people already waiting at the bar.

'Yep, I've still got the famous left foot.' Mike can hear the deep tone of David's voice from the bar despite the clamour of the heaving pub. 'I'll be there on Sunday as usual. Of course they'd be lost without me. Are you having another? I'll get you one in.'

David can never hide for long, the boom of his voice betrays him. The benefit and the curse of a private education, Mike has decided.

'Another two pints of your best, Mrs L. You're looking as

beautiful as ever, might I say? Off to Barbados for Christmas as usual?'

Mike turns his glass in his hand, wondering if he'll finish this pint, let alone another. The conversation drifts around him. 'Mrs L' is *so* David. She's Misty to everyone else, flame-haired bar manager and wife of the affable and obese landlord, Seamus. For a moment he wonders whether Misty is her real name – it seems such a cliché for a woman who once was a model of some sort but whose battle with the booze is evident from the slur of her voice to the tremor of her expensively ringed fingers.

'So you *were* thirsty,' David says, back in his seat. Mike's pint glass is empty. 'Been off with the fairies again, Mikey?'

Mike shakes his head, laughs and wonders where he's been without the dog, the black dog of depression, christened when it first snuck up on him at sixteen.

A black dog, he thinks, not a stork.

'Probably,' he smiles, shaking the unwelcome thought away. 'How's Antonia?'

'Fine, she's fine,' David answers, glancing towards the bar, the sparkle back in his bright blue eyes. 'At home with a DVD and guacamole. Jennifer Aniston's my bet. Actually Mikey, I wanted to ask you. Her birthday's coming up and I want to buy her something special, maybe something different for a change. Got any ideas? What would you buy Olivia?'

Mike scratches his chin, still smooth from its second shave of the day. He laughs. 'You mean, what do you buy the woman who has everything?'

'He treats her like a bloody doll,' his wife Olivia often remarks, spot on as ever. The statement reminds him of a cardboard dolly set his sister was given one Christmas. She asked him to play, and despite his desire to try out his new bicycle in the biting Irish winter outside, he knelt beside her and joined in the game at the warm kitchen table, detaching the paper outfits from the booklet, the dresses, the hats, the scarves and the shoes, then dressing the doll in different designs for each season of the year.

'I'm serious, Mikey.' David interrupts his thoughts. 'What would you buy Olivia?'

Mike takes a swig of his beer, then wipes the rim of the glass with his thumb. David's assumption that their respective wives fall into any remotely similar category makes him smile to himself.

'Vain and vacant. The sort of woman I can't stand,' Olivia said of Antonia after meeting her for the first time at one of David and Antonia's dinner parties. 'But as it happens, she's nice and I like her, which is really annoying.'

So what would he buy Olivia? What had he bought her last time? Mike can't remember, probably something she'd asked for, but then they don't make a fuss of their own birthdays, preferring to concentrate on their two lovely girls.

And there it is: like Winston Churchill's dog, his own black dog of despair, bounding back into the pub and sitting by him. Close, comfortable and devastating. He hears his own voice not long after it happened, trying for rationality: 'I didn't even know him. It could have been so much worse.'

There are times when Mike wonders if he's spoken aloud, made his words to the dog public. For a moment he's forgotten the question, but he's saved from an answer; David has turned towards the door.

'What bloody time do you call this?' he bellows, standing up and gesticulating towards the bar. Mike looks at his watch. It's getting on for last orders but Sami Richards grins and shrugs, holding out his palms in a dismissively apologetic gesture. Elegant and handsome, he strolls past the Friday regulars clustered at the bar, the turned-up collar of his black leather jacket matching the sheen of his skin.

'Why does he always look as though he's walked off the page of a fucking magazine?' David says, a little too aggressively, as he turns back towards Mike. He knocks back his pint, ready to get in more drinks.

'Things to do, people to see,' Sami replies easily as David walks away. He takes off his jacket and leans over the table to shake Mike's hand, careful as always not to catch his crisp cuff on the spillages. 'Hey, man, I bumped into Pete on site the other day. Sends his regards. He mentioned the Boot Room.'

Mike smiles. Bloody hell, yes, the Boot Room. It's what they named Sami's tiny office when they were working together as trainee surveyors. A happy memory. Before responsibility, marriage, kids. They'd spent lunchtimes in there: football talk over sandwiches, crisps and Coke in their city-centre office building, no women allowed.

'Was he wearing his Liverpool cufflinks?'

'Didn't catch the cufflinks. But he's just bought a Porsche 911. Lucky sod.'

'Better dash out and buy one, Sami,' David says, arriving back at the table with three pints and a whisky chaser. The whisky looks like a double.

'Might just do that, David, my man. A call here and there. You never know. Are you still driving that tank? Nought to eighty in three minutes?'

Mike watches them quietly. He's never quite worked it out, their friendship, if that's what it is. Happy-go-lucky, water-off-a-duck's-back, is David. Except when it comes to Sami. The barbed comments, the occasional belligerence. He becomes a different person.

Perhaps they're a little too alike, he thinks. In their late thirties, both from wealthy families, successful in their careers. Married to childhood friends Sophie and Antonia. Both childless. But there the similarities end. David sits back and lets wealth and fortune fall into his lap, whereas Sami's a hunter, a person who never rests on his laurels; he's always searching for something bigger, something better.

From the day they first met fifteen years ago, Mike had detected Sami's restlessness. He changed cars and hairstyles like a chameleon, but then, he could afford to. Yet as Mike gazes at him now, he seems happier, more grounded than ever before. Perhaps he's reached a plateau in life, a level of contentment which can be sustained for longer than usual. He hopes so; he likes Sami very much. Sami's one of the good guys.

He shakes himself back to the conversation, picks up his glass of Guinness, murky and dark beneath its creamy facade, and feels the dog's gentle nudge at his side.

Antonia loves the silence of the countryside, the tranquility of her and David's large home. It still feels pure and new. Yet she allows the telephone beside the bed to ring, insistent, loud and shrill, without answering. It's late and she's sleepy, drifting contentedly in and out of the final chapter of *Wuthering Heights*, another Brontë novel she should have read as a child.

She knows who's fruitlessly holding on at the other end of the telephone. Most people call her on her mobile, but years ago she decided to hold back from giving the number to her mother. It made her feel guilty. It still makes her feel mean. But it helps her feel free of the past. Just a little.

CHAPTER TWO

'I think it's Monday so I'm coming over for a coffee,' Sophie says, sounding groggy. 'Put the kettle on.'

It's what Sophie always says when she phones. Not, 'Are you in, are you busy, is it all right?' She expects Antonia to be in whenever she chooses to turn up.

It slightly irritated Antonia at one time, but it doesn't bother her now. After all, she's invariably in, alone in her huge home in the Cheshire countryside, going through the motions of being a housewife, whatever that is. Though she supposes cleaning and cooking pretty much cover it now the builders and plumbers and decorators have left. There's the highlight of the supermarket, of course, but she and David shop for clothes and the house most weekends, so she's content to stay in and order food online.

'For God's sake, what's David bought you now?' Sophie often jibes, pulling a face at the latest rug or vase or item of clothing.

'It's expensive,' she replies, feeling the inevitable and disappointing stab of Sophie's disapproval.

'That doesn't make it tasteful, darling.'

'Well, I think it's nice of him,' she says, leaving the sentence hanging. And Antonia does think it's nice. She thinks her home and its contents are really lovely. It's just that it's all a little too much. David's a little too much.

'I do love you very much, my beautiful girl,' he said as he left the house for work this morning, his grey pinstripe suit looking slightly tight.

'I know,' she replied, laughing. 'I think you might have mentioned it once or twice this weekend. Get to work, you big softie.'

Once, long ago, Antonia counted the number of times David declared his love in just one carefree night and she wrote the number in her diary to record it forever. Exhilarating and exciting, she never expected to be loved so much. But now she worries why he repeats the words. She knows he adores the person she's created, the one she sees in her reflection. But not her mother's 'Little Chinue'. He's never met her.

Making for the stairs, she catches her face in the mirror. 'Where's the trophy wife, then?' They were Olivia Turner's words, whispered to her husband Mike at the first dinner party she and David hosted. She hadn't heard the expression before, and as she hung back in the shadows of the hallway, she didn't twig that Olivia meant her.

'I'm sorry,' Olivia said, her pale face colouring when Antonia emerged with a hesitant smile. 'You must be Antonia. I've heard you're very beautiful and you are.'

But in Antonia's mind, the word *beautiful* has never stuck.

She turns away from the mirror, hoping Olivia likes her better now. She seemed tense at the last dinner party. 'Well, being the bloody office heartthrob . . .' she said pointedly to Mike several times. It seemed a strange thing to say. He looked embarrassed and perplexed. But perhaps they were all a little

11

too drunk, Sophie in particular, who turned up with two bottles. Still, the party went well. Of course Helen said the usual, 'For goodness sake, Antonia, sit here and talk. I won't bite,' but lovely Charlie was there with his genial wink, 'Oh, but she does and it's ferocious. I wouldn't risk it.'

She's still brushing her long hair when Sophie arrives at White Gables, so doesn't have time to straighten it completely.

'You look gorgeous, darling,' Sophie says as she wafts past her and into the large bright kitchen. 'But then you always do.'

She turns and studies Antonia. 'Why don't you do me a favour, just for once, and have a slob-out day? Just one day when you don't brush your hair or apply any make-up. Don't even clean your teeth or change your underwear. Twenty-four hours of not being perfect. Would you do that, just for me?'

Sophie's startling green eyes are on hers just a little too long before she breaks the gaze. 'But then you'd still look gorgeous and smell of lily of the valley on freshly baked wholegrain, wouldn't you?' She picks up a magazine from a low glass table and starts to flick the pages. 'The curl's coming back in your hair, Toni. Why don't you leave it this time? I like it curly.'

Antonia turns away as the telephone starts to ring. They have the hair conversation too often and she isn't in the mood for Sophie's amateur psychoanalysis today. Sophie has always been there for her since childhood, good times and bad, but sometimes her familiarity can be claustrophobic. She rubs the back of her neck. Her strained weekend with an unusually quiet David has left her tense.

'Aren't you going to answer the telephone?' Sophie asks. 'If you won't, I will.'

'No, Sophie, leave it. It'll be a call centre. I don't want to encourage them.'

'Then unplug the bloody thing.'

The telephone stops ringing and Antonia lets out her breath. Perhaps she should unplug it. But what about her mum?

Sophie flings the magazine on to the white leather sofa, following it herself with a huge sigh. 'Sami says I broke every taboo at dinner with the Henleys on Saturday.'

'Let me guess, you asked them how much they earned as well as how much their house was worth?'

'Well, I always ask that! But apparently I talked about sex rather a lot and I asked Tim whether he'd ever been unfaithful.'

'Ouch!'

Sophie laughs. 'I didn't think anyone else could hear and we're all gagging to know if the rumours are true. But I didn't talk about religion or politics.'

'That's all right then.'

'At least I don't think so. I drank far, far too much.'

Antonia fills the kettle from the tap at the centre of the gleaming granite-topped island and then perches on a chrome and leather bar stool before swivelling to examine her only real friend. Sophie does look pretty rough today, older than her thirty-one years. Her skin is blotchy, there are dark circles under her eyes, she's wearing no make-up and her auburn hair is chaotically tied with an elastic band at the nape of her neck. She looks remarkably like Norma, her mum, but Antonia knows better than to say so.

'I look terrible, don't I?'

'Well . . .' Antonia laughs. Sophie doesn't look her best, but with Sophie looks don't matter. Sometimes she looks plain, at other times dazzling, but however she appears, her personality shines through her brilliant eyes, entrancing all who come within her range.

'Well, what?' Sophie snaps.

'I was thinking about your butterfly and moth theory.'

'Bloody hell, you don't forget anything, do you? It wasn't meant as an insult. We were a winning team, Toni. You would attract the men with your butterfly beauty and I would keep them spellbound like moths around a light. Or something like that. Most people would prefer to be the butterfly!'

'I know. You ugly old moth, you.'

'Hmm. I guess some men prefer an easy win, while others prefer a bit of a challenge.'

Like Sami, Antonia thinks, still gazing at Sophie, and for a moment she drifts. Perhaps she is an easy win, but easy win or not, Sami wanted her first. It was her he wanted the night they all met. It was her he begged to go out with him, but she gave him to Sophie because Sophie wanted him so much.

'Antonia! My coffee. I'm waiting!'

Sophie is staring, her green eyes sharp. 'What are you smiling about? You really must stop that weird on another planet stuff you do. And turn off the radio, it's hurting my bloody head.'

'Our former lives,' Antonia replies, turning away and opening the white, high-gloss cupboards to take out a single pink-dotted teapot with a cup on top and a large mug with *Sophie's cappuccino* written on it. She arranges Belgian rolled wafers on a long ceramic dish. 'Life before marriage, life before you decided we should go more upmarket.'

'Yup, we bagged a surveyor and a solicitor. Didn't we do well!' Sophie replies, throwing her head back and laughing her deep guttural laugh.

Antonia studies her for a moment before taking the lid off the teapot, giving it a stir and breathing in the smell of peppermint. 'Do you really think so?' she says as she offers Sophie the wafers.

'Sami said David had a skinful on Friday. "Unbelievably rat

14

arsed" were his precise words. He wanted to have a fight over some harmless comment Sami made about you, apparently, which was pretty stupid when he could hardly walk,' Sophie says, ignoring Antonia's question. 'What was that all about then?'

'No idea. You probably know more than me.'

Antonia sweeps the crumbs into the sink as she contemplates last Friday night. She had been sound asleep and was awoken suddenly, the accusatory sound of the doorbell in the dead of night throwing her back to a time she tries hard to erase. She padded from her bedroom and down the limestone stairs, the sound of her heart loud in her ears, and there was Mike Turner peering through the peep hole while doing his best to hold David upright.

'Sorry, Antonia,' Mike said, and for a moment she gazed at him, her new name taking her by surprise, even after all these years. But then she rallied, shaking herself back to the dark cold night and the state of her husband.

Mike's eyes seemed watchful; she found she couldn't meet them. 'I know it's late but he's had a bit too much,' he said after a moment. 'And he couldn't find his keys. So I thought I'd better— Do you want me to help him upstairs?'

'I can get myself up my own fucking stairs.' David pulled himself upright and pushed Mike away. 'I could've found my way home too. Fuck off home and polish your halo, you fucking sanctimonious Irish prick.'

'Sorry, Mike,' she said, not knowing what else to say. Her heartbeat started to slow, but she felt panicky, that familiar metallic taste in her mouth.

Mike stood for a moment, looking unsteady on his feet and raking his hand through his dark messy hair. He opened his mouth, as though looking for the right words, but then turned away and lifted his hand. 'No problem, he won't remember in the morning. Taxi waiting. Night, Antonia. Take care.'

Antonia fleetingly wondered about David's surprising behaviour before climbing into bed beside his unconscious bulk. He could drink enormous quantities of booze, but was rarely drunk. She closed her eyes, hoping sleep would overcome the unsought memories jabbing at her mind. But just as she was finally drifting off, David woke up with a jerk. He stared at her face for what seemed like an age before starting to cry, loud, wretched sobs.

'I'm sorry, I'm so sorry, please forgive me,' he wept, pushing his face against her breast like a small helpless child. But then he fell back to sleep as swiftly as he'd woken. Antonia lay there, her silk nightdress stuck to her chest from the tears and saliva, feeling nothing but a queer blankness, tinged with memories of disgust.

'You're doing it again, Toni. Stop!'

Sophie's words bring Antonia back to the muggy September Monday and to the scrutinising eyes of her friend. She feels the tightness in her stomach, the burn of her cheeks and that mild taste of panic. 'Ready for a top-up?' she asks, turning away.

'Less coffee and more cream this time. And different biscuits,' Sophie replies, picking up the television remote control, pointing it at the huge flatscreen on the wall and flicking through the shopping channels. Then, after a few moments, 'You know you'll tell me eventually.'

CHAPTER THREE

'Lunch calls. Are you ready to go?' David asks, putting his head around Charlie Proctor's office door and inhaling the familiar smell of old books and leather.

'Is it that time already? Thought the old juices were giving me gyp. Turns out it's just my stomach rumbling for lunch!'

Charlie peers at the ancient oak grandfather clock which dominates the room. He places his hands on each arm of the leather chair, hauls himself up and then steadies himself against the desk. He clears his throat and adjusts his tie before reaching for his overcoat and umbrella.

'Charlie, it isn't cold or raining and you're forty-six, not sixty!' David might say. But that wouldn't be sporting or, indeed, nice. Besides, Charlie is Charlie, a cliché of his own creation. He was wearing a paisley smoking jacket and an avuncular smile the day they first met at boarding school. The eleven-year-old David had been allocated Charlie's study. 'How do. Ten years ago you would have been my new fag. Shame they scrapped them,' Charlie said by way of greeting that morning and yet it still took David days to work out that Charlie was a pupil, albeit an eighteen-year-old sixth former, and not a benign schoolmaster.

But today David's thoughts are with Antonia and their weekend. He woke late on Saturday to an empty house, a certainty in his gut that Antonia had left him. He misbehaved on Friday night. He made a scene at the pub, though he couldn't recall the details. But worse than that he cried in her arms; that he could remember.

Charlie closes his office door with a thud. The 'Senior Partner' brass plate shakes. It's left over from the days when the position of senior partner was handed down from father to son and when it meant something. Now it's incongruous, like Charlie himself. None of the other partners went to a public school; they went to grammar school or, in the case of the young guns, to a state comprehensive. The flavour of the partnership these days is political correctness, accountability and liberalism. Gone are the days of getting on because of the 'old school tie'. Nepotism died with Charlie's old man. David has learned to adapt, to tone down the open vowels and to voice slightly left-wing opinions he doesn't believe in, but Charlie seems oblivious to it all. Or perhaps that's part of his act, his survival.

They stroll pass the imposing eighteenth-century St Ann's church, past the al fresco diners huddling under chic canopies at its side, then continue through the cobbled alleyway to Sam's Chop House.

It's dark and quiet as usual on a Monday in Sam's. David brought Antonia here once, not long after they met. He wanted to show her off, his new stunning girlfriend, never dreaming that one day soon she'd say yes and become his wife. But she was withdrawn, she'd looked uncomfortable in the company of the older lunchtime lawyers and eventually asked if they could leave.

'Have you decided?'

David starts, his heart seeming to lurch out of place. Charlie is frowning at him, as though he can read his thoughts.

'Decided what?'

'What you're eating of course. The steak is always delicious here. But don't ask for rare. They don't bother cooking it at all. Are you all right, David? You're miles away.'

David glances at Charlie's face before dropping his gaze to the menu. His mind is in spasm. He's finding it difficult to focus. There are hugely worrying things to discuss, to confess, but it's all he can do not to put his head on the table and sleep. 'Yes, steak's a grand idea,' he says. He wonders if he'll manage to eat it. He worries whether he'll keep the food down. 'Shall we order? There's something I wanted to talk about. It's pretty—'

'Let's try a bottle of that rather nice Chianti. I've been stuck in the All England Reports this morning. No one reads case law any more, but they should, David. Back to basics, I say. Now at Cambridge . . .'

David's mind strays back to Antonia. Thank God, she came home. He didn't ask where she'd been. Her absence from White Gables for so long was strange, but it didn't matter. She was smiling; she was home.

'Do you know what I fancy doing?' she said, her cheek cold against his. 'But we don't have to if you don't want to.'

He watches as the glossy red wine is poured and then lifts the glass to his lips. Charlie is still talking, but he can't concentrate on anything but the wisps of chin hair he has omitted to shave, which are moving in time with his mouth.

'And I told George Briggs what I thought. Bloody Queen's Counsel. How they lord it over us mere solicitors. Waste of a Monday morning.'

David wasted his morning too. He sat in his sunlit office

with the insurance file on his desk, staring at its cover for hours, but seeing nothing. He needed to work things out in his head, but thoughts of his wife, her fresh face and her laughter, filtered in with the rays through the blinds.

'Been to the doctor . . .'

He puts down his fork and looks at Charlie with surprise. Now that Charlie has mentioned it, he does seem pallid, his face puffy and sweaty.

'Don't say a word to Helen, it's probably nothing. You know what these doctors are like, always protecting their own backs. That's what insurance is for!'

Insurance, David thinks, loosening his tie. That's nicely ironic.

'My blood pressure and cholesterol are sky high, apparently. He's given me some tablets, but he took an armful of blood for more tests and gave me a stern warning about lifestyle choices. You know the sort of rubbish they talk, less food, less alcohol, less stress. Hell, David, they're the things I live for, so I'm not telling Helen and neither must you.'

David nods, but he's meandered again. Ten-pin bowling, he's thinking. He and Antonia went bowling on Saturday afternoon and then stayed in the complex to eat burger and fries. He's nearly forty and he'd never been bowling before – and how Antonia had laughed. Like a girl. A beguiling girl he didn't know.

'And then there's Rupert,' Charlie continues, pouring more wine into David's empty glass. 'Helen thinks it's normal to experiment, to misbehave, to be downright rude at times. But if anything is causing my blood pressure to reach boiling point, it's him. We've got to meet the headmaster next weekend to convince the school why he shouldn't be expelled before he sits his Michaelmas exams. My questions to him will be "Where the hell do the pupils get the drugs from? Why doesn't the school do something about that?"'

David studies Charlie's face. It has changed from a grey sweaty white to a livid red, all the way down to his thick neck, housed in a too-tight white collar.

Now is definitely not the time to confess, he thinks. It'll just have to wait.

'We've decided to go through with IVF again,' Sophie says suddenly, pulling out the elastic band with some difficulty and then dragging her bitten nails through the thick mass of her hair.

Antonia raises her eyebrows but makes no comment. Nothing from Sophie's lips surprises her any more and it's best to allow her friend to spill it all out before making any remark. There are many occasions when Antonia is economical with the truth, or when she evades an answer by changing the subject, but Sophie can never hold anything in for long. As a child she was alarmingly honest about everything and everybody, her mum and her youngest brother targeted the most. 'Your breath smells, Uncle Frank. That dress makes you look fat, Mum. You know Dad loves me more than you, don't you, Harry? Does Grandpa have a foreskin?' That was just family: girls and boys at school were easy meat. An older girl once cornered her in the corridor. 'Do you know what a complete and utter cruel bitch you are?' she asked. 'No I'm not,' Sophie replied fearlessly. 'I'm just honest. If you don't like it, get out of my way.'

Antonia never got out of Sophie's way. Sometimes she dearly wishes she had. 'You're mixed race, Antonia. Or black if you like. So why don't you just admit it? There's nothing wrong with it.' Honest or cruel, Antonia has yet to decide.

'Don't look at me like that, Toni,' she now commands. 'I

know what you're thinking, but Sami wants us to try one last time. You know what he's like about family. Mother Martha had five kids and so she expects to have a hundred and twenty grandchildren or something. And if I'm up for all the prodding and poking, those bloody hormone injections . . .'

Antonia takes a breath. The real reason for Sophie's infertility is the one secret she has managed to keep. It has to be said.

'Sophie, why would you want to go through it again when you're pretty sure it won't work? Why put yourself through it? You hate hospitals! And it's hardly fair to Sami, you're giving him false hope.'

'Oh shut up, Antonia.'

Sophie stands and paces, her hands on her hips and her eyes ferocious. 'You really take your saintliness to extremes at times. Is there a Saint Antonia? Is that why you chose the bloody stupid name? Besides, you're the one with the problem if you really think having a baby is a fate worse than death. Most normal women want a child, it's what nature expects and I'm no different. You're the bloody freak, not me.'

It's ridiculous, Antonia knows, at thirty years old, but on these occasions she still wants to cry. Instead she stands, walks to the sink and turns on the tap. Sophie will never change; her best line of defence is to attack and the assault is invariably below the belt. But when it comes to babies, she doesn't care whether Sophie thinks she's unnatural or odd. She doesn't have and never has had any desire to procreate. There are enough unhappy people in the world without adding to their number. David understands. She told him from the start she didn't want children and he accepted it at face value, saying it was fine and that he'd have the snip. He's never broached the subject again and never asked why.

David, oh, David. The thought of Friday night catches her

breath again. He accepts her as she is, he doesn't ask questions, analyse or dig too deep like her former boyfriends. He doesn't want to control her, thank God. He's steady and reliable. Isn't he?

She feels Sophie's breath on her neck, then a hand on her back and the inevitable flutter somewhere deep in her stomach.

'I fancy a drink, Toni. Shall we open a bottle?'

Sophie kisses her cheek, then steps away to the glass-fronted wine fridge, crouching down to select a bottle.

'This looks expensive,' she says when she stands. 'Come on, darling, don't sulk, who knows what might happen?' She places her chin on Antonia's shoulder and softly blows a curl from her face. 'You will be there to hold my hand, won't you? All the way?'

'You know I will,' Antonia replies.

There's a tremor in David's large hand which he tries to ignore as he struggles to insert the tiny key into the lock of his bottom desk drawer. He extracts the yellow file and stares at its cover where his secretary has written 'Indemnity and Claims' in red marker pen.

He blows out his cheeks. Red for danger.

He glances at his closed office door before taking a deep breath. Then he opens the file quickly, like ripping off a plaster. As though that will make a difference. As though speed will alter the fact that the renewal date for the firm's insurance has passed, undeniably passed, and he hasn't done anything about it.

'Goodness me, the renewal date has passed. The practice has no insurance in place. If there are any claims for poor legal advice or mistakes, the partners will be personally liable! How did that happen?' He tries feigning surprise to himself, but it doesn't wash, even in his mildly inebriated state. As the partner in charge of indemnity and claims, he's always known about the date, roughly known, at least. But he's put it on the furthermost back burner of his mind. Because. Because he knows.

He'd opened a savings account with a great rate of interest a year back. A deposit account for the firm and for the partners, but with himself as the sole signatory.

'What shall we call it, David?' the bank manager had asked over a long lunch.

'Insurance,' he replied.

'But of course!' the manager laughed.

He paid in the huge premium up front. It was a great plan. There'd be less whingeing about the cost of ever-increasing insurance premiums from the partners when renewal came. A nice little nest egg of interest to put towards the following year's premium, too. It made sense. Charlie agreed. 'I knew you were the man for the job, David. Excellent work.' The other partners concurred and he enjoyed the rare praise.

He stares at the renewal notice in the file and then circles the premium figure with a pencil, whistling softly. Nearly a hundred thousand pounds and it has to be paid now. In a litigious society the firm must be covered for negligence claims. Claims for cock-ups, in short. He nods, his mind racing with thoughts of what to do. Cheque lost in the post? Yes. A back-dated letter for the file? Absolutely. But the thing is to get it paid. PDQ. But there's a problem, a huge heart-thrashing problem. Even though he hasn't been able to bring himself to look at the 'insurance account', he knows without a doubt the money isn't there.

CHAPTER FOUR

The Manchester rain hammers against the roof of Mike's car. The traffic is at a standstill, Princess Parkway chock-a-block, with no sign of movement. He looks to his left. The queue at the drive-through McDonald's is immobile with morose folk seeking their hunger-fix. Once, years ago, he and Olivia vowed their children would never eat junk. They wanted to do nothing but right for their girls. Mike sighs: how time and experience changes everything.

There must have been an accident, he thinks, as he strains to see beyond the line of traffic in front of him. No habitual impulse of a prayer pops into his head, he forced those thoughts out long ago. His Catholicism, drummed in during childhood, had once burned deep, creating a wound he thought would never heal. That profound belief or fear or superstition, or whatever it is, that there is a god. No, not a god, but The God. But that scar has healed; when he needs his faith, he finds it has gone.

He switches from Radio 4, to 2, to Capital, listens for a moment to Rihanna and thinks of his girls dancing, giggling,

25

showing their pretty white teeth. 'Look, Daddy. Watch us dance!' It's a happy thought, he knows this, but he's lost the feeling of happiness, its sense, its touch.

He turns off the radio and watches the rain splatter and spread against the windscreen. It's making shapes he's never noticed before. Interesting, he thinks, but the ruse doesn't work for long; his bleak thoughts are too dominant, too powerful for Rihanna, or the rain, or even his lovely girls.

Shaking himself, he tries to resurface, to focus on the traffic tailback and the noise of the vehicles happily jam-free on the flyover ahead. He looks at his watch, knowing that he should text Olivia, but wondering what he should say. 'Stuck in traffic' is the obvious choice, but he can predict the reply, 'How long will you be?'

How long will this go on? The gloom, the pestering, dark thoughts. He had them before as a teenager, but they were intermittent then, somehow controlled by the guilt of the priest's regular Sunday words, 'There's always someone worse off.' But this time it's been months and he bores himself. It's truly pathetic. Always the same, it's the little things that pull him down. He can go for hours without giving it a second thought and then something will happen to make the black dog bound in. Today it was an email circulating around the office inviting the staff to contribute to a present for one of the associates, the newly proud father of a healthy son. An everyday office occurrence, but enough to throw him.

A knock on his window makes him start. His mobile is still in his hand, text unsent.

'Are you all right, mate? Need a push or has the car just stalled?'

Mike notices the blare of horns behind him and the empty road ahead. It's still raining.

'Yeah, just stalled. Sorry.'

As he slips the car into gear, the black dog lurches forward and then settles in for the ride.

'Get up to your bedroom, now!' Olivia bellows as Mike walks through the front door of their semi-detached Victorian home. He shakes the rain from his hair and puts his briefcase down in its usual place by the stairs.

'What's going on?' he asks, looking from mother to daughter. It's unlike Olivia to scream at Rachel. Or at anyone. What is it that she always says when they watch *Question Time*? 'He's shouting. Ha! He's lost control of the conversation.'

'I will not have any daughter of mine speak to me like that,' Olivia replies breathlessly.

Rachel spins round on the stairs, the knuckles of her slim hand white against the stained wood of the banister. 'Well, it's true. You tell us to be honest. You've been a cow for weeks, Mum. We can't do anything right. We might as well not exist for all you bloody well care.'

'Rachel, go to your bedroom,' he says quietly. 'Your mum's right. Don't you ever speak to her like that again.'

Rachel stares at him, her face pained with reproach. 'I knew you'd take her side,' she says, before running up the rest of the stairs.

He stands for a moment, the slam of Rachel's bedroom door loud in his ears. He shakes off his jacket and looks at Olivia. She hasn't moved and her face is set. He's never seen her so angry. 'It's raining,' he murmurs, looking for time, wondering how best to handle such an unexpected situation.

'What's going on, Olivia? This isn't like you two.' He reaches out, placing his hands at the top of Olivia's arms to draw her in. She's trembling. He can feel the anger rising from her as she pushes him away, the flat of her hand firm against his damp shirt.

'And how would you know?'

He stands and stares. Is Olivia laughing? He isn't sure. He hardly recognises her.

'How would you know?' she repeats. 'Tell me, Mike. You're never here. And even when you are here you're in some unreachable place. You don't notice me, you don't notice the girls.'

'That isn't true.' He sees his daughters in his mind, dancing to Rihanna. 'Of course I notice you all. Come on, Olivia, this isn't like—'

'When was the last time you gave me a compliment?' Olivia isn't laughing, she's crying, but the soft contours of her pale face are gone. 'When was the last time you bought me a box of chocolates or some flowers? I had my hair cut last week and you didn't even notice.'

He gazes at her hair. It's blonde, elfin short; it suits her petite face and her frame. 'I did notice. Of course I noticed. It looks lovely. But flowers, chocolates? Come on, Olivia, you don't do chocolates.'

'Fuck the chocolates, then. Fuck everything. You just continue to take it for granted that I'm going to be here, the little wife with a smiling face when you come home, your bloody dinner waiting on the table.'

He catches his breath. This is Olivia, calm, capable, witty Olivia; Olivia who takes everything in her stride. She's never been and will never be 'the little wife'. She's clever, opinionated and strong. He stares again, aware that life has shifted, that the world has somehow moved without him noticing.

'What do I do on a Tuesday, Mike? You never ask me how I am, where I've been, what I've done. I could be anywhere, with anyone. You're just so used to me I've become invisible.'

28

'That isn't true. Really. You never said,' he replies quietly.

'I shouldn't have to say anything. If you loved me, Mike, you'd see, you'd know.'

She stares at him for a moment, searching his face, her amber eyes wide and sad. 'What's the point?' she mutters, then walks into the kitchen and closes the door.

A wisp of a thought enters Mike's head, an impulse to turn around and walk out of the door he entered only minutes earlier. But it's only a thought and only for a moment as his eyes catch the pink fur of Hannah's favourite slippers. She's under the stairs, hidden from view, her arms around her knees and her blonde head buried.

'Is it my fault, Daddy?'

'Of course it isn't.' Mike pulls her to him, his beautiful bag of bones, breathing in the cosy smell of shampoo and baked beans. 'It's Daddy's fault. Don't worry, I'll make it all better, I promise,' he says, hugging his warm living child tightly to his heart, wondering where on earth he should begin.

It's late. Antonia is in bed, asleep, her long hair spread away from her face like a fan on the pillow. David studies her features for a while, taking in her glossy skin, the definition of her jaw and the graceful length of her neck. He longs to trace his fingers from the small lobe of her ear to the hollow of her throat, but he doesn't want to wake her and spoil the moment. He slips in beside her, the clean sheets feeling crisp and cold, much like his sleeping wife.

In those few moments when the terror of his worries relaxed their grip, he thought of Antonia again today. He had a clear image of her in his mind; that of a honey marble statue, perfectly chiselled, incredibly beautiful, but cool and impenetrable.

Sleep doesn't come and when Antonia sighs, he rests his head on one arm, stroking a finger along her naked spine, counting the tiny moles on her back. He always wants her, even when he's too drunk to do anything about it and she's never denied him. She's soft, willing and compliant. But the reality is that even when he hungrily invades her, even when he comes with a thunderous rush of pleasure, even as she whispers, 'Please, David, please,' he doesn't really penetrate her. It's this insatiable desire, this urgent need to connect that makes him want her so badly.

'I've tried to give you everything,' he murmurs. 'I'm sorry.' He wants to add, 'I know you don't love me, but promise you won't leave me. Stay with me forever. I'm nothing without you.' But he's afraid that saying the words out loud will validate them. And if Antonia hears, she'll despise him for his weakness, of that much he's certain.

As the whisky slowly drags David into sleep, his mind replays the last two days: insurance, his bank manager; Charlie, Charlie ill; angry clients; too much alcohol, too many lies. And finally Antonia. She laughed at one of his jokes over dinner and just for an instant he glimpsed a different person, but the moment passed as quickly as it came.

As a small boy on a boating holiday abroad he'd seen the same look on his mother's face. 'Look, the sea's turquoise. Jump in, Mummy! I dare you!' He'd said those words knowing that Mummy would laugh and shake her head. But despite her carefully made-up face and her jewellery, she jumped into the sea without a moment's hesitation. He clapped his hands with delight as he watched from the side of the boat. Then he anxiously waited for his mother's copper hair to reappear from the salty depths of the ocean, caught with a sudden fear she might drown, that he might never see her again. But when she emerged from the sparkling sea, just for a second as the sun caught her face, he thought she was someone else. Someone young, happy and free. But the moment was lost when his father pulled the pipe from his mouth and cleared his throat noisily. He stared at his wife and shook his head before replacing the pipe and pointedly consulting the map.

Mike's head feels leaden on the pillow, crammed with listless negatives as he considers the day. Rachel, lovely Rachel, her face white with reproach. Little Hannah's tears. And Olivia, his wife Olivia, unrecognisable Olivia. And his associate's baby, a healthy son.

He closes his eyes, reviewing a scene at St Mary's maternity hospital from over a year ago. 'Just a routine scan,' the consultant obstetrician had said with easy charm. 'Nothing to worry about, the bump just seems a little small – probably a small baby.'

They'd strolled in for the scan, like many times before. But the face of the sonographer was blank as she looked at the screen. A face that told them everything.

'What's happened? What's wrong?' A look of panic on Olivia's face.

But Mike knew. Mike understood. There was no need to wait until Olivia had wiped the gel from her stomach and covered her naked bump. No need to wait in a room with a door, not a curtain. No need to hear the words, 'I'm sorry, there's no heartbeat, the baby has died.'

He sighs and turns in the dark. There's no point in rewinding the film. There's nothing he can do to change the past. Just like with his little sister, he can't bring them back. And it's late. With or without the dog, he must sleep. A voice echoes in his ears as he drifts off. 'Our Father, who art in Heaven.' The words repeat in his mind every night, like a mantra. But the words aren't his and they're hollow.

CHAPTER FIVE

'Morning, Mike, lovely weather still,' Judith says, glancing at him as she adjusts the collar of her blouse and wondering, as she seems to every day, whether she might have overdone her perfume. She does a double take. 'Are you OK? You look terrible!' She studies Mike's handsome face. He looks tired, with shadows beneath his dark blue eyes. 'Sorry. Perhaps not tactfully put, but I guess I'm not going to start being diplomatic after twelve years. Is everything all right?'

Mike looks away towards the window, squinting slightly in the way he always does. She once asked him if he had worn glasses as a child, but he looked perplexed and said, 'No, why?' with a friendly smile. She now knows it's just his thoughtful look. She's been his secretary since she was nineteen and knows more about Mike Turner than he knows himself, or so she jokes. And the truth is that they've grown up together, in a way. She's seen him through his marriage to Olivia and the birth of his girls; he's been her 'diamond, the sort of rock I like' through two marriages, four broken hearts and breast implants that have recently been removed.

'I didn't sleep very well,' he says, still gazing at something Judith can't see. She busies herself with filing. She knows there's no point in hurrying him, especially of late.

'Bloody typist, diarist, dogsbody and counsellor!' one of the secretaries declared yesterday over lunch, succinctly expanding on what her original job description had omitted. As Judith waits patiently for Mike to embellish on his lack of sleep, she understands what her friend means.

He eventually turns with an awkward smile before sitting at his desk.

'Turns out that I'm a rotten husband and a rubbish dad, Jude.' His face is slightly flushed. 'And there I was, thinking I was perfect!'

Judith smiles and wags a finger. 'That's because I'm always telling you you're perfect. I didn't think you were listening.'

'You've got it in one. I don't listen, apparently.' He puts his head in his hands for a moment and then rubs his eyes. 'But the truth is they're right. I haven't been looking or listening. I've taken my eye off the ball.'

'Trust you to use a football analogy, Mike,' she laughs. 'Is there anything I can do to help? Go into goal? Keep score?'

She sits down in the chair opposite him. There's plenty she'd like to do to help, she thinks affectionately as she strokes her ever-increasing bump, but that would certainly get in the way.

Mike Turner has been at the top of the secretaries' 'I wouldn't kick *him* out of bed' list for years. Christmas after Christmas various young hopefuls have tried to snog him at the office party, without success. Judith is certain that he's completely oblivious to these advances and to his charm. It's the way his hair is always scruffy from raking his hands through it, she decides, it makes him look both trendy and vulnerable at the same time. Those cheekbones too, a real man with cheekbones! And of course his thoughtful Irish eyes.

'I must make more of an effort, not just with Olivia but with the girls too.' He looks at Judith and grins. 'I would ask you for suggestions, but something tells me that would be cheating.'

'And so it would,' she replies, scooping up an armful of files from his muddled desk. Shame, she thinks as she leaves the room. Mike Turner isn't and will never be the sort of man who would go in for cheating.

Sami strides in late to the site meeting, looking sharp in his new navy suit.

'You've got a smile on your face,' the quantity surveyor comments. 'You are one jammy bastard, Richards. Who's the lucky woman this time?'

Sami puts down his briefcase and places the hard hat on his head, careful not to unsettle his hair. 'Who, me?' he grins. 'Well, since you ask. The wife. Really, Jack, the wife!'

'You're joking. I'm lucky if my wife cracks a smile, let alone . . .'

Sami pulls up the leg of his trousers at the knee, crouches down and spreads out the plans on the dusty concrete floor as he recalls an extremely pleasurable start to the day. Sophie was dead to the world when the alarm woke him at seven. But that's nothing new. She jacked in her job at the estate agents months ago ('too early, too boring!') and he suspects she sleeps in all morning during the week when he isn't there to cajole her into the land of the living. He'd done his press-ups, showered and finished the box of no-added-sugar muesli, and was just about to unlatch the walled garden door of his townhouse when Sophie called his name. He turned his head in surprise and there she was on their doorstep, naked save for fluffy slippers and the chunky glasses she wears first thing in the morning before her 'battle' with contact lenses.

'You haven't given me a kiss, darlink,' she called in her best Marlene Dietrich accent. He laughed. Her face looked crumpled and sleepy, her hair like a crow's nest, but her body was beautiful; rounded, plump and still tanned from their Antiguan summer.

'I haven't cleaned my teeth, so . . .' Sophie mumbled as she knelt on the floor of the hallway, the front door still ajar. She slipped one hand in the fly of his suit trousers and unbuckled his belt with the other. 'So I'll give you a different kiss goodbye.'

'That was a very nice treat,' he said afterwards. He stood at the lounge door for a moment and eyed Sophie thoughtfully. She'd put on the dressing gown he tries regularly to throw out and was lying on the sofa, the *Daily Mail* propped on her knees. 'Was there a particular reason why you were kind enough to . . .'

'I just like to keep you on your toes,' she replied, her face still hidden by the newspaper. 'Besides, you've been—'

'What?' Sami asked, his heart sinking just a little as he thought of the time. He knew that any heavy conversation about babies would make him very late for work.

Sophie narrowed her eyes as she lowered the paper. 'I don't know,' she said slowly, turning her head towards him. 'You seem happy.'

'I am happy. No, I'm absolutely delighted that we're going through with the IVF again. I know how hard it is for you with all the drugs, the hospital visits and stuff, but you know I'll be there. I'll be with you every step of the way, I promise.' He glanced at his Montblanc watch, which still gave him the rush of pleasure it had given him six months previously when he'd finally given in to temptation and bought it for himself. 'And

35

I think it's going to work this time, I don't know why, but I feel sure.'

Sophie turned back to the newspaper and the horoscopes. 'OK, you can bugger off to work now. Your usefulness is at an end.'

Sami now brushes the dust off his trousers as he straightens back up. Time to focus on work. 'Shall we start, Jack? Time is money and all that. Is the client coming or not?'

'What have you got that I haven't, Richards?' the quantity surveyor replies as he removes a pen from behind his ear and jots down some figures on his clipboard. 'On second thoughts, don't answer that,' he says with a dry laugh, 'we're not paid by the hour.'

Irony one: the morning nap has made Sophie tired. She yawns and looks at the calendar before opening the fridge. 'Coffee with Christine' is pencilled in for today, but it doesn't ring any bells. Irony two: the handwriting is hers, so she can blame no one but herself. The forgetfulness can be worrying, but only if she lets it, and anyway, she never forgets anything important.

She bends to pull out the carton of milk from the fridge and then changes her mind. It would be a shame to forego a glass of Chablis when it's so beautifully chilled, and besides, she bought a replacement bottle yesterday, just in case. She makes a mental note of the level of the wine before she pours. She's sure that Sami has too. Perhaps he's sketched a diagram and slipped it in his briefcase along with his work plans. She laughs as she closes the fridge. The big question for her is whether she'll remember.

Mike barely notices the door of his office close as Judith walks away. 'Mum got over it quite quickly.' It's his daughter's voice in his head, an echo of his own unspoken, festering words.

He picks up a letter and tries to focus on work and on today. But last night is still fresh, the memory raw in his mind.

He ate dinner alone in the high-ceilinged kitchen, knowing he should talk to Olivia, to clear the air somehow after her outburst. He wanted to be honest with her, but was afraid he would be too brutal. He took her a tea, then left her alone in their bedroom, her rigid back turned away from him.

But with Rachel it was different; he needed to make peace with her straight away. He was stunned at the way she'd behaved. She was bright and funny like her mum, but usually more mature than her twelve years. She was his little companion, always nearby, even when he watched the football on television.

'Grandma, Dad's buying me a season ticket next year,' she announced at the weekend.

'Girls don't go to the football!' his mother responded in horror.

'Of course they do, Grandma,' she replied. 'This is the age of equality. Anything a boy can do, a girl can do better,' she said boldly, making them all laugh.

'Can I come in?' Mike asked, tapping gently on her pine bedroom door. She was curled up on the bed, his little girl, with her face puffy and red from so much crying. 'Come here for a hug,' he said, the sight of her making him want to cry too. But he held it in; if he started he might never stop.

The story came out in a rush: 'Mum was livid. I've never seen her so cross. As soon as I put my key in the door she was there, shouting at me. She accused me of bunking off school but I promise you I wasn't. I felt ill so I came home. I didn't think she'd mind. I thought she'd understand. I thought she'd stick up for me and clear it with the teacher. I know I shouldn't have called her a cow, Dad, but she was one, really. Her face looked horrible and she said, "You don't look ill to me. What's in the bag? Have you been to the shops?"'

Mike studied Rachel's face. Her dark blue eyes looked sincere and hurt. She'd always been a daddy's girl, but Olivia adored her. 'Look,' he said. 'I bet Mum overreacted because we've heard so many bad things, not only about your school but all schools. You know, drugs, truanting, bullying and all the other things parents worry about. You're such a lovely girl that we'd hate you to get into any trouble.'

'Mum doesn't trust me. That makes it even worse.'

He nodded. He wasn't sure what the procedure was with illness and school, but he doubted that kids were allowed to wander off without consulting a parent. 'Well, of course we trust you . . .' he began.

Rachel hid her face in her hands. 'I called Mum's mobile loads of times, but it was off, so I had to go to the chemist all by myself and it was so embarrassing. Mum should have been there or bought them for me, but she didn't even care enough to ask what was wrong.'

He frowned; he'd lost the thread of the conversation.

'Dad, what are you like?' Rachel said, her angry eyes catching his for a moment before turning away. 'I had to go to the chemist to buy pads. I wasn't about to go to the school office and ask them. It's just so embarrassing.'

Mike raked his hands through his hair. He had no idea what to say. Thank God I'm not a single parent. Thank God I have Olivia, he thought. His sister Siobhan had been in and out of hospital when he was a boy. If she had started her periods at some point in his childhood, no one had told him about it. He knew nothing about a girl's puberty or menstruation, or any of that malarkey. He was rapidly discovering that he knew nothing about women at all.

'It's all right, Dad, I don't want to talk about it either,' Rachel said eventually with a small smile. She slipped her hand into his. 'By the way, I heard Mum shouting earlier. I'm not her number one fan at the moment, but it's true what she said. I mean, I don't want to upset you or anything, but sometimes you don't seem to hear what we say. You're not funny any more. You turn on the telly and just stare.'

She looked up into his face. 'Is it because of the baby? Is that why you're sad? Are you thinking about him?'

He took a breath and a moment to reply. Of course that was when the black dog returned, creeping in on its belly, almost unseen, before following him everywhere. 'How come you're so bright?' he asked, wondering how a twelve-year-old child could be so perceptive.

Rachel shrugged. 'You will get over it, you know,' she replied, blowing her nose with gusto. '"Time heals all wounds." People think it's Shakespeare, but it isn't. And look at Mum. She got over it quite quickly, didn't she?'

It is those words that burn in Mike's mind now, as he sips his cold coffee. He frowns and picks up another letter. Too quickly, he thinks, too bloody quickly.

CHAPTER SIX

'Toni, who is Christine and why is she on my calendar? I want to go out. Or stay in. Whatever. Should I be worried about standing her up?'

Antonia holds the iPhone between her ear and her shoulder as she sweeps crumbs from the granite work surface with one hand into the other. She can tell Sophie is being very careful to enunciate her words clearly and slowly.

'Do you want me to come over?' she replies.

'No, why?'

'Because it's a Wednesday morning and you don't usually start this early,' she says evenly. 'Has something happened to upset you?'

She unties her apron and sits down. The heady smell of the baked chocolate embraces her, but she won't be eating any. Her mother has put on a great deal of weight as she's got older; it could be genetic and she doesn't want to be fat.

'It's Sami's fault. If he didn't spy on me, I wouldn't have to drink a whole bottle. I could just have a civilised glass instead of a bloody great lecture. He's not there with you, is he?'

'No. Why, should he be?'

'No reason,' Sophie responds. 'There's the doorbell. It's probably Christine, whoever she is. I'll let you know later if she's your type, Toni. Bye.'

Antonia puts down the mobile carefully. Baking cookies earlier gave her a little high. Like a wide-eyed child she watched the TV chef make them and she copied him, stage by stage, from lining the trays with parchment, to pouring the pre-measured ingredients into a mixing bowl, to spooning the mixture out and to placing them in the oven. Then the waiting. Twenty minutes. Ping!

Of course she knows how to bake just about everything one can bake, but to do it under instruction, like an obedient school child, was surprisingly satisfying. But now she's wondering about Sophie, about what's bothering her so much that she's not letting on. The IVF treatment, she reasons, but then Sophie has already told her all about it, in every gory detail. Indeed, there isn't a lot about her life that hasn't been discussed, dissected and examined by the two of them over the years. The fact that Sophie is drinking is no surprise, it's her way of dealing with stress. But there's something else, definitely something else.

She looks at her watch and wonders whether she should nip round to Sophie's house to see what's going on. It's a twenty-mile round journey, but it's tempting because she doesn't like this uncertainty. Then again, she dislikes Sophie when she's drunk, she loathes anyone drunk, which makes her think again of David and the strange way he behaved last weekend.

'Don't look so bloody tragic,' Sophie said on the Monday, putting her arms around Antonia and holding her for a few moments before pulling away and stroking her arm from shoulder to elbow in that way she always does. 'Don't overreact. He was only pissed. It's not the end of the world.'

'I know,' she replied, thinking that perhaps it was the end

41

of the world and feeling tense, as always, from Sophie's touch.

'He's not your dad, you know, Toni.'

She flinched at Sophie's comment, but didn't reply. It was strange, hearing her dad mentioned twice within a week. There had been the telephone call a few days earlier, out of the blue. It was a friendly female voice, but then they'd always appeared friendly, the journalists.

'Hi, is that Jimmy Farrell's daughter? You've been difficult to track down! My name's Zara Singh. I'm a journalist and I'm looking into—'

She'd put down the phone as though it burned.

Antonia now sits silently at the kitchen table and stares through the open patio doors at the glinting fields and the hills beyond. It's still a bright September. She can see glowing green meadows, horses and cows, huge trees and stone walls. This is her life. There's nothing to say about her dad. He doesn't exist. She won't let him creep into her thoughts. And yet here he is today, looming large in her sunlit kitchen, amid the smell of cookies. 'She was asking for it, girl. She can go back to where she fucking belongs if she doesn't like it. And so can you.' Each memory is filed away, but still clear and in colour, like a series of framed photographs.

She remains motionless on the leather chair, the peppermint tea lukewarm in its cup, her mind cramped as it tries to regain order. It's just the alcohol; it changes people from normal decent human beings into something else, she reasons slowly and calmly, like a mother to a child. David isn't bad. He isn't a monster and nor is Sophie. There's nothing to worry about. She isn't afraid of them.

As she strides down the science faculty's main corridor, Helen Proctor thinks about snowmen. *The Snowman*, in fact, the film she watches every Christmas. She's never really understood the expression 'walking on air' until today. There's no doubt about it, today she is indeed walking on air, or perhaps in it, like The Snowman. She has to fight back the desire to announce it to her students, to blow her own trumpet (another silly expression) or to sing out loud (which she is known to do). They'll probably think she's completely deranged, but Helen is fully aware of her reputation for mild eccentricity and doesn't care.

Ted Edwards asked for a quiet word first thing. 'I have something to say to you, Helen. Perhaps a spot of lunch at the usual?' he said, lifting his black eyebrows which no longer matched his hair and adjusting his glasses. 'When all will be revealed!'

The reveal was unexpected but thrilling. Ted had clearly been pleased as he patted her hand.

It's only a secondment, nothing particularly special, she now chides herself. Another professor walking the other way gives her a sidelong look beneath his varifocals and she wonders whether she has spoken the thought out loud. But it's special to me, she continues with a shrug, an opportunity to teach and to research in America!

She looks at herself in the lavatory mirror as she washes her hands. She no longer notices the streaks of grey in her hair or the odd sprouting growth on her chin. She tried to pluck them at one time, those hairs, but they only grew back twofold, wasting time in which she could be doing something useful, like marking or reading, or chatting with Charlie.

'Oh, Charlie!' she says to the mirror. Her reflection looks startled, and a little downcast, as it wonders how on earth to break the news to him.

David puts his head around Charlie's office door to wish him goodnight, but to his surprise the room is dark, cold and empty.

He strolls in and swings round in Charlie's newly upholstered chair before opening the leather-bound diary to see where he is. It's an office rule that work diaries always stay on the premises on top of the fee earner's desk. David regularly 'forgets' this rule, preferring to risk censure than be pinned down. He studies Charlie's week: his 'school tie' handwriting shows he's been busy, but the page for this afternoon is blank, which means he's gone home early, which is unlike him, or that he's doing something he doesn't want the rest of the office to know about.

David gives a low whistle. The doctor. God, Charlie. He hopes he's all right. Charlie has always looked older than his years, even at school, using his bumbling act to hide the sharp intellect behind. But he isn't old really; David doesn't want him to be.

He sits back and gazes at the signed painting of a Lancaster bomber that Charlie has recently acquired as he tries to steady his breath. 'Lancaster Under Attack', the painting's called, and he knows how it feels. Over the last few days his heart has started to race, suddenly, without warning, like the hammer of a machine gun. Low blood pressure, high blood pressure, lack of fitness, whatever. It doesn't last long, so it really doesn't matter. The important thing is for him to focus. Not on the problem (which he's finally accepted exists), nor the fucking, fucking consequences (which make him want to vomit), but on the plan. And today he has focused. He's come up with a plan. At least a temporary one, which he now needs to put into action. *Velle est posse!* he remembers from school. Where there's a will, there's a way.

It's time to go home, but David isn't ready to do that. He wants to avoid his wife and her watchful eyes a little longer. It's as though Antonia knows. Her brown eyes are huge when she looks at him: perceptive, worried, knowing. 'Robbing Peter to pay Paul?' they say. 'Don't do it, David.'

Eyes like saucers, he thinks, to deflect his churning thoughts. The Tinderbox story. I have a wife with eyes like saucers. Who would have thought?

He picks up a gilt-framed photograph from the desk and smiles. It's of three generations of Proctors: Charlie, his father and his son Rupert, with only a nose in common. He remembers Charlie's father well. Harold, Harry to his friends, so much like Charlie, fair and genial, old fashioned to a fault. He thinks fondly of Charlie's mother, Valerie, a horsey woman both in hobby and looks who is still going strong. Always such a warm and welcoming family, eager to draw him into the fold of their love when his parents were absent.

'What would I have done without you, eh?' he says to the photograph.

A memory strikes him, of being clutched to Valerie's huge bosom. She was wearing a coat with a real fur collar and it made him sneeze. He'd been holding back the tears and the sneeze was such a relief.

'I was only a boy,' David mutters. The sneeze allowed him to cry.

He wonders when he last looked at a photograph of his own parents. Indeed, does he still have any? Has he ever shown one to Antonia? He doubts it; she's never asked. Their meeting at a night club and their simple yet heady marriage only months later at the registry office was like a natural start. They've never looked back to a life before then. It seems to suit them both.

And yet he'd adored his parents. He can still vividly recall the frenzied beating he'd given Smith-Bates at boarding school when he'd taunted that his father shagged his mother from behind. David called him a bloody great liar, told him to shut his ugly face. His father was stern but kind. He was certain his dad would never do such a repugnant thing to his flame-haired flawless mother, but Smith-Bates refused to back down. So David struck out, fuelled by longing and need for his parents, who were in Singapore at that time. When he was forcefully peeled away from Smith-Bates, the master asked him to explain why he'd done it, but he couldn't bear to repeat the profanity and so instead faced the consequences. Even as the lash was brought down on his small palms he was resolute. His pride at defending his mother's honour had been worth it.

'Live with honour. Die with pride,' he remembers, looking at his grown-up palms and desperately wishing the adult could match those words.

He glances at his watch and a thought occurs to him. He remembers Charlie's chuckle when he opened the desk drawer to show David his stash. 'There for times of trouble and strife, David!'

Leaning down he pulls open the drawer on the bottom right. The Glenfiddich bottle is more than half full. 'To trouble and strife! Cheers, Charlie,' he declares to the photograph, settling back down in Charlie's chair and taking his first liberal swig.

The ringtone penetrates the evening silence and Antonia answers immediately from her bedside telephone.

'Hello, Chinue, love. How are you keeping?' Candy Farrell asks in her small voice.

'It's Antonia, remember? I'm fine. How are you, Mum?'

'I was wondering if you were coming to visit. I haven't seen you for so long . . .'

'I was there on Sunday. I brought you some lovely flowers. And I'm coming again this Sunday, just as usual.'

'Will Jimmy be coming?'

Smoothing her hair, Antonia tenses, but keeps her voice even. 'No, Mum. Dad's dead. Remember?'

'Are you sure, love? I thought I saw him.'

'I'm absolutely sure, Mum. *EastEnders* will be on the telly soon. Why don't you check the television page and I'll see you on Sunday.'

Antonia replaces the receiver carefully and gazes at the tree whose branch taps at the shuttered bedroom window, reminding her to stand and view the garden from upstairs, to appreciate its size and splendour and to remember just how lucky she is.

'Human beings, we're all different, either inside or out,' her mother used to say. 'But we're all the Lord's children. There's good in everyone.'

She used to be full of wise words, her mum, even when she was bowed and bruised. But now that same person telephones her two or three times a day, forgetting a conversation she's had only moments earlier, sometimes completely oblivious of her daughter's weekly visits and yet still seeing the man who had no good in him at all.

She turns away from the window with a sigh, recovers her book from the pillow and continues to read.

CHAPTER SEVEN

Olivia is at the sink with her back turned as Mike enters the warm kitchen. He's come home from work earlier than usual and feels ridiculously nervous. A few days of staccato conversation have passed since her rollicking and he's been saying and doing nothing on the basis of least said soonest mended. It's one of his mother's many wise words, though she rarely practises what she preaches. But mid-afternoon at the office today, Judith tucked her blonde bob behind her ears and gave him one of her mind-reading looks. 'Still a crap husband?' she asked, handing over the post for signing.

'Possibly,' he replied. He couldn't help but smile as he looked at her. She was trying to find a hip on which to place her hand, but she was huge, far larger than he remembered Olivia being when pregnant. 'Why do you ask?'

'Well, you've worked late the last couple of days and I haven't seen you come back from lunch with a Thornton's bag or with a huge bunch of M&S flowers, and you don't seem the Interflora type of guy to me.'

Mike felt himself flush.

'Oh God, don't tell me you resorted to flowers from Netto. That's grounds for divorce!'

He sat back and raked a hand through his hair. 'To be honest, I've done nothing. Olivia hasn't said anything and I thought it might make things worse.'

So, Judith put him straight with her round, open, friendly face. She didn't know what the problem was, but doing or saying nothing was not an option. 'Venus and Mars and all that crap. It's true, men and women don't understand each other. But speaking on behalf of womankind, while chocolates and flowers don't solve anything, they certainly help. From the way you look, my guess is that you need to clear the air. So go home early, surprise her, tell her that you love her.'

So here he is. Olivia turns from the sink just as he reaches her. She looks worn and so very pale.

'For you,' he says, handing over a bunch of yellow roses with a wry smile. 'Not very imaginative, I know. It's just a token to say sorry.' He kisses her cheek and can sense the stifled sniggers of his girls sitting at the wooden table behind him. 'Can we talk later?'

Olivia smiles faintly, nods and takes the flowers.

'Aren't you going to snog?'

'Hannah!'

'Well that's what they do on the TV.'

'I think you mean kiss, young lady,' Olivia says. 'I'll put these in water.'

As Olivia moves away, Mike looks at Rachel, his face a question, but she shrugs her shoulders. 'I don't know,' she whispers.

'Well, these are for you two,' he says, pulling out two chocolate bars from his pocket and hiding them behind his back. 'Which hand? You go first, Hannah.'

Hannah pulls at his right sleeve. 'That one.' He brings out

49

an empty hand. Hannah starts to cry. 'That's mean, Daddy. It's not fair if Rachel gets two!'

Confectionery distribution woes salved, Mike sits down, pushes away the empty plates and studies his girls as they eat their treats. They're so different in looks and build and in chocolate-bar-eating technique, he thinks with a smile. No black dog today; he feels a sudden lightness, a sense of expectation, almost like optimism. I'm lucky, very lucky, he thinks. I must remember this more often.

'So, how was school?' he asks Hannah. 'Do you still fancy Dylan whatshisname?'

'I do not!'

'Yes, she does!'

'How do you know? You're not at St Theresa's any more. You go to Loreto where they all snog and smoke!'

'Well, *I* don't, you idiot.'

Olivia is back in the room. 'Don't call her an idiot, Rachel.'

'That's hardly fair, Mum. She just—'

'Life's not always fair, Rachel,' Olivia replies, sitting down at the table.

Mike feels a shiver and for a few moments they're all silent, but then he takes Olivia's hand and looks at her closed face. He still feels strangely buoyant. He squeezes gently. 'My darling wife . . . I would say you look a bit tired, but something tells me that wouldn't be a good thing to say.'

Olivia smiles, seeming to relent, just a little.

'However, since I'm home early, instead of going for a run, I can be your personal slave for the rest of the day. Feet up, cup of tea, dinner to follow. Your wish will be my command. What do you say?'

'And don't forget the snogging!' Hannah adds helpfully before bursting into giggles.

*

'My mother always called it stew. Very working class, I expect. You're looking old, Charles,' Helen says over the beef and kidney casserole in their Edwardian Cheshire home. 'Or is it my eyes? Turning fifty didn't bother me a jot, but I had twenty-twenty vision until then,' she adds, pouring Charlie another glass of claret. She's pulled the bottle out of the cellar so she knows it's a good year. She feels that perhaps he will take her news better if he's drunk a glass or two of the mellow, as he describes it.

'I suppose five years younger classes me as your toy boy, but sadly I've always looked old,' Charlie replies easily, wiping his plate with a crust of white bread. 'Perhaps you never noticed. Did you think you'd married a matinee star?'

Helen smiles. Neither has any delusions about their appearances and they often banter easily on the subject, ruminating at length about Rupert's unexpected good looks. 'He must have skipped a generation or two,' Charlie invariably comments. 'Or perhaps he's the butcher's son. He was a good-looking fella before he fell off the roof. Poor old chap, better not to survive than get old really. Like Rod Hull.'

'Oh yes, the chap from the *Marathon Man*. I like him.'

'Ah, film stars. Laurence Olivier? The mad Nazi dentist?'

'No. *The Graduate*. Little fellow with a nose, but something about him. One of those method actors.'

'Robert De Niro?'

'Charles, you are silly at times. What would I do with Robert De Niro?'

'You have your talents . . .'

'Which I save just for you! Birthdays and Christmas.'

They both laugh. 'Wouldn't mind another spoonful of the stew if you'd do the honours. Does Barbara still make these casseroles in that plug-in device?'

'I think she does. But don't ask me how it all works. I just

51

eat what she leaves. We must never lose her, Charles. Clean house, dinner, home-made bread. As if by magic.'

'Agreed. But she must be eighty, at least. Now *she* is old!'

Helen studies Charles's face as he wipes his chin with the napkin Barbara has laundered and laid. 'No, you're right. Old was the wrong word. Tired or drawn would be a more accurate description. More so than usual. Are you feeling all right?'

'I'm fine. In fact I'm delighted to be tired and drawn rather than old. It makes me feel like a boy!'

Charlie tucks into his second helping of Barbara's casserole, hoping Helen will change the subject. At times during their marriage, he's tried to deflect her long-winded inquisitions, but generally to no avail. Her tendency to see only the black and white in life means she can detect a lie or indeed a deflection a mile off. It's better to keep a low profile and eat up. He likes eating dinner with Helen, it's a wonderful combination of the three things he loves best in the world: food, wine and his wife.

A bloody diabetic, he ruminates inwardly as he savours the warmth of the wine on his throat. How preposterous. These women doctors don't know a thing.

Charlie's usual doctor, Simpson, is away, or so he was told by the fearsome receptionist when he visited the surgery that afternoon for his test results. One of the junior associates sat looking a little too comfortable in Simpson's seat, gazing at a computer screen. She looked so very young, like barbers and builders and general office staff.

He furtively glances again at Helen across the worn mahogany table. In either law or medicine, mistakes are easy to make when looking at other people's cases, computer or not. There's no point making a fuss until he speaks to Simpson. He'll worry about it then if he has to. For now his stomach is speaking. A touch of something sweet, it says, and then perhaps a small glass of golden dessert wine to finish.

'Now, what about pud?' he asks, lifting his spoon.

'I'm going to New York City in January, Charles,' Helen says bluntly. 'To New York University. I've been selected by Ted Edwards to teach and do some research on a secondment and I'm thrilled.'

'That's nice. Shall we move on to—'

'I'll be there for a year, Charles,' Helen interrupts firmly.

He puts down his spoon. 'Good God, Helen,' he replies. 'That's preposterous.' Charles Proctor doesn't need to be told anything twice.

The girls are in bed, Mike and Olivia are alone in the bay-windowed lounge and they have no more excuses. Mike takes a deep breath and looks at his wife on the sofa opposite. 'I'm sorry, Olivia. I realise I've . . .' he nearly uses the football analogy again, but he doesn't think Olivia will be amused. 'Well, I've had my mind on other things, I suppose. I didn't realise it until now. But I can see that I've neglected you and the girls and I'm sorry. I'll stop.'

Olivia examines her neatly trimmed nails. She speaks quietly and he has to lean towards her to hear. 'I need to know why, Mike. I don't want to know, but I need to know.' She's silent for a moment, and then she lifts her head to look him in the eye. She looks unbearably sad, her face pale, tears about to spill from her eyes. 'Please be honest with me.' She takes a deep breath. 'Are you having or have you had an affair?'

Mike almost flinches. It's the last thing he expects to hear. 'What the . . . no! Where on earth have you got that idea from?' he says, almost laughing with relief at the absurdity of her suggestion.

'Be honest, Mike.'

'I am! Absolutely.'

Mike prays the sincerity is showing on his face, and is rewarded when the relief almost visibly flows from Olivia's body. Limp and shaking, she bows her head, burying it in her hands.

For a moment he sits back in the armchair and watches, a surge of panic stopping him from reaching out to her. She's been so tense and unhappy, now she's so relieved at his reply. They live together, they sleep in the same bed. How has he missed all of this?

Olivia lifts her head, but still averts her eyes. 'I thought you'd stopped loving me,' she says quietly, the tears rolling down her ashen face. 'You seemed so disinterested, so remote. Then I thought of how Judith has thrown herself at you for all these years and it all made sense.'

'Jude's just friendly,' he replies with surprise. 'You know that. She's friendly with everyone, you included.' He feels mildly irked at the idea; it seems so silly. 'Besides, she's having a baby in two months.'

He sees Olivia's face harden and the penny drops. 'You didn't think . . .?' He can feel the heat rise, angry now, offended and alarmed that Olivia can even imagine such a thing.

'A devoted secretary who's always fancied you, pregnant with a man she won't name, you away with the fairies, what was I supposed to think?' Olivia's words cut through him like knives.

Much later, after Mike has been on a long run in the dark and drizzle, the black dog running alongside him on the wet pavements of Chorlton, the irritation he feels at Olivia's logic starts to recede. The idea of anyone he knows, let alone he or Olivia, having an affair is ridiculous. He knows some men occasionally have a quick shag if the opportunity presents itself, to satisfy a small desire, like the need to scratch an itch, but not the planning, the lies, the awful betrayal of a full-blown relationship. But his head has now cleared, and in fairness to Olivia, he understands he has been distant, something he didn't fully realise until a twelve-year-old told him straight.

Life still isn't all right, but there's some sense of relief that Olivia's strange behaviour has been explained. And when she steps naked into the shower beside him, his anger is replaced by an urgent desire to have her, to mark her, to show her he loves her, there in the shower, rough and fast, the water expunging her tears.

'I love you, Olivia,' he roars as he climaxes. 'I love you and only you. Do you hear me?'

Olivia nods and smiles, but as he wraps her in a towel and holds her in his arms, he thinks she looks sad.

CHAPTER EIGHT

Sami leans back in his chair and puts his feet on the office desk. For a moment he studies the shine on his shoes. They cost him a hundred and fifty quid, but they're worth every penny. 'Because quality really does count,' he mutters before going back to reading *Luxury Auto* magazine. He thumbs through the glossy pages, but he isn't really looking at it as he usually does, pawing over each photograph and article before comparing performance. He's too distracted for that, his mind swamped with thoughts of his afternoon meeting out of the office.

His eye catches the heading 'Size Has Clout' and he smiles for a moment before a mild but nagging anxiety sets in. 'Oh, piss off,' he says out loud. It's an unwelcome emotion, one which hasn't really bothered him since the day he discovered he was attractive. An overheard conversation between his eldest sister and her new friend from university when he was fourteen. 'Ramona, your little brother. His face – he's stunning!' he'd heard. He'd rushed to the bathroom and locked himself in, dared his eyes to the mirror expecting to see a fat boy, but had been astounded to find that the girl was right. His chubby cheeks had grown thin, his face was bony and chiselled. It was a turning point for Samuel Richards. Samuel became Sami. He stood tall and put anxiety behind him. But now it prods at him from a distance and he isn't entirely sure what it means.

He takes his feet off the desk and leans on the table, careful not to crease his tie. 'Why am I anxious?' he scribbles on the writing pad with the fibre-tip pen he bought to match his watch.

Reclining again, he swings in his chair, the pen to his mouth. Perhaps it's the huge project at Trafford and the commission he'll lose if it doesn't go through. Or maybe it's Sophie, his mother and the IVF. Or even the suit he forgot to collect from the cleaners. But he knows it's Friday, last Friday, when he should've been in the pub. The memory catches his breath and makes his skin tingle. It just isn't like him to care so much.

He crumples the paper into a ball and lobs it into the waste-paper bin, expecting to score as usual. It hits the edge and lands softly on the carpet. He stands, bends to pick it up and looks at it thoughtfully in his palm before dropping it directly into the bin. Then he stoops to look at himself in the mirror hung next to his surveying qualification certificates. Replacing one of the certificates, it's really too low for Sami's height. Everyone in the office laughs at this token of vanity, but he doesn't care. 'Have to keep up the standards,' he always says to anyone who comments. 'You should try it.' But the reality is that standards don't come into it, he's one handsome bastard and the mirror is there for him to strut and to preen, to confirm what he already knows. But today his reflection doesn't look quite right. It's as though his slight emotional imbalance is reflected in his striking face.

'No, really, piss off,' he says again before collecting his jacket and keys and then checking one last time that the words 'site meeting' are clearly legible in his diary for anyone who might look.

David feels breathless as he studies the backlog of letters that have accumulated on his office desk. He has work to do. Proper everyday work. Searches to make, title deeds to check, leases to read, contracts to exchange. But he has been preoccupied for days. Paralysed, almost.

'Routine commercial conveyancing isn't rocket science, David,' one of the other partners frequently goads. But that isn't entirely true. Conveyancing has its challenges, it can go pear-shaped, just like everything else in the law. And if a date is missed, a search omitted? Well, he's only human. One or two mistakes are easy to make.

His secretary has attached the letters to the front of their respective files with a yellow paper clip, in order of importance. 'I don't think there's anything imminent. Well, no exchanges this week, anyway,' she said earlier.

Yet every file he opens seems to sneer at him, to laugh and to say, 'I could be another mistake, David. Dig beneath the surface and you'll find me waiting for you.'

The sudden noise of the telephone makes him start. Everything makes him start. It's all he can do not to retch.

'Hi, David, it's Colin. A problem with one of my files seems to have come up. Can I have a word about it? How about in ten, fifteen minutes?'

He rests his head in his arms. God knows why the other partners have put him in charge of indemnity and claims, the majority seem to be on his own files. Perhaps that's why, he thinks wryly, they're so used to his cock-ups, they decided he may as well have the hassle of everyone else's as well.

'That's what insurance is for, David,' Charlie says whenever

David confesses to another small mistake over a glass of wine at the end of the day. 'Don't worry about it, it's only money. We all make mistakes, even me.'

Of course Charlie has never made a mistake. At least not one David is aware of. He wishes that he could be like Charlie, intelligent and able, ploughing through the work with simple ease. Yet if he's honest, he knows Charlie's success comes from hard graft as well as ability and that he's stupid and lazy in comparison. Every hole he finds himself in is his own bloody fault. Forgetting to diarise important dates, cutting corners, occasionally being less than honest. David knows it, and he despises himself for it.

But at least his initial desperate need to confess to Charlie has abated slightly and is on the back burner again. He and the Glenfiddich accessed the client accounts on the computer the other night. They found a commercial property transaction with a substantial amount of money waiting in the account, one that wouldn't be completed for months, and then put the temporary solution into play, transferring the money from that account to the insurance account and then paying the outstanding indemnity premium with a click of a mouse. Indemnity insurance paid, claims will now be covered, immediate problem rectified.

David picks up another file, feels the battering of his heart and tries to breathe. He can't bear to contemplate what will happen regarding claims arising before today or how he'll repay the funds he has borrowed from Peter to pay Paul. That's something he needs to discuss with Charlie. The trouble is that Charlie doesn't seem to be in the mood for listening.

Antonia's stomach rumbles for its lunch as she pulls off her green buckled wellies on the steps. Her mum called three times before nine this morning, so she escaped to the garden with her secateurs. Snip, snip, snip. She's been savage with her pruning, savagery that usually works.

She steps back for a moment in her socks, lifting her head and taking in her home's clean white facade. Bless David. She never asked for a house like this, but as he often says, he'd promised it from their very first date. She can still picture it clearly.

It was a Sunday. He'd arrived ten minutes early in a low sports car. She couldn't have told you the make, but it was small, shiny and sleek, and rather than soundless as she expected, it was loud, booming with noise, much like the man who drove it.

'Hope you like poussin,' he'd said at the traffic lights. Then after a moment, putting his hand on hers, 'Only chicken. We're having a picnic. The hamper's in the boot. Is that OK?'

She'd nodded, feeling foolish. She hadn't dressed for a picnic. Not knowing what to expect, she'd worn a pale pink shift dress and high heels.

David had driven towards Derbyshire, chatting all the way, then turned off the main road at some gates, parking up, jumping out to open her door and holding out his hand.

'Welcome to Lyme Hall!' He'd deliberately said it as though it was his and she'd laughed, pleased he was so easy to be with despite her *faux pas* with the heels.

Spreading out a blanket on a manicured lawn at the front of the house, David had opened the basket. Not just tiny chickens, but glossy pork pies, Scotch eggs, stuffed peppers and champagne.

'Please take a seat,' he'd said, gesturing to the ground. For a moment she'd frozen. The shoes were sharp-heeled, the dress fitted. Then, thinking what Sophie would do, she'd slightly

60

hitched up her dress and slipped off her shoes. 'This is lovely,' she'd said.

'And so are you,' he'd replied.

Much later, topping up her wine, he'd grinned at her. 'I've done nothing but talk. Now it's your turn. Tell me about you.'

The mild panic was there as always, but he hadn't told her anything really. He was a solicitor, he lived somewhere in Cheshire, he played football on a Sunday, but nothing personal, somehow. She found she liked it; she liked that he talked incessantly, but didn't say anything profound.

'Well . . .' she'd begun, but as though sensing her hesitation, he'd put up his hand.

'No, don't tell me anything. You're perfect just as you are.'

But after all the arguments with her last boyfriend, she hadn't wanted to appear odd, wanted to get it out of the way. 'I run a hair salon, share a flat with two friends. My dad died way back, but I still have my mum. She's a bit fragile so she's in a care home.' She'd smiled, embarrassed. 'No brothers or sisters, so there's pretty much just me.'

David had gazed at her, but after a few moments the intensity in his eyes was replaced with a smile. 'Me too. Parents died long ago. See? I knew you were perfect.' He'd leaned back and stretched out his legs. 'Told you last night you were the woman I'd marry.' Turning to the grand facade of Lyme Hall, he'd nodded. 'Did I mention I'm going to buy you one of these?'

Antonia now smiles and shakes her head at the memory. It had been the first time she'd visited a National Trust property and David had watched her face as she'd gazed wide-eyed and open-mouthed at its magnificence and splendour. Though considerably smaller, it's what his clients and visitors say of White Gables all the time: 'The renovation is magnificent. Must have cost a fortune.' She can see that and she's proud, but it's the garden which pleases her. She feels she's had more of an input. Not planting, necessarily, though she did all the bedding plants herself, but nurturing. She nurtures the plants, the beds and the bushes and they respond in kind.

'Antonia, darling, you do have green fingers!' Naomi the neighbour shouts from over the fence, her voice startling Antonia as she stands on the doorstep. She feels suddenly shy.

'Perhaps I do,' she replies with a guilty clutch of conceit as she blushes in acknowledgement.

It relaxes her usually; the garden, the fresh air, the birds and the hills reaching up to the steep ridge of The Edge. But today she's agitated and even gardening hasn't settled her. She goes inside, takes off her waxed jacket in the hall and strokes her arm. The cut has started to scab and it's itchy. It always is when the healing process is underway. Like a little reminder.

'The Chablis has been staring at me again,' Sophie joked the other day.

'Then don't have it in the house,' Antonia replied sternly.

But she understood completely. A tempting treat at the tip of one's fingertips. It's just a question of how long each of them can resist.

'That's a nasty cut,' David had commented, not so long ago. 'How did you do that?'

They were in bed and a shaft of light slanting through the shutters lit her naked body.

'Gardening. Those hawthorns can be vicious,' she'd replied brightly, turning towards him and pulling him into an embrace. But she'd caught his troubled look, that frown of love he has when he doesn't know she's looking. She must be more careful.

The answerphone light in the kitchen is flashing. She sighs and stares for a moment, then walks briskly to the telephone, quickly presses play, turns her back and busies herself loudly at the sink as though that will swamp the sound of the inevitable.

'Hi, it's Zara Singh again. The journalist? I think we got cut off. I'd really appreciate it if you could call me back?' The rise in tone makes it sound like a question. And then she hears Candy's hesitant voice, for the fourth time today. 'Hello, Chinue, love. It's Mum. Are you there?'

Olivia pushes the washing-machine door to, programmes a light wash and then leans against it, staring out of the utility room window which, she notes with a sigh, needs cleaning both inside and out. She knows she's been moody and uncommunicative with the girls again today and feels vaguely guilty, but the truth is she can't help herself.

She looks at her hands, which still have a slight tremor. Her jaw is aching from clenching her teeth. She's seething. She seethed silently all night and all day and the churning hasn't abated, not even a drop.

'The bastard, the absolute bastard.' The sheer anger and frustration brings tears to her eyes while his words repeat in a galling loop in her head. She marches into the kitchen and puts on the kettle before collapsing on to a chair. 'Fuck you, Mike,' she says out loud.

She considers phoning her sister, regaling her with last night's conversation word for word. But she knows what her sister will say. 'Come on, Olivia. He's only human. Everything's fine now you know he's not having an affair with his tarty secretary or anyone else. I told you so.'

Her sister likes Mike. Everybody likes bloody Mike. But not everyone agreed to bear him another child. She really didn't want a third child but she did it for him. She went through yet another amniocentesis to check for Down's Syndrome and then experienced the worst of her pregnancies with horrendous sickness and overwhelming tiredness while having to care for two other young demanding children. It was she who gave birth to a dead baby; it was she who felt the pain and the fear, the impotence, the failure.

'Fuck you, Mike!' she declares again. And then, 'God, what a cow' as she leans down to pick up a piece of ceramic she's missed from the floor. She looks at Hannah's empty seat and feels another wave of emotion. Hannah is only five, accidents are bound to happen and it's only a broken cereal bowl. How she wishes she hadn't shouted quite so loudly and for quite so long. Hannah cried so much at school that the teacher had to peel her away from Olivia's arms. Then she walked away swiftly, down the long corridor, past all the happy pictures and paintings and books, fearful that the teacher would call her back and suggest she take Hannah home.

Olivia sighs loudly. An awful mother and murderous to boot. Focusing on Hannah, her anger recedes for a spell. She'll make it up to her after school, she thinks, her mind racing with ideas. She'll make her a cake or buy her a treat and say sorry. She'll try to be patient, she'll try to be kind.

Lifting her head, she glances at the clock to check the time, but her eyes catch the wedding portrait of her and Mike hanging against the dark red wallpaper in the hall, still not replaced from when they moved in nine years ago. That couple was happy, she thinks, look how they laughed.

Stepping forward, she studies the photograph. She hasn't looked at it, really looked at it, for a long time and yet she walks past it maybe twelve times a day. Perhaps that's what's happened to their marriage, she thinks, perhaps they've grown so used to each other that they just walk past without seeing.

She gazes at Mike's striking face in the photograph. She can see no resemblance between him and the man who said those hurtful words about the miscarriage to her last night, even though they look much the same. The person in the photograph was fun, he was open and loving, a man who wore his heart on his sleeve. Not a man given to irrational deep thought.

Olivia shakes her head as the anger resurfaces. The bastard implied she was somehow responsible for the miscarriage, for the death of their son. She still can't believe it; it was an unforgivable thing to say, but an even worse thing to actually believe.

Antonia looks at her watch and continues her pacing from the lofty hallway, around the staircase to the lounge. She feels guilty. Hot and guilty. She's aware that it's a terrible betrayal, but she can't help herself. She's spent half an hour reapplying her make-up and has changed her clothes twice. It's ridiculous, she knows, but she's nervous, more nervous than she ever expected. She catches her face in the hall mirror and somebody else stares back with long, straight, dark hair looking polished, calm and relaxed.

It's not as though I don't know him, she thinks. It's me who instigated it and now I must see it through with no regrets.

She glances at her watch one more time, the white-gold strap bright against her honey-coloured skin. He'll be here any minute and it wouldn't do to be waiting at the door. She walks into the silent lounge and puts on an Adele CD for company. Standing for a moment, she listens, but even Adele's intoxicating voice doesn't seem right, so she turns it off and plumps up the sofa cushions yet again.

The doorbell is shrill in the silence. Antonia stands up, touches her hair and then takes a deep breath. Then she walks to the front door, straightens her shoulders and opens it.

'Hello, Sami,' she says.

CHAPTER NINE

Olivia is running late as she leaves her untidy house to collect Hannah from school. The afternoon has flown by as it always does and she feels hot as she searches for her keys, but the cold air swipes her cheeks at the door, so she turns back to fetch her coat. It's only then that she stops to study the wedding photograph again. She doesn't look at the man this time, but at the girl. She has pale hair and pastel eyes but a bright, confident smile. She holds a single bunch of yellow roses and her dress is traditional but plain. There are no feathers or frills in her hair. This isn't a girl who needs chocolates or flowers to tell her she is loved. This isn't a girl who craves flattery or attention to give her self-worth. This is a girl who's said 'for better or for worse' and who means it.

'Here's the post for signing, Mike,' Judith says as she neatens a letter escaping from the tidy rectangle of her long day's endeavours.

Mike looks up at her and nods, then drops his head again, continuing to punch numbers into a calculator, which spews out digits on a tiny receipt. She turns away towards the filing cabinet, feeling contemplative. The filing is up to date, but she hovers for a moment, busying herself by opening cabinet drawers, tidying the hanging baskets and closing them again. Mike hasn't said much to her at all today. He looks tired and unhappy, and she wonders how the flowers fared last night. Pretty badly, by the looks of it, she concludes.

She casts a final glance at Mike and notes that his frown line seems more pronounced than usual. It is, she reflects, the one slight imperfection in an otherwise perfect face.

She has her hand on the handle when he abruptly speaks. 'Who's the father of your baby, Jude?' he asks.

Judith turns, blurting out a laugh of surprise. It's the first time in all the years she's known him that he's asked such a personal question. 'Bloody hell, Mike. Am I dreaming or did you really ask me that?'

He drops his intense gaze and picks up a pen. 'Sorry,' he says. 'None of my business.'

Judith studies his slightly flushed face. There's something vulnerable about him, she thinks, like a little lost boy who needs a big cuddle from the wicked witch or the snow queen, to be led by the hand into the land of temptation . . . he just doesn't know it.

She toys with the idea of teasing him, perhaps asking if he realises his question is tantamount to sexual harassment, or something similar, but he looked so sincere when he posed the question that a straight answer seems only fair.

'No, that's fine,' she says, pulling out the client chair and sitting heavily, grateful to be off her feet for a minute or two. 'Actually, no one in particular, as it happens. Just someone who was tall and pleasant for an evening or two. With hair and good shoes. And, of course, with straight white teeth.' She smiles. 'Some things you can't compromise on.'

She watches him absorb her reply and then laughs at the look of mild shock on his face when he realises her answer is serious. 'For a leftie, you're very conservative at times. I don't know why you're surprised, Mike. You of all people know I've tried them all, big, small, black, white. I even married a couple and they all ended in disaster. So I figured there's me and my mum and that's all the baby needs.'

She stops for a moment, her head cocked. She can almost see the slow chug of Mike's mind trying to keep up, to understand. 'Ask yourself this, Mike: what's better, to have a dad who buggers off after two minutes, to have one who gives the odd slap, or not to have one at all? Well, I know which one I'd prefer, the one with the least heartache.'

It's dusk outside, the office empty save, perhaps, for one or two other surveyors who are still at their work stations clocking up chargeable hours before the end of the month. Mike sits at his desk for a long time without moving. It's the first time in twelve years of marriage that he doesn't want to rush home at the end of the day. He has no idea what awaits him. Olivia busied herself with the girls and their school bags when he left this morning, avoiding all eye contact with him.

It has been a day of maybes, his mind fit to burst with the awful uncertainty of it all. Maybe Olivia will forgive him for the things that he said. Maybe life will go on as before. He wants it to, of course, but there's an iota of a maybe that still hangs around, suggesting there's no smoke without fire. Maybe he was right.

Last night everything was fine. After the frisson of the shower he took Olivia to bed, dried her body with kisses and eventually she smiled and said, 'Yes, just there. That's so nice. Oh, Mike, where have you been?' It was love at its best, hearing her come, the sweetest of sounds and one he can never get enough of, before releasing himself.

'You didn't explain why,' she said later as they lay entwined in the dark. 'Why you went away in here,' she said, kissing his temple.

Mike sighed. His fears now felt foolish and childish. He'd hoped she wouldn't ask. 'It doesn't matter now,' he said, drawing her close.

'It matters to me,' Olivia said, pulling away from him. She turned on the bedside lamp and looked intently at his face. 'What was it, Mike? Was it the miscarriage? I thought we grieved together and put it behind us.'

He sat up, staring ahead at nothing in particular. He suddenly felt angry, really angry. He could feel the heat rise in his body, the colour flood his face. '*You* put it behind us, Olivia. You wiped the slate clean and said "never mind".'

He could feel her flinch, heard her intake of breath, but he knew he wouldn't stop. 'But you didn't pause for one moment to consider how I felt. Everyone was there with their condolences and their sympathy. We're so sorry, Olivia, how are you, Olivia, can I do anything, Olivia. He was my child too, my loss. It was me who wanted him, not you.'

'That isn't fair, Mike. You have no idea what it's like to be pregnant, let alone give bloody birth. I was as sick as a dog, in and out of hospital with the vomiting. It was bloody awful but I did it for you. Because you had some stupid hang-up about wanting a son. How do you think the girls would feel if they knew that they weren't good enough for you, just because of their gender? We live in the twenty-first century for God's sake, women are equal and our girls are wonderful.'

He turned his head and stared at Olivia. He could feel a

69

throb in his temple. 'That's crap and you know it. I wanted another child, Olivia. Another *child*. It might have been a girl, and that would have been great.'

'But it was a boy, Mike, and you couldn't conceal your delight, could you? It was written all over your face when they told us, your son and heir, just what you always wanted. Until that moment I didn't realise how much I'd disappointed you with mere daughters.'

Part of Mike wanted to shout. Part of him wanted to take Olivia by the throat and shake the unfairness of her words out of her. But instead he dropped his head, the cold despair he'd felt for months seeping through his body, dispersing the heat. 'Don't you dare say that. You're not being fair. I adore my girls, you know I do.'

They sat for a moment and listened to the gentle thrum of the traffic from the far-off motorway.

'Then why the total withdrawal and the silent treatment for so long?' Olivia asked quietly.

He looked at her then. The harshness had gone from her face. Her pale eyes were sad, soft, concerned. He was hurting her. He was hurting himself. He understood this and yet he knew he had to push ahead through the numbness, to at least try to focus his mind and put his thoughts into words.

'Because try as I did, I couldn't put it him to rest, Olivia. I've spent months asking myself why. Why did our little boy die? No one had a reason, he wasn't Down's or disabled. He was perfect, wasn't he?'

Olivia nodded, her head propped on her knees, her fingers playing with the quilt and so he continued, trying to marshal his thoughts and frame them into words. 'And because we got no answers from the hospital or the consultant, my mind has tormented me with its own.'

'And they are?' Olivia asked slowly, turning her head to look at him.

Mike was silent for a while, but he had come so far, he knew it had to be said, to exorcise those ugly pestering thoughts, if nothing else. The frequent picture he had in his mind of Olivia with a glass of wine in one hand and a cigarette in the other flashed before his eyes. She hadn't touched a drop of alcohol when pregnant with the girls. Prawns and eggs and all manner of other foods had been off the menu too. 'That you did something. God, I don't know. It sounds so stupid now, but I felt that by thought, or by word or by deed you did something. Something to cause the miscarriage.'

For a moment Olivia didn't move, her unfathomable gaze fixed on his face. Seconds ticked by as he waited for an answer, a reaction. The moment he had voiced his innermost ugly thoughts, he knew how unworthy and pathetic they were.

She eventually stood from the bed and walked into the en-suite bathroom, closing the door quietly behind her. He watched and waited, numb, wretched and unbelievably tired. He had wanted to say it for so long that the desire to confess had become overwhelming. But now the words were out, he felt bereft and empty. As though someone had put their hand in his chest and pulled out his heart.

He'd started to drift off by the time Olivia returned to the bed. 'You bastard,' she said, quite clearly, as she turned off the lamp.

The unmistakable and sickening sound of two cars colliding on the busy main road outside Mike's office building jolts him back to the present. 'You bastard', he still hears, but he knows it's time to go home.

'When you're feeling sorry for yourself, remember there's always someone worse off,' his grandpa often said when life had gone awry and little Michael sought him out for a hug. Same words as the priest, but delivered so much more kindly. Mike nods in acknowledgement, hoping that no one has been hurt in the collision below. He collects his jacket from the back of his chair. But still he can hear the tip-tap of the dog's claws on the laminate behind him as he turns off the light and heads for home.

Olivia smooths the clean sheets on the bed, then stares into space for a few breathless moments before trudging wearily down the stairs. She waits for Mike in the lounge, her head resting on the sofa's curved arm. She's exhausted; complete physical and mental exhaustion. Anger has sapped her and she wants to sleep. But at least it's gone, or even if not completely, it has receded, to be replaced by that old, familiar feeling of self-loathing.

As a small child her temper was the family joke, her tantrums legendary. 'Short-fuse Olivia,' her dad regularly teased with his soft Geordie accent. As much as she tried, she was unable to count to ten, to bite her tongue, breathe deeply or any of the other things she knew she should do to control it. But coming down south to university in Manchester changed her. By writing, debating and using self-styled anger management, she stopped her knee-jerk reactions, she put her sharp mind and sharp tongue to good use.

But 'short-fuse Olivia' is still there, she fears, increasingly pestering to break free. She hates being a cow, even when she's being a 'justifiable' cow, she hates it. She despises herself for allowing short-fuse Olivia and her knee-jerk reactions to escape.

She checks her mobile again. Still no word from Mike. He always sends a text when he's leaving the office. Perhaps he's still working; perhaps he's angry; perhaps he's buggered off forever. It's difficult to judge. Last night she was a cow. Last night they were strangers.

She's tried to make amends with the girls by buying Hannah a chocolate cake from Morrisons, undoubtedly full of hyper-activity-inducing additives which they'll pay for tomorrow, and then covering it with sweets to make it look home-baked. She's given Rachel a 'don't tell Dad' expensive mascara. But with Mike it's more difficult. Now that she's calm she knows everything is fine, actually. He said some crazy things last night, but he was honest. Wasn't that what the couple in the wedding photograph used to do? Be honest and open and talk? Talk for hours. About everything. Sometimes all night. She needs to say sorry, to get things back on track. 'Sorry, Mike,' she should say. As simple as that. And as difficult. Olivia struggles with that word. She always has.

She feels the vibration of her mobile under the cushion. Holds her breath as she opens the message from Mike.

On my way home, it reads.

CHAPTER TEN

'Mum's driving over on Sunday. I thought we could eat out. Catch a bite in the village,' Sami shouts from the bathroom.

Sophie marks the page of the book club choice with a bookmark from Waterstones. She hates it when people fold the corner of the page. It's just about the only thing she's fastidious about and she vaguely wonders what that says about her.

She stretches and yawns, still sleepy from her afternoon nap. 'You know she'll think I'm not looking after you if we do that,' she calls back. 'She'll think I'm a bad wife.'

'No she won't. Mum likes to go out.'

Sophie reaches for her glasses and regards Sami as he rubs his hair dry with a thick stripy towel. She's pretty sure he has no inkling of how much his mother dislikes her. Martha made it clear from the start that she didn't approve of her beloved only son's choice of wife. Sophie doubts any woman would have been good enough, but a neat, compliant and privately educated posh girl might have done the job. 'I know what you are,' she once hissed when Sami's back was turned. 'You're a fraud and you're not good enough for my son.' And the hostile relationship has continued unabated in private ever since.

Sophie has no intention of making Sami aware of his mother's barbed comments, however bad they get. There's just the tiniest fear at the tips of her toes that if Sami knows his mother's real feelings he may be swayed by them and she isn't going to take that chance.

She pulls back the duvet and stands up. Her breasts seem huge, but so do her legs and her belly; too much Chablis is making her fat. She needs to rein it in.

'Whatever you want, my handsome husband. But if you'd like me to cook, it's not a problem. I like to make the effort for Martha.'

Martha and her comments are better ignored. She finds that fairly easy, but wishes she could do the same with Sami's occasional dalliances. 'So, you don't mind my son sleeping with other women?' Martha had asked conversationally, having drawn her to one side during their third wedding anniversary celebrations. If anyone was looking, they'd have seen mother and daughter-in-law, happy, smiling, chatty.

The pain was intense, deep and physical. Sophie extracted herself from the tête-à-tête with her head held high, a smile on her face, but threw up moments later alone in the bathroom. She stared at her blanched face in the mirror, bewildered that she didn't know. Sassy, streetwise Sophie, who knew everything and everyone, didn't know that her husband was unfaithful. She could picture schoolgirl faces laughing, taunting and gleeful. It was all she could do not to run to her mother, despite their differences, to howl in her lap, to beg her to make it all go away. But she knew that she had to be strong if she wanted to keep Sami, she had to be willing to fight. 'As long as he isn't fucking you, Martha, it's not a problem,' she'd replied.

'I'll rustle up something tasty,' Sophie now says, wondering which ready meal to buy from the small M&S local in the village. She'll do the usual, buy soup or a casserole and throw in some fresh mushrooms and herbs to make it look authentic. It never fools Martha, but if Sami's aware that his wife hasn't spent hours over a hot stove just for the love of his mum, he isn't letting on.

'A touch of arsenic on toast for the good lady, I think,' Sophie jokes with Antonia. But of course she's never mentioned Sami's infidelity, not even to her.

The thoughts of his unfaithfulness are there, always there, like a blade in her heart, but Sophie isn't going to dwell on them today. She stands next to Sami in the mirror and looks at him with narrowed eyes. I'll never let you go, never, she thinks, watching carefully as he splashes aftershave liberally on his newly shaved chin.

'It's only the lads' Friday night in the pub, Sami. I don't suppose they give two hoots how delicious you smell.'

'It's all to do with standards, woman. How many times do I have to tell you?' he replies laughing, catching her around her waist, then kissing the side of her head. 'Thanks for offering to cook for Mum. I appreciate it. She's really excited about the IVF.'

He pauses for a moment before turning back to the mirror, carefully stroking strands of his fringe back into place, then collects his watch and slips it over his long, slim fingers. All without making eye contact with anyone but himself.

Sophie takes a deep hot breath. 'Sami? We agreed not to tell your mum about the IVF. What have you—'

'Talk later,' he interrupts. 'Can't be late for the lads.' And with that he leaves.

Helen puts down her fork. She knows Charlie hates her to eat with only a fork. 'So bloody American. Too lazy to use both hands,' is his usual comment. But it's only pasta and a bit too al dente, in her view. She has difficulty either scooping or stabbing the shells, she'll use a spoon next time.

She looks at Charlie. His face has all the charm of a petulant three-year-old and his accusing stare follows the fork. She almost wants to laugh, but she's never pandered to Charlie's silly whims and she isn't going to start now.

'There's no point in sulking, Charles. Ted Edwards nominated me out of a whole department of very clever people. I'm not going to change my mind,' she says, wondering how long he's going to play his puerile game of silence.

She's been patient up to now, but Charlie's juvenile behaviour is starting to annoy her. After her New York announcement on Wednesday, his face became worryingly tomato-hued and he briefly tried to argue with her. He even said, 'No, I won't allow it!' to which she replied, 'Don't be ridiculous, Charles!' Then he stomped out of the dining room and didn't say another word until he discovered, mid-evacuation, that the toilet roll had run out.

There was something of a tussle with the duvet when they eventually got to bed that night, but Charlie maintained his silence all the way up to and then throughout breakfast, which Helen thought was absurd when he made so much noise eating his toast. She decided that ignoring him was the best policy. Rupert had occasionally sulked as a child and she found that disregarding it was best. He soon realised that it simply wouldn't work and wasn't worth the effort. Helen hopes that's precisely what Charlie will do, but so far the strategy isn't working.

She stares a moment longer at Charlie before rising from the table. She and Charlie hardly disagree on any matter and she doesn't like it when they do. Of course she's aware of his stubborn streak, but she's seldom been subjected to it. It's Friday now and he's still sulking but she sees no other way than holding her ground.

She deftly operates her new espresso coffee machine. Helen rarely spends money on frivolities and this has set her back three hundred pounds, but she can't get enough of it. It's like a shiny new toy at Christmas and has even aroused feelings of empathy in her for Rupert and his hoard of electronic gadgets. She'll miss her coffee machine, but she supposes that they have such luxuries in New York and, if they don't, it won't be the end of the world. She pours an espresso into the tiny cup, the caffeine from the last one already working its magic, and then she frowns at her husband, her patience almost gone.

'For goodness sake, Charles, it's been days, you'll have to speak soon. We can't possibly drive all the way to Staffordshire without saying a word and it'll look rather odd in front of the headmaster if we don't agree a riposte. He'll think that Rupert's a druggy because of bad parenting.'

'Well, he'd be right, wouldn't he?' Charlie blurts.

Helen's tempted to crow for having provoked him into speech, but she thinks better of it and silently watches him take a large gulp of air before his inevitable onslaught.

'You are a bad parent if you're buggering off to America without giving us a second thought. Rupert needs you here. I need you here, as well you know.' Charlie's face goes from frenzied to truculent. He puts his hand on his chest and makes a small cough. 'Besides, I'm not going to see the headmaster or anyone else.'

'Why on earth not? Do you want him to be expelled?' Helen replies with surprise. It's a response she hadn't expected.

'Perhaps I do want him to be expelled if it'll stop you from waltzing off to God knows where. I have a job, Helen, an important job and I couldn't possibly be left in charge of a juvenile delinquent on my own. I don't suppose you've given a second's thought to what we'll do with Rupert in the holidays.'

'Oh, for goodness sake, Charles, our son is not a juvenile

delinquent, as you so generously put it, he's just growing up and experimenting. It's natural. Don't tell me you didn't try the odd puff or tab at university. I certainly did.'

Charlie stares at Helen for a few moments. She thinks of Paddington Bear and his hard stare, except Charlie's eyes are grey, not brown. The blue dressing gown he usually likes to wear for breakfast adds to the mental image and she has to try very hard not to chuckle.

'Well, that explains a lot,' he eventually replies before scraping the chair back and stomping off in his slippers, slamming the oak-panelled door behind him.

Sophie waits for the click of the front door, then lowers herself on to the toilet seat, puts her hands to her face and weeps. Heavy tears. Frustration, anger, anxiety and despair blending with the intoxicating aroma of Sami's aftershave. The tears soon stop, but she doesn't move, she doesn't have the energy. Or the inclination. And it's only the ladies book club. She can go back to bed and ignore the doorbell. They can all sod off somewhere else. But eventually Sophie remembers the glorious chilled wine waiting in the fridge and by the time Antonia arrives, first as always, she's cleaned her teeth, done battle with her contact lenses, applied make-up, got dressed in a too-tight lycra bodycon dress, danced to some Beyoncé and drunk two large glasses of wine.

'He's told his fucking mother!' she announces at the open front door.

'Can I get in first? He's told his fucking mother what?'

'About the IVF.'

'Oh.' Antonia shakes her umbrella and looks at it doubtfully. 'It's raining. Where should I put this?'

Sophie ambles to the lounge. 'It pisses me off. He pisses me off. It's always the same. If he's got something to say that he knows I won't like, he lets it out as a parting shot when he's halfway out of the front door. He's afraid of confrontation. He's a fucking coward.'

'Aren't we all?'

Sophie follows Antonia's eyes and shrugs. 'I couldn't be bothered with tidying. But I did buy Kettle Crisps. Oh, and wine. I've started, join me. Of course he knows I'll simmer down. No doubt he thinks I'll be nicely caramelised by the time he gets home. More like anaesthetised.' She looks thoughtful for a moment, then smiles. 'But it's the book club, so Sami can't possibly complain about wine, sweet wine. At least that's a result.'

Antonia stoops to the coffee table, collects some dirty mugs and heads for the kitchen. 'Shall I open the crisps?' she asks.

'And why has he told her now?' Sophie continues, following Antonia into the kitchen. 'He didn't before. Understandably. He hates failure. I mean, what does one say to one's mother who has so many kids that she obviously couldn't say no?'

'Sophie! That's not—'

'He's told her because he doesn't want me to back out. Of course that's a joke; it shows just how little he sees. If he understood anything at all, he'd know that the last thing his mother wants is the tie of a grandchild, she'll never get rid of me then.' Sophie puts her hands on her hips and frowns.

'I'm sure Martha—'

'Oh God. The fat old cow'll put her oar in every step of the way. What if she wants to come to appointments and pretend to hold my hand when Sami's at work? Suppose she asks the doctor questions?'

Antonia puts a hand either side of Sophie's shoulders and holds her firmly. 'Sophie, calm down. Everything's fine. Really. And there's the doorbell. I hope you've read the book this time.'

CHAPTER ELEVEN

Antonia drops David off outside the Royal Oak as usual, but after waving her off, he walks away from the pub, past Aladdin's, the deli and Cartridge World towards the huge Victorian houses on Parsonage Road, most of which have been converted into flats.

David had lived in Withington as a student at Manchester Poly and he still feels a tremendous affection for it, for its buzz, its strange mix of young and old, its pubs and late drinking clubs. The best kebab take-out in South Manchester too, still going strong at midnight over twenty years on.

He'd got a place at the polytechnic through clearing to read law at pretty much the last moment and had to search for digs. It had been a lonely search. School and the Proctors had been his family until then, but suddenly he was eighteen, he had three duff A levels and the trustees who'd carefully nurtured his parents' wealth just handed it over to him, job done. Still officially under his aunt's roof in Matlock, he'd gone a little wild at first, buying a silver soft-top MG and spending the summer visiting school mates dotted around the country, dishing the dosh. But Charlie intervened when David crashed the MG on a lonely Derbyshire lane. He'd taken to the narrow tree-lined lanes when he was bored at his aunt's, 'to test the motor to its limit', and on one of those days of boredom, 'a bend appeared in the road which hadn't been there before', as he laughingly told Charlie.

David walked away from the collision without a scratch, but the car was written off. Charlie was livid, as never before or since. 'You could've died or been crippled, you fool. Didn't you learn anything from your parents' death?' he'd shouted down the telephone. 'Stop being a failure, David. Bloody well grow up and get on a law course somewhere, for God's sake.'

David was surprised at Charlie's reaction, even more so at the uncalled-for mention of his mother and father and ultimately quite offended. 'It was black ice, not speeding, actually,' he'd replied. But he loved Charlie enough to phone around the polytechnics until he secured a place through economy with the truth and his usual lavish charm.

His aunt had reluctantly offered to come and look at some digs in Withington he found through the Manchester student union. He'd said no to her offer, but as he stepped off the bus, he felt a little Dutch courage was in order before meeting the three postgrad foreign language students he'd be sharing with and there, immediately in front of him, was the Royal Oak with its multi-flowered window boxes and friendly white facade.

'What's up, lad. Somebody died?' the huge, curly-haired and sweaty barman had asked with a grin as he pulled a pint of the local beer. 'I'm Seamus, by the way. The landlord of this establishment. Welcome to Withington.'

David had looked around him. The pub strangely reminded him of his house study at school with its tatty but aesthetic furniture, its low beams, nooks and crannies. For a moment he'd stood still, listening to the hum of conversation around him. Then he'd sniffed the air, felt the warmth, breathed in the feeling of comfort. 'On the hunt for digs, Seamus,' he'd replied. 'Don't suppose you've got a spare room upstairs?'

He pulls up the collar of his coat as he continues to walk past the bay windows of the old houses along Parsonage Road, peering into people's lives. White Gables is an old house too, but it was gutted for the renovation, completely stripped of its past and so it feels like new. New for him and Antonia, a couple happily without a past. Yet here he is again, walking in his own footsteps.

As he strolls, he thinks about Antonia. She looked beautiful tonight, all dressed up for the book club at Sophie's. He wanted to chat with her over dinner or in the car. Not about all the work crap consuming his thoughts, but about anything and nothing, just to connect. But she seemed far away, distracted. Once, in a rare moment when they touched upon the past, he'd tried to explain how lonely it was being an orphan. How he was better with noise, in a crowd. 'I suppose I'm sort of an orphan too, so I do understand the loneliness,' she had replied, holding his hand to her cheek. 'But I quite like it.'

'How are you doing, man?' Sami asks.

He shakes Mike's hand at the bar of the Royal Oak. It started as a joke, the handshake, but neither of them can recall why. There were so many quips and so much laughter in the Boot Room that this particular lore has got lost. 'Are you off to the match tomorrow?'

'I am, but I'm not renewing next season if they carry on playing so bloody badly. All that money and they're still rubbish. They need a new manager,' Mike replies.

'Funny, I feel as though I've heard that before. Now if you

stuck with one manager instead of binning them every two minutes . . .'

'Yeah, well, even for twenty championships I wouldn't have had Beetroot Face if he was the last manager in the land. You still pretending to be a Red, Sami?'

'Only when a client invites me for champagne and prawn sandwiches. Come on, even you wouldn't turn down a corporate freebie.'

'You're right.'

'I'm always right, man. Though trying to convince the wife is another matter.'

Mike inwardly winces at the expression 'the wife'. 'She has a name, you know. You are so bloody sexist,' Olivia reprimands Sami whenever she hears him use it.

He glances at Sami. 'Everything OK?' he asks.

'You know Sophie.' Sami looks thoughtful for a moment then laughs. 'Nothing I can't sort out. What's going on in here? It's bloody empty tonight. Maybe it's the scaffolding. Always said this place would fall down.'

'Easy bet, Sam. It is seventeenth century! A pint or a pint?'

'Hello, chaps. Hope I'm not interrupting anything.'

Mike and Sami turn towards the voice. It's Charlie Proctor, white-faced and sweaty. 'Bloody hell, Charlie, what are you doing here?' Mike laughs. 'Has Helen let you out or did you escape?'

'Thought Friday nights were spent in bed with your *experienced* older wife,' Sami teases.

'I escaped and I'm here to get legless,' Charlie replies, breathing heavily. 'Be a good man and get me a whisky, would you? It's bloody cold out there. Has David arrived yet? He's not answering his phone, but I tried Antonia and she said he was here.'

84

'Perhaps he's got, er, *waylaid*?' Sami replies glancing at Mike with a grin.

Mike studies Charlie's baffled face. There's something innocent and childlike about his expression, even though he usually looks far older than his years.

'I'm sure he'll be here in a couple of minutes,' he says, putting a reassuring hand on Charlie's arm. Then he grins. 'Come on Charlie, spill the beans, what's Helen done to upset you?'

'Should we talk about the book at some point?' Antonia asks no one in particular. The other women are Sophie's friends. They're deep in discussion about local gossip, the latest series on Netflix and the Kardashians, leaving Antonia in her familiar place on the periphery. She likes to talk about the book choice. Her secretly made notes are stashed in her handbag. Hopeless at school, leaving with only a few low-grade GCSEs to her name, she's recently discovered novels and can't get enough of them. But a hum of women with lots to say surrounds her in Sophie's warm, brightly coloured front room, none of it about the book.

'I've read the book!' Sophie announced earlier to the eight or so book clubbers in the room. 'Though maybe not all of it.'

Which is progress, Antonia thinks. Sophie usually reads a summary of the chosen novel on the internet and still manages to have an opinion. Still, it's Sophie who suggested the book club originally, so Antonia isn't complaining, and one or two of the women are nice. She leans over to Sophie, whose unusually heavy eye make-up has smudged quite noticeably.

'Couldn't Olivia come?' she asks.

'Was I supposed to invite her?' Sophie replies with a shrug. 'Where have all the crisps gone?'

'Sophie, that's not fair. Olivia is nice and we've known her for ages. How would you like it if you weren't included?'

'Well, I wouldn't know, would I? Anyway it's Olivia's fault for being so forgettable.'

'What's that supposed to mean?'

'She's so mumsy with all that right-on Chorlton-cum-Hardy *Breast Is Best* stuff. All she ever talks about are those boring children. "Rachel's so clever, she could recite Karl Marx when she was in the womb." And the other one who cries all the time, whatever her name is, "So awfully, awfully cute." And they go to state school, don't you know. Well, so did we! I don't remember anyone giving us a medal.'

Antonia lowers her voice. 'If children are so boring, Sophie, why are you trying to have one?'

'Oh sod off, Antonia. At times you're as dull as she is.'

Sophie's voice is harsh and the other book clubber heads twitch towards hers, too polite to stare, but Antonia is sure their ears are open wide. Sophie's voice drops, the husky catch more prominent than when she's sober. 'Anyway, Toni, why are you so bothered? I didn't think mumsies were your type. Thought you only loved me. Why don't you have a drink and chill out?'

Antonia stands up and straightens her skirt. She's aware that the other women are now openly staring; she wishes they wouldn't. 'I'd rather go home, actually.'

Sophie guffaws, the red wine splattering over the side of her glass. 'Don't be such a drama queen. Anyway, you can't go, we haven't discussed the book yet and I believe it was your choice.'

Antonia sits down, her handbag clutched on her knee and she gazes at the drops of red wine as they seep into the carpet. So very much like blood, she thinks.

*

The glazed chintz curtains of the high-ceilinged room are drawn and the lamp is dimmed by a matching fringed shade.

'What's up, David? You've gone quiet again. I told Seamus I'd take over the bar at ten.'

'Sorry, I'm in a funny mood.'

'I gathered that, love. Cheer up or you'll make me think I'm losing my touch.'

'I'd like to talk more. It's just . . . Or don't you have time?'

Misty peers at her watch, the gold wristband loose on the tanned skin of her wrist. 'If it was up to me you could stay all night, you know that. But I'm not the person you should be talking to, am I? I'm hardly Brain of Britain, but I can see that you need to talk to Charlie. As soon as. Or Seamus might be able to help, he knows people with money. Maybe a short-term loan would do the trick?'

David shakes his head, his eyes on the wallpapered ceiling. As usual with Misty, he's said too much. It usually helps; him wittering, her listening, her eyes kind and supportive. Knowing she won't tell another soul. But that was just stuff, small irritations, petty concerns, things forgotten the moment they're voiced. Whereas this problem is huge and talking just made it seem bigger. He doesn't want to think about it any more.

'And there's Irish Mike. You like him, don't you? He seems kind and discreet. He might be able to help.'

He strokes the back of Misty's hand absentmindedly. She's in her fifties now and the flesh is loosening, but it's soft, it's welcoming. 'At least you don't suggest a friendly little chat with Sami.'

'He's all right. A bit full of himself, perhaps. I don't know why you have it in for him. He seems pleasant enough.'

Feeling the heat rise to his cheeks, he roughly shakes his head. 'There's no way I'd let Sami have one over me.'

Misty glances at him and smiles. 'Because he knew Antonia before you did? That's silly. He married Sophie, not her.'

It's something David has never asked. Was there prior history between Sami and Antonia? He doesn't really think so, certainly not if Sophie had anything to do with it. But occasionally he thinks of Sami's dark hands on Antonia's flawless skin.

Propping his head on his hand, he studies Misty's dimmed beauty for a moment. 'How many years has it been now? At least twenty since you and Seamus took in a poor orphan! God knows where I'd be without this, without you—'

'A pleasure,' Misty says with a soft smile. 'But, seriously, love, you need to speak to Charlie. To sort things out, not just for you, for Antonia too.'

David leans against her shoulder and closes his eyes. He can feel her fiery-coloured hair soft against his cheek. 'Trust me, I know,' he replies. 'I know.'

CHAPTER TWELVE

Antonia expects a wall of heat and the usual fetid smell as she's beeped through the door of The Ridings. As the door opens, the heat is still there but the smell is long gone. If Antonia looked, she'd see sofas with cheerful cushions in the reception area, wallpapered walls, fresh flowers and chirpy staff. But Antonia doesn't look. She hasn't looked since she was a teenager.

Candy is in the lounge in her usual chair by the window. Jeremy Kyle is mouthing silent words on the television screen, his frown prominent. She is looking at her hands, examining their backs and then turning them over to gaze at her palms, as though the answer is there. Antonia notices that someone has painted her mother's fingernails and it gives her a jolt of memory and of surprise. Candy has put on weight over the years and there's little resemblance between mother and daughter, but Antonia has Candy's hands, her youthful soft hands with long slim fingers and nails that are now painted bright red.

The flash from childhood hits Antonia's chest and for a moment she's breathless. But as usual she rallies. 'Hello, Mum.'

She bends and kisses her mother's solid cheek and then pulls up a seat, careful not to disturb an elderly man in the next chair. His eyes are closed, his mouth wide open. He might be sleeping, he might be dead. She supposes the former as two of the carers stand chatting in a corner with folded arms. 'How are you, Mum?'

Candy lifts her head and after a moment her large eyes focus on her daughter. 'Hello, love. Oh, look at you. Don't you look lovely.' Reaching out her hand, she softly strokes Antonia's hair. 'Your hair has grown long again!' She breaks her gaze after a moment and turns to the carrier bag. 'Have you been shopping?'

'Not today, Mum. But I've bought you some new slippers and a box of chocolates. What have you been up to then?'

It's the question Antonia always asks and Candy always replies that she's been to see Sacha, the German shepherd they owned when Antonia was a child.

'She was so pleased to see me, jumping all over and she licked my face. I took her some treats.'

There was a time when Antonia tried to put her mother straight, to tell her she was wrong or forgetful. She wanted to argue, to shout at her, to shake the mother she missed so much out of this placid, blown-up version.

'That's nice,' she says instead. It's all there is to say.

'Has Jimmy come with you?' The light shines behind Candy's brown eyes as she looks to the door and she struggles to heave her body from the chair.

Antonia opens her mouth to reply. It's the same every week. Her mother's excitement and her hope. Then her tears. It's exhausting.

'Now we've talked about Jimmy, haven't we, Candy?' The loud reply comes from behind Antonia, saving her from saying the words yet again. 'Jimmy can't visit because he died a long

90

time ago. But your lovely girl here comes every Sunday, rain or shine. So are you going to give her a smile and tell her what you've been up to all week?'

Antonia nods her thanks to the carer, hoping to conceal the irritation she feels. She understands the staff are there to help, but she hates the lack of privacy, the way her mother and her history are public property. They once spoke so blaringly that she declared, 'Mum isn't deaf, you know!' but she's learned to be compliant, to keep her mouth shut. She's swallowed the furious words that she's wanted so often to scream at the do-gooders, the social workers and the doctors, 'Where were you all when we needed you?'

'So, Mum, tell me all about Sacha,' she says brightly. She shakes her head, but not so you'd notice. She hated that dog. It belonged to her father.

Sundays are good, David loves them. Antonia goes early to visit her mum in Stoke but he has a lie-in, picking at the continental breakfast she leaves by the bed. Later, he has a pub lunch with the lads, a lazy afternoon in front of the TV and more often than not Antonia's superb lasagne for dinner. But the best part is football, Sunday football for a local team. Eleven o'clock kick-off.

He turns on the shower in the changing rooms, his mind and limbs still buzzing from the match. It was a tough game in the best possible way. He really got stuck in, though the result was a 'dirty draw', as one of the lads put it.

David's the oldest player by far. 'Hey, I'm not forty yet!' he says to the youngsters repeatedly when they take the piss. But he will be soon. Still, forty is only a number and the lads let him play every Sunday, hangover or not. 'Go, Dave!' they laugh when he shows some of the left-footed skill he was famous for at school and at uni.

It's ridiculous, he knows, the desire to crow, 'I was the captain of the first eleven football and cricket team every year at school,' even after all these years. 'Yeah, Dave. Whatever,' would be the inevitable eye-rolling reply. But it was great, it was bloody fantastic to be talented at something and sport, like drama, came so easily to him.

'Larger than life. And bright with it,' Charlie says of him to anyone who's listening. But David isn't bright, he knows that, he struggles with anything too intellectual or demanding. He's just good at talking, or at least pretending.

He sings, bellowing out an old song about a great pretender, as the hot water of the shower smacks his face.

'Don't give up the day job,' someone calls from the changing rooms. 'See you next week, chief.'

At that moment David is happy. Sport makes him happy. It doesn't give him time to think.

Helen feels the heat of Charlie's anger ballooning as she drives down the leafy lanes of Staffordshire towards home. He'll burst if he doesn't let it out soon, she muses to herself. But now isn't the time for an argument. Rupert is slumped in the back seat of the car, cocooned in an enormous pair of headphones which she thinks look strikingly similar to the ear muffs she had as a child back in Scotland.

She could be angry too if she wanted to, but an astonishingly wide tractor has inhibited her view of the road ahead and she needs to concentrate on any opportunity to overtake it. She hasn't time to be stuck here all day. There's tomorrow's lecture plan to complete and some marking to do. Her 'daily dose' of yoga too. She hopes to crack the *Karnapidasana* position before bed. Followed by the *Savasana*, the corpse posture, which isn't as easy as it looks.

She glances at Charlie's face, still beetroot-coloured from his explosion of squawks and spittle at the school. She hadn't for a moment expected him to behave so bloody childishly in front of Rupert's headmaster. He's normally mature and sensible about everything, so cool in times of crisis. But then they are other people's crises, not theirs. *Crisis? What Crisis?* she thinks randomly. A boy at Durham had bought her the Supertramp album of that name and they'd listened to it time after time, completely stoned. An early precursor to *the corpse*, she smiles.

'It's only suspension for two weeks, Dad. I don't know why you're so stressed,' Rupert declares, the unexpected sound making Helen and the car lurch. 'Tell him, Mum.'

'I think he heard, darling. And you've promised faithfully to revise.'

Helen nods to herself as she negotiates a hump-backed bridge. She's outwitted the road hog by taking an alternative route, and despite Charlie's petulance in front of the headmaster, she's negotiated a return for Rupert to sit his exams and then to go back to the school for a fresh start after October half term. All sorted without having to resort to *Virabhadrasana*, the warrior, she chuckles inwardly. She hums a tune as she drives. Everything will be in place and running smoothly by the time she's on the aeroplane to New York, she's sure of it.

David lugs his football kit from the boot of his old Land Rover and stops to admire the new paving on the drive of White Gables. No sign of moss at all. As usual Antonia has done a fantastic job of organising it, he thinks automatically. But he's suddenly caught by a thought. Paving half an acre is expensive. Has it been paid for? He has no idea. He merely glances at the bank statement when it arrives to check that it's in credit. That it doesn't need topping up. That's all he's ever needed to know.

'Can we afford it?' Antonia asked every step of the way through the year-long renovation.

'Of course we can,' he always replied. 'And don't worry about the price, darling. You get what you pay for and you're absolutely worth it.'

Antonia pays the workmen by debit or credit card. But it's his account, the statements come addressed to him, private and confidential. He's always topped up when he's needed to. But what now? What now if extra money is needed? He takes a deep breath, reminding himself that it's only the snagging which remains outstanding and that's already been paid for, in theory at least. And Antonia doesn't pry, thank God she doesn't pry.

He shakes off the thought of money, trying to rekindle the warm glow of the football match. But as he heads towards the steps he notices the steam of his breath in the cold air and there's that familiar clasp of apprehension in his chest, the one he's had since boyhood. He hopes Antonia has driven carefully, it's a long way to Stoke and he worries about the weather.

'Afternoon, David. I've got something for you,' a voice calls, interrupting his thoughts.

His neighbour, Naomi, disappears from the fence which separates the land their houses are built on, and then returns a moment later waving his brown wallet in the air. She's wearing her dressing gown, he notices. But then she's always wearing her dressing gown. He and Antonia have a laugh when they speculate why.

'Someone dropped it off this morning, but Antonia was out, so he left it with me.'

David strides to the end of the drive and hops over the long damp grass. He looked for the wallet yesterday but couldn't find it. There was a small flash of concern that there might be something in it that shouldn't be there when he realised it was missing. But as he focuses on Naomi's long painted nails, he remembers that he paid for the last round in the pub on Friday, so he must have lost it there. Of course. Charlie! It was strange to see Charlie out of place in the Royal Oak. Surprisingly pissed too. He must've picked it up at the bar and forgotten to hand it back.

The football spark dulls just a little more. It was another missed opportunity to speak to Charlie alone.

'Who was that then?' he asks Naomi with a smile. 'Charlie Proctor, I assume.'

'No, not Charlie, that other friend of yours. He was here in the week.' Naomi's cheeks flush. 'Do you know, I can never remember his name? He's . . . well, he's tall, rather good looking, drives a sports car?'

David nods, feeling the cold.

Naomi tightens her belt. 'He's very charming, isn't he? And good of him to bring it round so quickly. I hate it when anything goes missing.'

'Very good.' David nods again, feeling rooted to the spot despite his dampening feet, wanting to ask questions, but not knowing what to ask or how to begin.

The house is in darkness when Antonia arrives home from Stoke. She flicks on the lights of the hallway and the kitchen, then walks into the dim lounge, wondering idly where David might be.

'You're home.'

'David! You made me jump. Why are you sitting in the dark?'

She bends to turn on a small table lamp next to the sofa. 'You look sad. Are you OK?'

'I was worried about the ice, that's all,' he says, holding out his arm.

She takes his large hand for a moment and then places it against her cheek as she kneels by the side of his armchair. 'There wasn't any ice.'

'There might have been black ice,' David says. 'It's there but you can't see it.'

Antonia nods, bringing David's hand to her mouth and kissing it gently. Once long ago, in a moment of frivolity, she gave Charlie a clumsy hug. 'Thank you for always looking out for us. You're the best dad anyone could have!' She'd turned to David. 'Don't you agree, David? Charlie's a brilliant dad?' Charlie didn't return the hug. He frowned and Antonia immediately regretted her words. She'd meant them affectionately, with love. Of course Charlie wasn't nearly as old as anyone's dad, he just looked it. She'd obviously offended him. It was only later, when they were alone, that he explained in a gruff voice how David had suffered when his parents died. Of course she knew they were dead, but David had never said when it had happened or how.

'He was twelve. Still a boy. A car crash on the ice,' Charlie told her. 'On a country road, just turning a corner. Losing both parents in the blink of an eye. Tragic. Very tragic.'

David now breaks the silence. 'How's your mum?' he asks. 'You know I'd come too, if you wanted me to.'

'I know, love.' Then after a moment. 'She's fine, thanks,' she says, her automatic reply which needs no further detail. 'Look at the time. I'll put the lasagne in the oven, shall I?'

'Sounds nice,' David replies. But still he keeps hold of her hand.

CHAPTER THIRTEEN

Antonia climbs out of her car and looks up. It's a substantial and imposing period home, bay-fronted and semi-detached in a tree-lined cul-de-sac near the centre of Chorlton. A large property, probably five or six bedrooms, yet a far cry from White Gables. Olivia and Mike Turner have neighbours immediately either side for a start.

She stands for a moment looking around. There's a small boy with his mum digging in the next garden. She's wearing a spectacular African dress. A young man in lycra squats down by his bike, another man in a white turban washes his van in the road. The house opposite has been converted into flats. She can smell the sweet aroma of spices from one flat, hear the thump of music from another. It reminds her of childhood. But the people, the noises and the smells feel friendly here.

The doorbell sounds loud to Antonia's ears as she presses it, almost insistent. Perhaps she should've knocked. Clasping the flowers with one hand, she puts the other in the pocket of her wool coat and stands back. There's a very thin crack between the panels of the red front door and she wonders if it lets in the cold breeze. She breathes in, and then out. It's silly to feel nervous. She's been here several times before. But never for coffee and not on her own.

The door opens, letting out a rush of warm air, which blows the newly fallen autumn leaves around Antonia's ankles. The telephone's ringing inside.

'Hi! Come on in.' Olivia smiles. 'Let me grab the phone and I'll be right with you.'

Antonia steps into the hall. She can't describe how exactly, but the house smells different from the one she shares with David. Not an unpleasant smell, but layers of smell, of children, of cooking, of family. Not that her childhood home smelt this way. Tobacco, beer and dog is all she can recall on the rare occasions she allows her mind to wander. She glances at the pink and white freesias still clutched in her hand as she walks into the kitchen, regretting her choice. It's clearly a family home. Perhaps chocolates or biscuits would have been better.

The kitchen's a jumble. Half-eaten bowls of cereal, toast, fruit juice and crumbs. Discarded spoons and spilt milk. A red plastic basket full of damp washing sits on the floor. A solitary piece of buttered, seeded toast lies on the work surface with just one bite missing.

Olivia returns from her phone call, her cheeks slightly pink. 'Sorry,' they both say at once.

Olivia is wearing jeans and a checked shirt tied in a knot at her waist. She always looks fresh, Antonia thinks, fresh and healthy and hearty, even though she's so petite. 'That was my sister. I'll ring her back later. What were you about to say?'

Antonia nods towards the toast. 'Oh, it was just that . . . I've interrupted your breakfast.'

'Oh, don't worry. It's usually lunchtime before I realise that I haven't eaten anything, but my stomach felt a bit dodgy this morning. Another bug brought home by Hannah, no doubt. Reception is the worst possible class for it. Earache one day, the runs the next. And, of course, the dreaded head lice.'

Olivia catches Antonia's slight grimace and laughs. 'Don't worry. The nits were a couple of weeks ago. Even Mike was enlisted to do some wet combing, much to the girls' dismay. Men just don't understand long hair and knots, do they?'

Men and long hair. Long curly hair, Antonia immediately thinks. She replaces it with a smile and a much fonder memory. The nit nurse from school, when she and Sophie went in together, holding hands. Sophie's head teemed with nits, hers didn't. 'It's the curls,' the nit nurse had said, as though Antonia had done something wrong. 'Nits don't like them.'

'I don't suppose men do,' Antonia replies, wondering if Olivia knows she used to be a hairdresser in her 'former life', as she calls it in her head. Of course there's nothing wrong with hairdressing, but a clean sheet starting with David feels so much easier. 'I brought you some flowers.'

'What a lovely smell. Thank you. Let me just fill the washing machine with some bedding and then I'll put on the coffee. Feel free to clear yourself a space at the table.'

Antonia sits down on a chair for a moment before standing up again and taking the pots and cutlery from the table to the sink. Something tells her that a real friend doesn't stand on ceremony, but gets stuck in with the chores. By the time Olivia comes back with her arms full of bedding, Antonia has cleared the table, washed up the crockery and put the kettle on.

Olivia smiles as she surveys the results. 'You can come again,' she laughs.

The traffic lights on Princess Parkway are on red. They always seem to turn from amber to red the moment the car reaches sixty and purrs like a cat. Sami usually bears down on the accelerator, hoping to jump the lights with only a second to spare, just for the soft thrill, but today his thoughts are elsewhere.

God, I want her now, right now, he sighs. I wonder if she's been thinking about me.

The thought is uninvited and for a moment Sami wonders if he's said it out loud.

'Stop it, man,' he chides, deliberately aloud to test the sound. He adjusts the mirror and then glances to the right, his sixth sense telling him he's being admired. An attractive woman in sunglasses is appraising him from a shiny black Mercedes sports car. He glances at the wheels, noting the discreet badge of the performance-tuning company. See? he thinks, grinning back with a nod. Plenty of shapes and sizes to be had. I mustn't get hung up. It's only temporary fun. It's only a laugh.

Yet as he presses his foot on the accelerator of his car and listens to the throb of the engine, his mind's with her, with him and her, her touch, her breath and her skin, so unbelievably soft. His body is tingling, alert. He wants her now as much as he ever has.

'Fuck,' he says as the road opens out. Fuck, fuck. It isn't supposed to be this way.

Charlie sits opposite David in his office, talking. His face is puce and he's gesticulating far more than usual, so perhaps ranting would be a more accurate description. But David isn't listening. He's thinking about God. The God he doesn't believe in, if anyone asks. Not just thinking, but talking. He finds it helps when his heart starts to race, the chat slows it down and helps him breathe. He isn't sure whether he actually talks to God, or just to himself. He doesn't go to church, he hasn't been to church since belting out the words to 'Jerusalem' at school every Sunday morning, but he finds it helpful to say, 'Dear God' or 'Dear Lord God', when he's talking to himself. When he's hoping and praying and trying to stay calm.

'I mean who pays the blasted school fees?' David eventually hears.

He tries to focus on Charlie and for a moment he watches the animation of Charlie's mouth. Small bubbles of saliva are accumulating at one corner.

'That's what I said to the bloody headmaster. I've probably paid for a whole new tennis court with the charitable donations alone,' Charlie rants.

David was brought up by his parents to say his prayers at night, tucked up in bed before sleep. Eyes closed and palms together, the Lord's Prayer voiced in unison. It was the one moment of demonstrative affection between father and son.

His parents weren't churchgoers. 'It would be strange, listening to sermons in all those different languages,' David's father had explained.

'Different but interesting,' his mother had retorted.

'So you do believe in God?' young David had asked, with surprise.

'Only the God of love,' his mother had laughed, dismissing his father's frown with a wave of her elegant hand.

When he was sent away to school, his prayers were like a mantra. To God, or to the God of love, so long as he said his prayers every night and at chapel every day, his parents would be safe, he would see them soon.

'So now we've got Rupert at home sleeping in until lunch and then disappearing off to God knows where until he needs to be fed. He's meant to be bloody revising, not acting like a domestic pet. Could you have a word with him, David? He's always loved you. He might listen.'

David nods. Charlie looks exhausted, old. 'Course I will, though I doubt he'll listen to me.' Insurance, Antonia, his parents and money. Prayers work, he thinks, but only to a point.

Sami sits at his desk, thinking. He's held back from texting. Waiting for her to text him, which she hasn't, which does his head in. He isn't used to this. Since being a tiny, asthmatic child, what Sami Richards wants, Sami gets.

'Baby of the family and the only boy. Well, that explains it. You are unbelievably spoilt. You do know that, don't you?' Sophie stated on their first proper date.

'No I'm not! Why do you say that?' He was genuinely surprised. He didn't feel spoilt. He used his charm to good effect, he knew, but spoilt? Spoilt wasn't a pleasant word.

'Your sisters do your supermarket shopping, your mum travels from Yorkshire to clean your flat. Leaves little love notes "from Momma".'

The spoilt list went on. Charm, he insisted. Spoilt, she retorted. They agreed to disagree, eventually.

Sami drums his fingers on the desk and then pulls out his iPhone. *Tomorrow? What time?* he types, ponders for a moment, then adds, *Thinking wicked thoughts. Can't wait to see you.* He presses send.

His private line rings almost instantaneously. 'Ha!' his ego sings.

Still sitting at Olivia's kitchen table, Antonia looks at her watch, surprised at the time. As she lay in bed fretting about the visit here last night, she expected to stay for an hour at most. She expected to be tense and shy, to feel inadequate and stupid.

Olivia has always been friendly, but she's clever, she's educated, reads the *Guardian* and has opinions. But time has flown by, the coffee interrupted by telephone calls, the window cleaner, a crying neighbour with her crying baby and the insistent beep of the washing machine. There has been no time to feel tense.

When they finally sit down on the long sofa in the lounge, Antonia studies Olivia's face. Perhaps there's a hint of tiredness around her eyes, smudges of pale grey on her fair skin. 'So you were up at five with Hannah, you made breakfast and lunch boxes, walked the girls to different schools, had a word with Rachel's teacher, visited a new mum and her baby on the way home, changed the bedding . . .' Antonia laughs as she counts the chores on her fingers, marvelling at how much Olivia manages to fit in to a weekday morning. By eleven she'd made David a bacon sandwich, had tea in bed and got dressed.

'The bedding wasn't until you came. But you've forgotten Tesco local for bread and milk on the way back from school.'

'Tesco, of course!'

Antonia smiles, but her mind is on the white bap bacon sandwich which she found untouched on the kitchen island when she came down from the shower. It looked forlorn, abandoned. She should've said goodbye to David before he left, she should've given him a kiss.

She goes back to Olivia. 'I don't know how you do it, Olivia. Don't you get fed up at times?' The words are out, and Antonia winces. She hadn't intended them to sound as they did, like a criticism of Olivia's life.

'Actually, I do get fed up sometimes and I take it out on Mike, which probably isn't fair of me.' Olivia's pale eyes drift away and she frowns. 'He was the first to go to Hannah this morning,' she comments, as though to herself.

'If you ever want a break, I'd be happy to look after the girls.'

There they are again, Antonia's thoughts popping out as words. But she says them quietly, her body rigid with the anticipation of rejection. 'Seriously, I'd love to help, it would make me feel useful.'

'Aren't you lovely,' Olivia replies, her face flushing with unexpected colour. She leans forward and gives Antonia a brief hug. 'I might just take you up on that. But they'll run rings around you, so don't say you haven't been warned!'

CHAPTER FOURTEEN

Antonia drives straight down Barlow Moor Road from Olivia's house to Southern Cemetery. She even buys flowers from the extortionately priced shop on the busy road catering for the bereaved. And busy husbands, she thinks with a smile. Two bunches in a single day, though the petals of the red chrysanthemums she clutches in her hand are already browning at the tips.

She parks her car between two trees on Nell Lane and notices that a block of pale-brick apartments with trendy wooden balconies has been built since last she came. The wood looks weathered already. She fleetingly wonders whether she'll remember where to go, but her feet seem to know the way as she tiptoes between plots to prevent the heels of her boots sinking in the grass. She ponders why she's come. She hasn't visited the cemetery for a long, long time. Perhaps it's Olivia's words about family and the smell of a home. Or perhaps it's that rarely felt need to be normal, to belong.

'God knows, we try our best to be good parents, but we

don't always get it right,' Olivia said earlier, her face pensive and almost tearful.

'"They fuck you up, your mum and dad",' Antonia responded bravely, hoping she'd quoted the poem correctly. '"They may not mean to . . ."'

'Absolutely! I love that poem,' Olivia replied, her face clearing, leaving Antonia feeling inordinately pleased.

'Your dad's in pain. And sometimes he gets full of anger and disappointment, that's all,' her mother would say, ever forgiving. 'It's the drink that's talking, not him. He doesn't mean it, Chinue.'

Candy's love and tolerance for Jimmy was constant. It must have been mutual once, that adoration, Antonia muses as she walks into the breeze. They were people before they were parents. As a small child she'd seen the photographs, a bundle of sticky snapshots tied together with a perished rubber band. She'd found them at the back of a drawer in an old shoebox, along with her birth certificate and a few one-pound premium bonds. An array of happy photographs taken at the seaside. Her dad thickset with sideburns and a quiff and her mum, stunning in a headscarf, larking around on the sand and the pier with another grinning couple. The snaps fascinated her. She took to gazing at them in secret when her parents were still in bed in the morning, trying to reconcile the smiling man with her angry father. But then one day she became complacent, she laid the photographs out on the threadbare carpet like a pack of cards, guessing the order in which they were taken. So absorbed, she didn't hear the groan of the stairs or the creak of the opening door, just the sound of his gravelly voice behind her.

'What have you got there? Pass it here.' So she stood with jelly knees, turned and handed him the bundle she'd frantically scraped together from the floor, her eyes fixed on the swirls of the brown carpet, waiting with breath taut in her lungs.

'That's Scarborough,' her father said eventually, his voice smiling. 'Bloody hell! That's a blast from the past. With Marcie and Ben. Call your mum down for a laugh. Just look at my hair!'

Sophie isn't a person given to nerves. Except when it comes to anything medical, which she knows is stupid. Even more so, given that both Norma and Barry are nurses. Or perhaps that's why. Bloody parents. But then there's the dentist too. Her mum dragged her kicking and squealing for the twice-yearly check-up as a child.

'It's your fault,' she said to Norma when they were last friends. 'My dental phobia. You made me go to that bloody maniac when we were small.' But the reality is that Sophie didn't have one single filling as a child, it's only as an adult, when she can choose not to go, that she has the problems. Indescribable toothache from an abscess just a few months ago. Pain nearly as bad as the 'I told you so' look on her mum's face when Sophie asked her to go with her to the bloody maniac, who was as kind and as patient as he'd always been.

'Fuck!' Sophie says to herself in Sami's full-length mirror. Even without her contact lenses, she can see she looks a mess. She's stayed in bed all morning, valiantly resisting the urge to have a glass of wine and go back to sleep. But sleep isn't an option when she's worried, when her mind is churning out thoughts and spiky memories.

'You did go for that smear appointment, didn't you?' Norma asked when Sophie still lived at home, when her mum could still nosey through her post, even if she didn't go so far as to open it.

'Yes! Get off my case!' Sophie replied, the usual retort. But Sophie assumed that a cervical smear would be as bad as the dentist, only at the other end of her anatomy. She couldn't bear the thought of it. She'd been obsessed with an irrational fear of having one ever since she'd spied a photograph of the barbaric instrument of torture they used for the procedure when she was about ten.

The science books were on the top shelf of the bookcase at home, but Sophie was tall and could reach. She'd pile the books on the soft carpet and flick through them cross-legged, her mum actually thinking she was taking an interest in medicine, a short-lived hope that her offspring might one day become a doctor.

Of course Sophie and her cousin were glued to the science books in the hope of finding pictures of bollocks and dicks. Or an account of having it off. Preferably with photographs. Instead it was graphic and biological, more of a horror story than Sophie and her cousin had ever expected. 'Which is why, which is why . . .' Sophie now says to her blurry self.

She climbs back into bed. The sheets feel slightly dank from sweat, from worry. She's spilt some coffee, a spreading stain on the silky cream throw. Staring at the stain, she examines the spirals of colour that fade from dark brown to beige. Antonia will clean it for her, she thinks, she'll spray on some newly-advertised-on-the-shopping-channel product then hand-wash it in the sink and the stain will disappear, like magic.

She picks up the cold coffee cup and takes a sip to ease down the paracetamol that's stuck in her throat. Her colleagues at the estate agents used to joke that it was a good idea to have a large gin and tonic before a smear, to help them relax. Sophie laughed and dismissed the thought at the time and yet when she started the last round of IVF, she drank a couple of large

glasses of wine before leaving for the clinic. The doctor immediately smelled the alcohol on her breath and reprimanded her
severely, saying she didn't deserve the procedure if she was
going to endanger it. Sophie tried to laugh it off, asking where
all the 'tea and sympathy' had gone and mocking the doctor
for being a member of the 'grin and bear it brigade'. Yet the
doctor's disapproval helped her be brave, to grit her teeth and
let them get on with what they had to do without the prop of
alcohol. Last time, at least.

Sophie stops biting her nails and groans out loud, lifts her
mobile close to her eyes so she can see, taps in a message to
Antonia, *Where the fuck are you? I've called three times*, then
inches further down into bed, waiting for a reply, wishing for
magic.

Olivia throws the last of her drink down the sink before leaving
the house for the school pick-up. It's a new range of 'real' coffee
advertised by handsome actors who persuade their female audi-
ence with a beautiful, deep and languid voice to have a 'coffee
moment'.

She and Antonia laughed about the advert as they sipped
their coffee this morning. 'Coffee moment! The power of adver-
tising. I can't believe that I actually went out and bought it.
You'd never believe I was *highly educated* and a feminist at uni
to boot. And it tastes vile!'

But Antonia lowered her eyes and looked into her mug. 'Oh,
really? I didn't go to university,' she said quietly.

The conversation had flowed until then. Olivia was left feeling
she'd somehow humiliated Antonia and to cover up her own
embarrassment she invited her to stay for lunch, even though
she had a million other things to do. But they got back on
track; Antonia insisted on making them her 'club sandwich

special', which she produced ten minutes later with a flourish, complete with cocktail sticks from God knows where and even a paper napkin.

'Look at the time! Sorry for imposing for so long,' Antonia said as she left. But it wasn't an imposition at all, Olivia thinks, as she strolls in the weak autumn sunshine towards the primary school gates. She's surprised at how effortless it was to talk to her. Or perhaps to talk at, she muses. She did all the talking, probably too much.

'Oh, we all need to have a rant from time to time,' Antonia said when Olivia apologised for going on. 'Or all the time, in Sophie's case,' she added, laughing.

'Were you two at school together?' Olivia asked to be polite, not particularly wanting to talk about Sophie.

'Yes, Sale High, from Year Seven. Sorry, I interrupted. You were saying about your dad.'

And so it went on. Olivia ranting. Ranting that she couldn't rant to her sister or to her dad because they wouldn't have a bad word said about Mike. Not that she wanted to rant, because she was lucky to have Mike as a partner, but that sometimes being married to somebody whom everyone else thought perfect was annoying and made her feel bad for wanting to rant because, really, she had nothing to rant about.

Hannah darts out of the green school door waving something in her hand, a look of sheer happiness on her pink shiny face. 'It's a party invitation, Mummy! To make a bear! Can I go?'

Olivia lifts Hannah, hugging her tightly, the pleasure of holding her youngest child still as intense as the day she was born. But a thought pinches her chest and the euphoria of unburdening herself fades, just a little. She'd confided in Antonia about the miscarriage and what Mike had said. Perhaps she'd said too much; she doesn't know her that well, but the flow of words and hurt, concern and confusion were unstoppable.

Of course she didn't tell Antonia everything. Olivia still has no idea why she didn't want the last baby, the boy. In her mind she blames the toll of pregnancy and childbirth, the burden of looking after yet another child, but they aren't the real reasons for her rejection of him. She still can't put her finger on it, but the awful truth is that she didn't want their son, she resented each step of the way until she lost him and once he was gone she felt nothing but guilty relief.

Maybe there was something in what Mike said, she thinks as she kisses Hannah's warm chubby face. Not by deed, but perhaps by unwholesome feelings or by thought she did something to make her unborn baby die. It's a frightening thought, one she shared with Antonia. 'Thoughts don't kill, Olivia,' she replied, her brown eyes kind, understanding. 'Much as we would like them to at times. It's the deed that counts.'

Sophie peers at her mobile again before flinging it from the bed and on to the floor where it makes a soft thudding noise of protest. She feels another surge of breathlessness. She wants to feel brave, she really does, but sometimes it's hard, the erect head, the bright smile, the flippancy for the 'camera' which everyone expects.

So many injections. The prodding, the poking, the pain. The fucking humiliation of it all. She knows what's coming this time and she doesn't feel brave at all.

She lies with her face in the pillow, like she did as a child, resisting the urge to kick her legs and howl. Then after a few moments she leans over and scoops her phone from the carpet. She sits up cross-legged and stares at the name in her contacts list. 'Carrot or stick?' she muses aloud. She knows she could wait for Antonia to call her back, but she's temporarily annoyed with her, and besides, she knows she needs a much firmer hand to help her through. She takes a deep breath and presses call. It's answered after three rings, which Sophie finds herself counting. 'Hello, Mum,' she says. 'It's me.'

Antonia fingers the bunch of flowers as she stares at the mossy, weathered headstone. In memory of. Name, date of birth and date of death. No loving this, or much missed that. Her dry eyes flick back to the flowers. It's a large bouquet, albeit common chrysanthemums, bought impulsively when her heart was full of poetry.

The slant of sunlight behind her moves and she feels her heels sink into the grass. It's fine. She has tissues in her bag to wipe her boots, so she won't soil the car. She gazes at the weed-strewn grave of Jimmy Farrell a moment longer and then shakes her head and turns away, berating herself for dwelling on the good moments, which were far too few. There's no point brooding on the dead, it's the living who count. She has David to think of and what to create for his dinner. Something he likes, a delicacy to please him. Perhaps poussin, she thinks, he'd see the funny side of that.

As she hurries towards the exit gate, a bird chirps from a tall tree and the wind ripples the flowers' cellophane wrapping, reminding her they're there. She stops and turns her head towards the direction of her father's grave, then sighs, tucks her hair behind her ears and bends to lay the flowers gently on the closest naked grave.

CHAPTER FIFTEEN

'I don't really think she'll go through with it. Do you?' David asks from the other end of the new Italian contemporary dining table. 'Antonia?'

Antonia lifts her head, her face blank for a moment in the light of the dinner candle. 'Oh, do you mean Helen and this America thing? Not if she knows that Charlie is ill, surely. Though you never know with Helen. Has he told her?'

David shakes his head. He's tried several times to broach the subject of the doctor and the test results, but Charlie ducks the issue by saying it isn't important, that there's too much else to think about. Talking to Charlie about anything just now seems impossible.

'Should you say something? To Helen?'

'God, no. I promised Charlie. He'd go ape.'

With her dark eyebrows slightly raised, David thinks Antonia looks sceptical, and as he gazes at her lovely face, he wonders if he could try to explain that old school rule of 'not splitting on a friend', whatever the consequences. It was an unspoken drill learned early at boarding school, one of loyalty, allegiance and honour. A rewarding lesson he was proud of, often taking the flak for his friends, as they would do for him.

As Charlie has always done and surely always will?

David waits for his heartbeat to slow, then leans towards his wife. Antonia has such a tight friendship with Sophie, he thinks she might understand. But she's drifted away again, her face contemplative, even softer than usual. He wants to say, 'A penny for your thoughts?' or, more specifically, 'Where did you go yesterday after you left Olivia's house at three? I called, but you weren't at home,' but he's too afraid to ask. He's too afraid to say, even casually, 'Naomi mentioned that Sami popped by last week. What did he want?'

He moves the pasta around the bowl with his fork. Creamy spaghetti carbonara made with chunks of gammon. It's just as he likes it but he doesn't feel hungry. 'Do you mind if I nip over to Charlie's tonight? He wants me to talk to Rupert about school.' It's on the tip of his tongue to say he doesn't know why. Who is he to offer advice when it comes to academia? Or children, for that matter? But he suspects that Antonia would be disappointed in him for showing weakness or failure. 'Do you want to come? Keep me company in the car?' he adds instead.

Antonia shakes her head as she stands to collect the plates. 'No, I'd better stay in to phone Sophie and catch up. She's left half a dozen messages and I've ignored them all. Keep your ears peeled, I'm expecting a big telling off!' She bends to kiss David's cheek. 'Good luck with Rupert though, love. A fifteen-year-old incommunicative boy. You're a sweetie for saying yes. I wouldn't know where to begin.'

Lifting her mobile, Antonia sighs. She usually responds to Sophie's messages straight away; she's not entirely sure why she hasn't this time.

Sophie answers almost immediately. 'Toni! Well, it's about bloody time,' she says heatedly. 'Where have you been all week?'

'Here and there,' Antonia replies, surprising herself by not instantly telling Sophie about every intricate detail of her day with Olivia. 'How about you? What've you been up to?'

Tightening the belt of her dressing gown, Antonia props her bare feet on the edge of the coffee table, her mind wandering. She enjoyed her time with Olivia yesterday and she doesn't want Sophie to belittle it somehow, to call Olivia 'mumsy' or 'boring', which is the last thing she actually is. Besides, she increasingly feels the need to keep some aspects of her life apart from Sophie and it's slightly liberating to feel that she isn't completely in her friend's pocket. Not like at school when she was taunted regularly by other girls from her estate who were once her friends. 'Sophie's shadow, Sophie's pathetic little shadow. Watch out or we might say boo!'

'Well, as it happens, you've got a lot to answer for, Toni *here and there*,' Sophie replies. 'You were ignoring me, so I telephoned Mum.'

Antonia pulls down her feet and sits up straight. 'Really? Did you apologise?'

'No. What have I got to apologise about?'

Antonia wants to laugh. Sophie's so thick-skinned, or at least pretends to be. But then so is Sophie's mum, the one person who sees her daughter for what she is, a 'selfish spoilt madam', as Norma bluntly puts it, even in front of Sophie's friends. Which is why the two of them haven't been on speaking terms for several months. The final spat was in the presence of Antonia and another of Sophie's friends one afternoon in the garden. It was toe-curling, both mother and daughter having clearly forgotten the visitors were there.

'Why are you drinking wine when the rest of us are drinking coffee?' Norma had demanded. 'You're drinking too much, Sophie. It's bad for your health and no one likes a drunk. Sort yourself out before Sami sees you for what you are.'

'And what's that supposed to mean?' Sophie retorted, her voice too loud and slightly slurred. 'What am I then?'

'A person who manipulates everyone who loves them,' Norma replied firmly, as though it were a well-rehearsed comment.

'What's that got to do with the price of wine? Oh, I get it, you're still peeved because Dad always loved me more than you. You're pissed off with me because he left home as soon as I did. Well, that's not my fault. Did it never occur to you that he couldn't stand living with you any longer?'

Even Norma couldn't mask the hurt. 'Don't contact me unless you're ready to apologise,' was all she said as she left, leaving Antonia and the friend wide-eyed and wondering how they would skulk out of Sophie's townhouse garden without catching the tail end of her wrath.

'But I did say that I missed her, which is true,' Sophie now continues down the line. 'Then she said, "I suppose that's the closest I'll get to an apology." The cheek of it! But at least we're officially friends again. And I've missed you too, Toni. What time can you come over and give me some TLC? I have chocolate and mango. You know you love mango.'

Antonia smiles on the other end of the phone. 'A person who manipulates.' Norma knows her daughter well. She's tempted to see Sophie, but not tonight; she doesn't want to bump into Sami.

'Not tonight, Soph, I'm tired. But I'll be over tomorrow, as I promised.'

'You'd better be. Sami's neglecting me, so you'll have to be as sweet as ever.'

Sweet, Antonia thinks as she ends the call. She carefully peels back the damp flannel and inspects the neat slash at the top of her arm. The beads of seeping blood have finally given up. Sweet? I've no idea who that person is, she thinks to herself.

'How are things going, Rupe?' David asks.

Although only a few weeks have passed, Rupert looks considerably taller than the last time they met, but he's still spider-thin. He's slumped full length on the worn leather Chesterfield sofa in Charlie's chilly lounge with his long legs dressed in torn jeans, not dissimilar to those David wore on 'dress-down' days at school. David supposes that Rupert is staring vacantly into space, the remote control having been confiscated by Charlie, but he can't be sure because Rupert's fringe is so long that he can't see his eyes.

'Come on, Rupe, don't look so miserable. It's your old Uncle Dave. I'm hardly going to give you an ear bashing, am I?'

'Ear bashing? Is that a twentieth-century expression or something?'

But Rupert is smiling. He hitches up his legs, pulls his fringe behind one ear and makes eye contact with David. 'They're just so irritating. Both of them. They don't get anything.'

David stiffens for a moment, bracing himself for the inevitable, 'I wish they were dead.'

The reply is clear in his mind, but he wonders whether he's able to voice the words: 'Appreciate what you've got, Rupert. My parents were dead when I was your age. Coming to see me on a leave-out at school. Only they never arrived.'

It was a time of indescribable agony. Two days had passed before he was called into the housemaster's study. Two days of unbearable pain. He'd read and re-read the letter from his mother, the aroma of her perfume still there in his imagination, if not in the paper. *We're in the UK next weekend, first port of call being you, darling boy! We'll see you on Saturday. Can't wait. Love always, Mummy xxx.*

He doesn't know how his words to Rupert will come out, whether he'll shout or cry. Or laugh, perhaps, as he did at school, with that protective bonhomie masking the grief. But Rupert is quiet, his fringe has fallen forward again and David is reprieved.

'Hmm. Irritating parents. Well, that's good news at least!' he replies with a laugh, sitting down in the space Rupert has made. 'I pronounce you a normal healthy fifteen-year-old lad.'

'What's all this about drugs then?' he asks, suddenly aware that moments have passed and that Rupert is watching him.

'Everyone does it. It's only weed.'

'Good point.' He was in the minority at school by not smoking tobacco, cannabis or anything going. But that was only because it made him chesty and sport came first. 'But that doesn't mean you have to. Believe it or not, school work and exams do matter. Take it from me, Rupe, you do not want to have to re-sit those bastards!'

'You said you weren't going to give me an ear bashing.'

'I lied,' says David, giving Rupert a playful thump. 'Just remember he's a good bloke, your dad. A really good bloke. Come on, let's put on the box and see if there's some sport on Sky before your mum comes and inspects your transformation from devil to angel. Oh, and by the way you'd be doing me a favour if you acted the part too. You know, the odd civil word here, bit of revision there, maybe even an occasional thank you. Get the picture?'

'Got it,' Rupert replies looking towards the television screen. 'I think the switch is on the side, Uncle Dave. Or you could ask Dad for the remote.'

*

Antonia is still trying to get to grips with Sylvia Plath's poems, but even when she doesn't really comprehend the words, she gets the gist, she understands the struggle, the desire to be something else. She's read 'Resolve' ten, twenty times, maybe more tonight. Shyly and out loud to the listening walls of the lounge, but to no one else.

She'd started reading poetry after a conversation between Olivia and Helen at a dinner party a year or so ago. It was a debate about music and poetry. Olivia argued that music *was* poetry and Helen was dismissive, declaring poetry to be silly and pointless. Olivia disagreed, listing reasons why everyone should read it, specifying poems and poets who had influenced her life. Antonia had sat dumbly and listened, but it was the fervour in Olivia's eyes, the passion of her argument which enthralled her. She had headed for the laptop to make an order as soon as they left, a feeling of anticipation in her chest until the slim collections arrived in the post.

David's late, chatting to Charlie over a bottle of whisky, she supposes. So she hasn't gone to bed, but lies on the sofa, covered in a soft blanket, Sylvia whispering softly in her ear as she waits for David's call to collect and drive him home. But she's fallen asleep and so suddenly, so deeply, that the dream is real. Her father is there and so is she, like a vicious, dancing cat. Scratching, hissing, spitting and goading him to hit her again. 'Come on, Dad. Don't be afraid just because I'm a big girl now. Hit me, insult me, show me how brave you really are.'

David slouches at the bar of the Royal Oak waiting for Misty to appear. She hasn't replied to his texts but sometimes she's busy. One of her kids might be visiting or Seamus might be at the table begging for home-cooked food. So he's driven from

Charlie's home in Hale all the way to Withington. To do what, to say what, he doesn't know.

He feels untouched by the three double whiskies he drank in a wine bar in Hale, nor by the pint of bitter he's just downed. Nothing has dimmed since his confession to Charlie. Not the look on his face, not his anger, his lack of understanding or forgiveness. Nor Rupert's confusion as he darted into the study, looking fearful and so very young. 'Dad, what's going on? You can't say that. It's Uncle Dave. Why does he have to get out of the house? It's my house too. And Mum's.'

'David. David? Are you listening?' he eventually hears through the whirl of whetted images. 'You need to go home. How much have you had? I'll call you a taxi.'

Misty's there behind the bar, her tanned fingers spread wide on the bar top but her eyes not reaching his. Seamus's bulk is a presence in the background.

'I thought we could talk,' David replies, his attempt at a whisper emerging too loudly.

'Not tonight. Not any night soon.' Misty glances over her shoulder. Seamus is pulling a pint, the frown seeming to puncture his usual plump friendly face. 'People have been talking again, David. I'll see you. Now off you go home.'

'Fine to drive. Sober as a judge,' he calls to Seamus with a wave as he stumbles from the pub. Then again as he catches his clown face in the car mirror. 'I am as sober as a judge, Your Honour!'

He puts his keys into the ignition and heads the Land Rover down the A road towards home, not bothering with the seat belt.

Sober as a judge. It makes him laugh at first, the irony of the expression. Then eventually he cries. He weeps so much that he can't see, but still he drives along the dark autumnal lanes towards his Cheshire home, wondering if it's normal for a nearly forty-year-old man to miss his mother quite so much after so many years. Occasionally he can smell her perfume at the theatre or in the street, and it's all he can do not to halt the passer-by, to clutch on to her and sink his face against her neck to inhale the aroma on living skin.

Like a vampire, he muses. What a complete and utter fuckup I am.

He briefly glimpses a tiny pair of hollow eyes in the head-lights and feels a small thud against the car. Another dead bunny, he thinks, wiping his nose with a sleeve.

He feels inordinately sad for all those dead rabbits. There was a badger too, once. Far larger than he expected, it had stared at him from the muddy roadside with dead, reproachful eyes. Is that how his mother looked, her beautiful face intact, but her body broken and crushed against the steering wheel? Then there was a small, red fox cub, many years ago, when he dated a schoolteacher. The head was mangled and trampled. He should have been brave, but he wanted to heave.

He nearly shoots past the drive of White Gables; he always does.

'Slow down immediately after the sign for Mottram, then it's first right, just after the bend.' That's what he says to visitors, but forgets to do it himself.

He chuckles – every bloody time, he ought to have learned by now. But he manages to skid into the driveway, the vehicle clipping the gatepost and then sliding and lurching before coming to a sudden hard stop against a raised garden wall.

Lifting his head from the steering wheel, David opens the car door eventually. He knows time has passed but he's unsure if he's been unconscious or asleep. The moody sky is lit with glinting stars and there's drizzle in the air. Part of the small wall has collapsed from the collision, the soil spilt, as though making a pathetic bid for freedom along with the roots of some flowering plants. He closes the car door with care but the sound of his feet seems unduly loud on the wet paving as he stumbles towards his front door. His nose feels matted and it throbs from the thrust against the steering wheel. He vaguely wonders if it's broken, but it doesn't really matter, he's home.

'Sober as a judge,' he whispers, as he opens the front door of White Gables.

CHAPTER SIXTEEN

Antonia's awake, listening to the smack of the rain on the shutters. She wonders if she's slept at all, but she supposes she must have done at some point, as the thin early morning light sighs through the wooden panels. David's asleep next to her in the bed, breathing softly through his mouth. Remains of clotted blood are flecked around his nose and mouth and yet his face is relaxed and peaceful.

She looks at his pillow, soiled and smeared with red and brown traces of blood, and she briefly replaces her feelings of guilt with questions about what on earth happened to David last night. But her quest for answers doesn't last long. The overwhelming guilt is far stronger, more insistent. She wants to wake David, to explain her own behaviour. But where would she begin?

Slipping out of bed, she feels the warmth of the underfloor heating against the soles of her feet. The words which echoed through the night are still fresh in her mind. 'I am so lucky. To have all this. To have David. Remember to tell him.' She looks at her watch. It's still only six-thirty. She'll give him an extra hour in bed and then wake him up with his breakfast, ready on a tray. Then she'll say, 'I love you, David. I appreciate you so much, I really do.'

The sound of the telephone breaks her thoughts and she snatches it up, not wanting it to wake her sleeping, damaged husband.

'Auntie Antonia? It's Rupert.'

'Oh, hello Rupert, how are you?' Her mind rushes. Why is Rupert calling at this time? Questions unanswered. A feeling of slight panic. What has David done? 'It's OK to call me Antonia, Rupert, Auntie makes me sound old.' She's talking too much, procrastinating.

'Well, the thing is, Mum's asked me to telephone.' His voice sounds strangled. 'Dad was taken into hospital last night. Macclesfield hospital. She went with him. An ambulance came, paramedics and everything. They think he's had a diabetic coma or something. I mean, fuck, I didn't even know he was a diabetic.'

Not David, thank God. 'Oh Rupert, I didn't know either. Poor you. Do you want to come here? Shall I come and fetch you?'

Relief floods her mind. She needs to concentrate, be practical. 'How is he, how's your dad?'

'Well, Mum called and I think he's OK. But I don't really know. She told me to stay here. Suppose I'd only get in the way.'

His voice is thick with emotion. He wants to cry, Antonia knows. She understands this, the need to cry, to sob and to scream, but the need to hide it even greater.

'Mum said Dad's all wired up because his blood pressure is really high and he needs loads of different drugs.'

Poor boy. Bloody insensitive parents. But who am I to judge? she thinks, glancing at the peaceful face of her husband.

'David's still in bed, Rupert, but I'll wake him. He'll want to go to the hospital straight away,' she says. Her mind is sticky, rebelling against the sudden change of plan. She should drive. David reeks of booze, he'll be over the limit. 'So I'll drop off David at the hospital and then come over to your house and keep you company for a bit. How's that?'

David feels Antonia's hand on his shoulder, bringing him back from a dream. 'David, love, wake up, Charlie's in hospital,' she says clearly.

'I know,' he replies from the pillow. 'He's dead, isn't he?'

He rolls away from her waking hand and bunches up his body like a huge fist. Reality has hit him immediately on waking, his mind prodding viciously with a stream of recrimination. Fool, fool, fool. Debts, huge debts. Insurance, indemnity, money – client money, ethics and rules. And theft, oh God, theft. Charlie's fury, his disappointment. 'A failure, David. Again. Get out of my sight.'

David scrunches up his eyes, willing reality to disperse, wanting to climb back into his dream, the dream he hasn't had for many years. The one of a small boy gliding to and fro on a pond thick with ice. A smiling fir tree glistens in the middle, its lights like warm eyes winking. Then the ice begins to crack, a thunderous black noise in his ears. But despite the screams all around him, the boy isn't afraid. He doesn't fear the face slowly rising to the surface, or the hand, white with death, reaching to pull him in. For the man-boy has been in this dream before. He knows not to fear the stinging slap of the icy water but to welcome the touch, the comfort and love as he slides into death. Not into the cold black ice of a pond, but hand in hand with his mother, into the warm soapy sleep of the ocean.

'No, he's stable, he's alive, love,' Antonia says, still standing beside the bed. 'Why would you think that? But you need to wake up. Rupert's all alone, so I'll drop you at the hospital and then drive on to Hale.'

David averts his eyes from his watchful wife as he climbs from the bed and reaches for some clothes. He feels leaden with grogginess and his head hurts badly, from the alcohol, from the impact. He fumbles with the buttons on his shirt then gives up, rips it off his hot torso and pulls a jumper over his head. He can feel Antonia's eyes on him, wondering what he meant. Eyes like saucers, he thinks.

'Divine justice,' he mutters in reply. But it's fine. He doesn't mind divine intervention. It all makes sense really.

'I do love you, you know,' Mike says as he leaves the house. A glint of sunshine through the clouds catches the top of Olivia's face. He means it. He really means it. 'I'm not always good at showing it, but I do.'

'I know,' she replies, rearranging his ruffled hair with a half-smile. 'It's a good job I love you anyway.'

He grins as he climbs into his car. His heart hasn't felt this light for as long as he can remember. The black dog is missing, gone for now at least. He arrived home from work yesterday evening as usual, trying to leave his feelings of boring, dull despondency in the car for the sake of the girls, but immediately he stepped into the house, Olivia pulled him into the kitchen, away from the girls who were watching television in the lounge. 'Let's be friends again. I've missed you,' she rushed, putting her arms tightly around him and burying her head against his chest until Hannah appeared and elbowed into the hug.

Mike is loath to leave the house and drive into Manchester today. His feelings of contentment and relief spread like osmosis, giving the whole house a party atmosphere throughout last night and again this morning at breakfast. It made him realise just how much his happiness or otherwise with Olivia affects the girls.

He thinks back to his own childhood as his car crawls with the other early commuters into town. It was happy, both parents loving and supportive, his sister joyful despite her disabilities, but he can still remember the cold dreadful atmosphere when his dad was in one of his dark moods. It was never physical, there was only shouting and stomping, but still it frightened the family into silent submission every time. Mike doesn't generally shout, instead he withdraws, which he now understands can be just as bad. His father was vocal, so at least the family knew what was eating him. Silence is infinitely more difficult to interpret.

I must try harder, he muses, as he bounds up the stairs into work. Family is everything.

Antonia's mind is buzzing as she drives from the hospital to the Proctors' house in Hale. David was quiet in the car on the way to see Charlie, far too quiet. She put her hand on his and gave it a squeeze. He smiled in reply, a soft shy smile, but he was miles away. She wanted to apologise, to say the words of love that had been snatched away, but it felt too indulgent when Charlie was in hospital. Then there's Sophie. Bloody Sophie. Antonia called her to say that she wouldn't be able to go round to her house this morning, perhaps not all day, but Sami answered the telephone and it was strained, embarrassing.

'What does she want at this time?' Antonia heard Sophie grumble from the background. There was a muffled conversation between Sophie and Sami; Sami's voice was raised. Then

Sophie came on the line, angry and petulant. 'He's a teenager, isn't he? Why does Rupert need you to hold his hand? You promised you'd be here. I thought we'd go out for lunch.'

Antonia ended the call without saying goodbye. First time ever and so easy. 'You're being completely selfish, Sophie. I'm not speaking to you when you're like this.'

Then there was last night, when David got home in the early hours. The sharp memory of her words and her actions needles her as she drives. She was still in the dream with her father; she thought David was him. Oh God, what she said, what she did. There's no point thinking about it now. But still she does.

'He's asleep,' Helen says flatly. She's swung from an intense fear that Charlie is going to die, to a mild irritation that bloody diabetes might put a spanner in the works (an expression she does understand) of New York. The stress of it all has created an irresistible urge to sleep, but here's David, his sheepish face unshaven and bruised. 'What on earth . . .' she begins, but David is staring down at Charlie with a look of sheer hopelessness on his pallid face. 'Sit down, David, before you fall down. You look worse than he does. He isn't dead or dying. At least they don't think so.'

She waits for David to sit down and to speak, but he remains silent, pale and impassive, so she continues to talk. 'The main problem is diabetes. It's buggered up his blood sugar, which they'll have to balance with insulin, and his blood pressure and cholesterol levels are alarming too. He's lucky not to have had a heart attack, but there could well be one in the pipeline.'

She removes her glasses, automatically polishing the lenses with her blouse. 'Of course I didn't know anything about it.' Replacing her glasses, she looks pointedly at David. His swollen nose and stubble make him look like a cliché of a criminal. His eyes shifty and hooded, he looks guilty too. 'Did you know he was ill? David?' she demands. 'David? Be honest.'

'Well, he did mention something.'

'When? When was this?'

'A while ago.'

'And you didn't say anything to me? You didn't force him to go to the doctors or to speak to me about it? For goodness sake David, what sort of friend are you? Charlie could have died. He might still do if he's not very careful, his arteries will be caked.'

She's silent for a moment, embarrassed by the shrill tone of her words, knowing she's unfairly taking out her anger and frustration on David, when it's Charlie's fault for not confiding in her and perhaps her fault for not being amenable to such a confidence. But she's cross, cross with David, cross with Charlie, cross with herself and so she can't stop.

'And what was all that about last night in the study? All that shouting and swearing? Demanding that you leave? I've never seen him so upset. That's probably what brought it on. You're meant to be his closest friend, David. I don't know what you've done but . . .'

Helen rages at some length as she stares at the three differently coloured lines on the monitor above Charlie's bed, aware that she's fully attributing blame to David when both she and Rupert have played their parts. When she turns her head to inspect David's guilt-ridden face, he's gone.

'Cheer up, Rupert. Stable is good, isn't it?' Antonia smiles encouragingly. 'Why don't you give your mum a ring to see how he is now?'

It's still only ten-thirty in the morning. She's made Rupert several drinks, ranging from Ovaltine to a glass of soda from an antique-looking syphon, but they've all gone untouched. Rupert remains slumped in an armchair chewing his thumb. She's been through Helen's kitchen cupboards in search of something a youth might like to eat – crisps, biscuits, even jam for toast.

'My parents don't do junk, treats, whatever you'd call them. "Not very healthy" they say, which is ironic, considering,' he mutters. So Antonia resorts to creating something from the ingredients she can find, trying not to pay too much attention to the long-gone 'best before' dates.

'Like *Ready Steady Cook*,' she declares, which is rewarded with the slightest of smiles. 'Flour, sugar and butter. That's all it takes to make a biscuit, right? Come on, you need to help me out here, Rupert. I hated domestic science. Always skived it at school.'

'You're joking, right? Come on, Auntie Antonia, Dad's always on about your fantastic cooking. I bet you were the perfect schoolgirl, top of the class, star of the week, every week.'

It strikes her then how little anyone really knows about anybody else. But Rupert is animated, at least for a while, as the warm shortbread is eaten. Then time hangs again with nothing to say and Rupert retreats to his chair.

'Mum should have called me by now. I'm her son. She's meant to care about my fucking feelings. She's never loved me, neither of them has.'

Antonia tries to argue, to cajole and reason with him. 'Of course they love you, Rupert, of course they do,' but her words aren't convincing. Not even to her. Helen and Charlie sent him away from the local primary school in Hale where he was happy and settled, to a far-away boarding school, a fragile only child who needed his mum. Then when he was home for the holidays, they barely noticed he was there, leaving him alone for long days with their elderly housekeeper.

For a moment, but only for a moment, the thought pops into Antonia's head that perhaps it was better to have her father, as terrible as he was, rather than to have no father at all. But then she remembers the dream on the sofa last night, so deep and intense that she thought it was real, that her father was real. And her words to poor David when she thought he was him. 'Get off. You disgust me. Don't touch me. Never again. Do you hear?'

She checks her mobile with a sigh. There's no answer from David to her texts, but that's not surprising. He's at the hospital with Charlie where no mobiles are allowed. They're probably laughing about old times, Helen looking on, bored. She'll try again later.

'I know, Rupert. How about a game of Snap?'

A groan in reply from Rupert. 'I'm not ten, Auntie Antonia.' But at least there's a smile.

CHAPTER SEVENTEEN

Sami's face is tight, his body tense as he strides past the flurry of lunchtime shoppers in St Ann's Square. He's angry with her for humiliating him, for making him look like a fool. But most of all he's angry with himself. He's said too much to her, he's exposed his inner self and let emotion get in the way.

As a cautionary measure against Sophie's snooping, their texting over the past few weeks has been infrequent, though he'd never been so meticulous about it with women before. It was always easy to shrug and to say to Sophie, 'The girls at work having a laugh, you know what they're like.' But this time it was too close to home, too difficult to explain away and it mattered. Only God knew why, but it mattered.

She was usually at home in the mornings but her car was missing and the house was empty, so he waited for her a distance away, hoping the neighbours wouldn't think it odd that a man in a smart suit was waiting and watching, alone in his newly polished car. The sports pages of the *Telegraph* bounced in rhythm with his impatiently jiggling knee, but he didn't read a word.

Their last tryst had been sublime. He'd relived it in his imagination time and again. Before leaving her bed, he completely covered her soft naked body with his, lying perfectly still, trying to preserve the moment.

'We're a perfect fit,' he whispered.

'Lying down, yes,' she laughed in reply.

He didn't want to leave. Unusually for him and his occasional conquests, he wanted to stay. To inhale that special smell, to chat, to cuddle and to kiss. He had to wrench himself from her bed, from her, but she promised to call him at work on his private line.

'Soon,' she said in answer to his question as to when they would meet. 'Soon,' she said in answer to when she would call.

Over the last few days he found himself sitting idly at his desk, watching the telephone like a silly bloody teenager. But no call came and he began creating different scenarios in his head as to why she hadn't called. The sex was fantastic for them both, he was confident of that. So what was the problem? He liked her and she liked him, no one else knew about it, so it wasn't hurting anyone.

As he waited down the road this morning, he caught himself in the car mirror, adjusted it to see his whole face and grinned. He was looking good. He smelled good, his body was nicely toned from the gym. He couldn't imagine that she might have gone off him. No one ever got bored with Sami Richards before he became bored with them.

'Hey, Sami,' a voice shouts.

Sami looks across the cobbled square. It's Mike, who's seen him first, so there's no chance of escape. Dodging a heave of sandwich shoppers, Mike approaches with a look of friendly concern. 'Are you OK? You look as though City have scored six times!'

133

Wrenching his focus to Mike, he tries for normality. Mike is carrying a large blue and silver brolly with the name of an accountancy firm printed on it in huge letters. Sami lifts the collar of his coat. He hadn't noticed the rain.

Sami nods at the umbrella. 'And you have the cheek to call me a corporate freebie bitch. Those bastards too!'

'Not guilty.' Mike laughs. 'Found it in the boot of my car.'

'With the bodies? That's what they all say.' The need for distraction suddenly overwhelming, Sami nods in the direction of Sam's Chop House. 'Man, am I glad to see a friendly face. I've had a shit morning. Do you fancy a quick pint?'

Mike looks apologetic. Sami has forgotten how Mike hates to let anyone down. 'Sorry, Sam. I'm on an errand for Olivia and I've an appointment in the office at two. How about tomorrow?'

'You're getting soft in your old age, man. Lunchtime used to be boys only, remember?' He manoeuvres himself under Mike's umbrella, shakes away the stab of rebuff. 'And what is it that you're buying for your lovely wife?'

Mike lifts a green shopping bag. 'Not buying. M&S returns, actually. Not very macho, is it? I bet the Boot Room boys would be disappointed in me.'

'Too bloody right.'

Sami laughs, but he's disappointed. Despite his conflicting emotions, it would be good to talk to Mike. He always has a knack of turning the downside of life on its head and seeing the comedy. And more to the point, just when it's needed, he'll gently take the piss out of 'Sami and his pedestal', which no one else is allowed to do.

Sami shrugs off the thought; he needs to get out of his own head somehow. 'I'll walk with you and the brolly bastards. Don't want to spoil my lovely locks in this piss.' He looks at his watch, still pleased with its e-Strap. 'Besides, I think a bit of retail therapy is just what the doctor ordered.'

Antonia picks up the bundle of bills on the doormat, flicking through the envelopes absently before leaving White Gables yet again. She looks at herself briefly in the hall mirror, surprised at how composed she looks. The packed morning has been a nightmare from start to finish. Her hand is trembling and she feels slightly breathless. It's all she can do not to retreat back into the house and search out the razor blade she hides beneath her old diaphragm in its box. But she knows the calm it gives her is only ever temporary and she has things to do, Sophie for a start.

She doesn't feel guilty about having reprimanded Sophie for her selfishness. It's surprisingly satisfying. But she is aware of a feeling of culpability, even though she was trying to put things right. She sat at her kitchen table with an espresso for at least half an hour, mulling things over and trying to calm herself, but the rare caffeine boost is having the opposite effect. Still, it gives her the energy to move. And with Sophie I'll need energy, she muses, as she climbs into the car.

Rupert's outburst troubles Antonia as she drives. Once he started to tell her his problems, he couldn't stop and they tumbled out in a deluge along with his tears. It's the detail in which he related every incident, she thinks, from his mum's failure to join his class on school trips like the other mums, to being left alone with his chronic asthma in hotel rooms, while his parents, oblivious to his loneliness and panic, ate their dinner *à deux* in the restaurant downstairs.

Her heart went out to him and yet still she found it difficult to give him her full attention. She found her mind kept straying to another only boy who'd been left all alone at such an early age. 'Be careful driving, darling. It could be icy. It's the black ice I worry about. You can't always see it.' David's words of concern, so often repeated. Yet they've been married for five years and never specifically had the 'How did your parents die?' conversation. The 'What happened? How old were you? How did you feel?' discussion. What little she knows of David's parents' death comes from Charlie, a snippet here and there, spilled out quickly when David's not in the room. But of course that's her fault. Any wife would ask, wouldn't they? But if she asks, he'll reciprocate and what then?

A beep from the car behind makes her start and she puts her mobile down on the passenger seat. Still no reply from David. Or from Helen, for that matter. She suspects Helen is angry with her for interfering, but she doesn't much care. She still feels empowered by her sudden decision. 'Come on, Rupert, you need to see what's happening at the hospital for yourself. I'll text your mum and tell her we're on the way.' It makes her feel like a real grown-up; not only the empathy and understanding she feels for Rupert, but the decision to do something about it.

There's absolutely no doubt, she thinks, as she slips the car into gear, it feels good to make decisions and be useful. And for once, useful to somebody other than Sophie.

Sami lobs the half-eaten Big Mac back into its cosy little box.

I don't even like McDonald's, he thinks morosely, and yet I'm here, sitting on a plastic seat made for kids, rubbing shoulders with a take-out full of chavs.

A middle-aged geezer wearing a shabby tweed jacket stares at the red tray with bloodshot eyes. Sami stands, picks up the tray and places it before the man. 'Here you go, mate. Nuggets and fries untouched.'

The man doesn't look the least bit offended. 'Cheers.' He

cocks his head to one side. 'Would you like to join me?' he asks, nodding to the vacant bench opposite him.

Sami sits down, wondering what the fuck he's doing. He's the only person here in a suit, his hair looks shit, his eyes sting and he's bought an expensive green dress for Sophie that she's sure to detest.

'Escape from the office?' the man asks, delicately dipping individual fries into a small plastic box of tomato ketchup.

Sami pictures the telephone on his office desk, knows it will torment him when he gets back. Clients and his mum have his private number too. Still, he'd probably best unplug it for a while. He gazes at the man, notes that his cheeks resemble red sandpaper and wonders for a moment what has brought him so low.

'Ever made a complete arse of yourself?' Sami asks.

The man smiles. Some teeth are missing, the others are brown. He has an eloquent voice. 'Too often to remember. Booze. I like it more than I like anything else.'

'I don't even have that excuse.'

Sami rubs his eyes as he thinks about earlier. He scrambled out of his car and followed her to the house as soon as she returned, eager, smiling and stupid.

'What are you doing here, Sami?' she asked. 'I've had a really busy morning.' Her face was impassive with just a hint of colour in her cheeks.

'I thought you'd be pleased to see me,' Sami found himself saying to her. Pathetically. Like a petulant child.

The man opposite regards him with curious eyes and nibbles carefully at the chicken nuggets. But Sami drifts, picturing the frown of uncertainty on her lovely face. What is it about her? he wonders. What yanks at his heart? He's always thought she's attractive, but there's something more. Something he can't quite define, which bizarrely reminds him of his feisty eldest sister, the one who was always there for him when he was picked on at school. Ramona would laugh her socks off if he told her his heart was hurting. Indeed he would like to confide in her, she'd put him straight in a trice. But Ramona lives in America with her brood and a broken love affair isn't something he can discuss over the telephone, even on his private bloody line.

'Aren't you pleased to see me?' he had asked again to cover his lover's silence.

She didn't reply but put her keys in the lock and softly pulled him by the hand into the house, closing the door, but remaining in the hall. 'Look, Sami, I don't think we should do this any more.'

She's finishing with me, he thought, his mind pitching. She's fucking finishing with me.

'Oh, and what is "this"?' he asked. Defensive. Stunned. Hurt.

'Seeing each other,' she replied. 'Having sex.'

'I thought we made love,' he said, almost shouting. No pride. No fucking pride.

She reached again for his hand. Her voice was gentle, kind. It made him feel so much worse. He felt like crying. 'Come on, Sami, we've always been friends, let's keep it that way.'

An argument at the counter brings Sami back to Thursday lunch at McDonald's. He shakes his head, feeling a chesty tightness in his lungs from the fried oil in the atmosphere, just like the young Samuel who'd stuff down his burger and fries ferociously despite the discomfort. He knows the stinging eyes and the tightness comes from rejection and humiliation, too. Like fat boy Samuel, the boy who had no friends.

Sami clears his clogged throat, aware that the man is openly gazing. 'Penny for them?' the man asks.

'I've been a complete wanker,' Sami replies. 'But I'll get over it. Come on, let's get out of here. I'll buy you a pint.'

CHAPTER EIGHTEEN

David walks. His plan is to catch a taxi, a taxi home to shower and shave. That's as much of a plan as his muddled mind can manage. His head is inordinately painful and he's so very tired. It vaguely occurs to him that perhaps he's concussed from the crack to his forehead and nose last night and he smiles an ironic little smile. He's leaving a hospital. A more sensible man would turn around and get himself checked out. But David isn't bothered. *Res ipsa loquitur*, the matter speaks for itself. He's clearly not a sensible man. The foolishness of the past week and month, hell, the past year, are ample evidence of that. Besides, the hurting head blocks out all his guilt, his lies, and complaining about a headache seems childish, indulgent and unfair given Charlie's condition.

He wanted to puke in the hospital. He was shocked by all the tubes and wires and drips attached to Charlie's body, the spiteful winking monitors and he wanted to vomit.

'He's sleeping,' Helen said. She said those words clearly, but he hadn't heard, not really heard. Then Charlie's body twitched and the relief drained him of speech, of movement, of thought.

139

It was all he could do not to climb on to the bed next to him, to hold on to him tightly and sleep. But then Helen started to talk.

Busy roads have become country lanes, the town of Macclesfield is behind him, the opportunity to catch a taxi long gone. But the autumn sun is warm on his back, the walk is clearing his head, helping him to focus on the conversation with Antonia in the early hours, to remember what she said.

It was the perfume, he now recalls. He was thinking about his mother's scent on and off all day yesterday. He doesn't want to contemplate his visit to Charlie's house or to recall his behaviour in the pub, but he knows that he drove home like a blockhead, that he eventually stumbled through the front door of White Gables and into the lounge. To his surprise, there was Antonia, asleep on the sofa, so beautiful, icy and still, that he knelt down by her side to listen for her breath. The smell of her perfume, so like Mummy's perfume, and the soft warmth of her throat. They overwhelmed him.

'So you decided to come.' Sophie turns away from the door and stomps back into the townhouse. 'I'm honoured.'

Antonia follows her into the lounge with a feeling of mild panic rising in her chest. Sophie's eyelids are swollen and her face looks crumpled. It's not like her to cry. 'Has something happened, Soph? Are you OK?'

'No, I'm not OK.' Sophie roughly pushes a copy of *Cosmopolitan* magazine off the sofa and thumps heavily into its place. 'You and Sami.'

She throws a bunched-up tissue into the wicker basket and then looks up at Antonia for a few seconds, her green eyes sharp. 'You're never here when I need you.'

Antonia lets out the breath she's holding, sits down on the

sofa and rubs Sophie's knee. 'Sorry, Soph, it's been one of those days. Come on, tell me, what's up?'

Sophie takes a deep breath. 'It's my own bloody fault, isn't it? I can't give Sami what he really wants from me and he'll leave, I know he will.'

Antonia relaxes and sighs. She doesn't really know what to say that she hasn't already said a hundred times before. 'It isn't your fault. Chlamydia is a silent infection. Millions of women contract it. You were just unlucky.' And then there's the usual, 'Tell Sami the truth. You're not being fair. He needs to know.' Part of her feels that there is no point, that nothing she can say will make any difference once Sophie has made up her mind. Yet on the other hand, she always feels she should try.

'Of course he won't leave you. He adores you. You have to stop beating yourself up about it and come clean,' she says today.

Sophie's face darkens and she pulls away from Antonia's touch. 'Oh, fuck off. You really annoy me at times with your sanctimonious crap. As though you've never told a lie, *Antonia*. Preacher heal thyself and all that.'

'This isn't about me.' Antonia stands up. 'I'm not the one demanding attention twenty-four seven. I've had a hard morning so if you're going to be horrible, I'm not hanging around.'

'Oh, for Christ's sake sit down and don't be so bloody sensitive. You're here now, Sami's working late and I'm a bundle of nerves.'

Antonia doesn't move. Her jaw is clenched.

'Come on, Toni.' Sophie stands too and puts her warm bare arms around Antonia. She kisses her cheek several times, the way she always does when she's pushed things too far. 'Hey, believe it or not, I don't even want wine.'

'Well, every cloud . . .' Antonia relents with a small smile. She sits down, taking up Sophie's position on the sofa. 'I've had a busy day so you can wait on me for a change. I'll have a cup of tea and something to eat, please. I'm starving.'

Helen is back at Charlie's bedside, still reeling from the shock of her altercation with Antonia, of all people. She supposes that Antonia is beautiful, if you like that sort of thing, but she always finds her hollow and uninteresting. Any conversation is a staccato 'yes' or 'no' on the girl's part. Not that she sees much of her outside David's dinner parties and they don't count as the silly girl is never at the table, choosing instead to fuss in the kitchen and produce unnaturally perfectly presented food with only a dash of sauce or gravy. Helen infinitely prefers Barbara's sturdy casseroles, whatever the other guests might say about Antonia's 'splendid cuisine'.

'She's a nice, sweet girl, that's all,' Charlie would say. 'You probably intimidate her.'

'Good God, I hope so!' Helen would reply.

Helen's still holding the mobile tightly in her white-knuckled hand as she reviews her conversation with Antonia, who didn't seem the least bit intimidated on the telephone. The discussion went along the lines of, 'I dropped Rupert at the hospital because I thought it would be better for him to be with his father.'

To which Helen replied, 'As his mother, Antonia, I think that I'm best placed to judge.'

And she replied, 'Well, as his mother, Helen, I think you should put yourself in his shoes occasionally and see how it feels.'

Charlie puts his hand on hers and nods at the mobile phone. 'Everything all right, my love?'

'Oh it's nothing,' she replies. 'You're looking much better than you did at five this morning.'

'Even handsome chaps like me don't look their best at five in the morning.'

Helen smiles. It's good to have Charlie back. He finally woke late in the morning and immediately spotted Rupert. 'Is that you, Rupert?' he said. 'Come and give your old man a hug.'

She looks over at her son, sitting in the chair next to the hospital bed. His head is down towards some gadget or other, his ears covered with the huge muffler headphones, but there's an air of calm about him. She's rarely wrong about anything, but this time she wonders. She had assumed Rupert would wind Charlie up, get in the way and make his condition worse, but father and son seem content together.

Perhaps, she thinks buoyantly, her spat with Antonia already forgotten, perhaps everything will come together by Christmas and I'll be on that aeroplane in the New Year.

David's memory is starting to coming back, but in snatches. Antonia and Charlie, Charlie and Antonia. Misty too. Her eyes strangely hidden. Her voice low.

He's been sitting on a dry-stone wall for a while, gazing over the rugged green fields to the rocky splendour of The Edge high above. People are walking their dogs, appearing miniature on the horizon. He'd once suggested adopting an old Labrador retriever left homeless by a deceased client, but Antonia said, no, sorry, she was allergic to dogs. She'd like a kitten though, he thinks, to keep her company while he's at work. Or perhaps one of those small dogs they breed especially for owners with allergies. If he hasn't messed things up completely. If it isn't too late.

He tries to block out Charlie's angry voice, still shrilling in his head. 'Ethics, David. Ethics! Solicitors are supposed to be honest. Of the highest integrity, David. Ring any bells?'

He'd longed for a dog as a small boy. 'Please, Mummy, please,' he'd frequently begged. They lived in Derbyshire then, in a small medieval village near Chatsworth with a church, a school and a post office that had a cafe serving cream teas to the tourists. That was before Shell Oil International sent them away to their 'far-flung adventures', as his mother described them. Even now, he feels a strange uncertainty when his eye catches the familiar yellow Shell sign, and he remembers how his father refused to buy petrol from any other garage even if it meant driving miles out of his way. 'Really, darling?' his mother would breathe through her ruby-red lips. David loved and loathed the 'far-flung adventures' in equal measures.

Charlie's voice is still piercing. 'Spent it on the house? You won't have a house, David. You won't have a job, for God's sake. You'll be prosecuted, imprisoned, disgraced.'

The cows come up close to David, used to him now, their beautiful eyes deep and unreadable. Eyes like saucers, he thinks.

'Please, Mummy, please. Let me have a dog!'

His mother would point to her inappropriate-for-Derbyshire heels. 'How could I possibly walk a dog with those cobbles outside?' and she'd laugh.

But of course she'd eventually relented. His father had arrived home early from work one day with a feeble black-and-white Border collie puppy in a cardboard box. 'The runt. She's got a twisted leg,' he explained, his voice gruff. 'The farmer's wife refused to drown it, so now she's yours. All yours. Look after her properly, son.'

The afternoon darkens. David eventually registers the cold, wipes the tears from his face, says goodbye to the cows and continues to walk.

The perfume, of course. Last night is now in focus. His mind is clear. He stumbled into White Gables and there was his wife, asleep on the sofa, beautiful, icy and still. He knelt down beside her, felt her breath, inhaled the aroma and softly kissed her neck. Her reaction was immediate.

'Get off. You disgust me,' she cried. Eyes cold with loathing as she hit him. 'Don't touch me. Never again. Do you hear?'

And of course Misty at the bar. Her voice low, her eyes hidden from his. He repulsed even her.

He pulls up his collar, wraps his arms around himself and walks on. His mind is blank, there's no point straining it any more. It's started to shower. A car passes occasionally. Then a tractor.

'Look after her properly, son,' his father said.

Sophie carries the mug of tea in one hand and a slice of toast in the other. The mug is overfull and milky drink spills on to the carpet. Colour has returned to her cheeks and she's grinning. Only Sophie can transform so easily, Antonia thinks.

'A plate would be nice,' she says, looking at the sad slice of toasted white bread. 'Have you pâté or something to go with that?'

Sophie narrows her eyes. 'Pâté? Listen to you!' she declares. 'No one would know you came from a grotty council estate in Northern Moor with benefit cheats and drug dealers as neighbours.'

'Not everyone was like that, Soph. You read rubbish too often. Mr Bennett next door was nice, remember? Just an old man.'

'He had a rusty oven in his front garden, Toni.'

'Probably because no one offered him a lift to the tip. Anyway, it wasn't so far from your house in Northenden.'

145

'Ahem, a private house in the posh part of Northenden. Good job I was there to drag you out.'

'For which I'm eternally grateful,' she replies laughing.

'Then promise me you'll stay and keep me company until Sami comes home.'

Antonia looks at Sophie, but doesn't reply. Even when they joke about old times, there's always that tiny underlying message of 'Never forget you owe me,' or sometimes even, 'I can expose you if I want to.' But as she sits there on Sophie's garish sofa, she realises that she doesn't care any more. There isn't much to expose. Does it really matter if she was christened with another name and told a few white lies along the way? Doesn't everyone do that somehow in their lives, either to themselves or to others?

'I'll go when I'm ready to, Sophie,' she replies evenly, gazing at the look of surprise on Sophie's face. I want to get home to David, she thinks. She feels empowered by the events of the day. She didn't jump the moment Sophie asked her to this morning. She decided it was best for Rupert to be with Charlie at the hospital and did something about it. She even argued with Helen. For once she's stood up and been counted, and now she wants to go home to her husband, to explain about her dream last night, to apologise for her harsh words and to say, 'Talk to me, tell me who you are, what you feel, how you are. Let's be a couple, let's communicate.' She takes a deep breath and smiles; it feels like a challenge and she can't wait.

David continues to walk towards home, one foot in front of the other, not noticing the rain or the countryside, his mind fitful.

Antonia must already know what he's done. That explains

it, he thinks. She knows about the money. Not just borrowing, but theft.

It makes sense of her words last night. Her anger, her hatred. 'You disgust me,' she said. She never really loved him and now he's let her down. He's made her unhappy, disappointed. In the worst possible way. And there is Sami Richards in the wings, with his arms open wide.

Life without Antonia. The thought is unbearable.

'Look after her properly, son.'

He's tried. He's tried so hard to give her everything.

But as ever, he's a failure.

The rain has become heavy. David tries to quicken his pace but the drum of his heart is loud in his ears, beating faster and faster, slowing him down. He suddenly understands that if he doesn't rest, he'll faint, so he sits where he stops, on a muddy verge with the rain teeming down.

He should call, ask for help, he thinks vaguely. But who would he call? Antonia or Charlie? Even Misty. He's lost them all. So instead he closes his eyes and he drifts into an oblivion of sorts.

A vibration at his chest eventually rouses him: the mobile in his inside pocket. He'd forgotten it was there. His fingertips white with cold, he squints at the bright screen full of received messages.

But only one counts, *Antonia (3)*

He takes a deep breath, blows life into his hands and reads.

Everything OK? Dropping Rupert at the hospital. Sounds like Charlie's stable, so that's good.

Assume you're busy at work. Going to Sophie's now. I'm very late. Wish me luck!

Love you xxx PS Can we have a long talk later?

David puts his hands to his face, then shakes his head, looks to the murky sky and smiles. *Love you xxx*, the message says.

The grin pulls at the bruises on his face, but he doesn't mind, not a bit. He needs to get home. There's a garden nursery not far ahead. If he increases his pace, he can get there before it closes and buy a plant or a shrub or, if he's blessed, the biggest bouquet of cut flowers they sell.

He stands up, breathes deeply and walks on.

Lucky, he remembers. They had named his collie dog Lucky.

CHAPTER NINETEEN

The afternoon is fun and Sophie is on form, pulling out snaps from high school, pointing to various faces and reminding Antonia of memories and moments she's all but forgotten.

'Look at this one, Toni. Year Eleven prom. My Big Fat Gypsy Wedding or what! Oh, God, look at Shannon Rocketry's hair. Can you believe those shoes? The chavs always made more of an effort than us.'

'Us? You called me a council estate chav many a time.'

'That was before I decided you were mine, all mine. Anyway, you say you can't remember anything.'

It's true. There are enormous gaps in her memories of those secondary school years. Even when Sophie describes some events in detail, Antonia struggles to remember. Perhaps she was too successful in erasing that time, but it's got to the point where it's embarrassing.

'I remember some stuff,' she replies. 'When we were older and went "upmarket", as you like to put it.'

'From Baa Baa to Panacea! Thank God we did. Pretty boys in the park were all very well but there comes a time when one needs men who can grow stubble. And have enough cash to pay for champagne!'

Antonia smiles and thinks again of David. She'd met him on a Saturday night at Panacea, the place to be seen in Manchester, even then. The DJ had been playing soul and rare groove, the bar buzzing with energy. Beautiful people pouted and posed and there among them, sticking out like a sore thumb, was her future husband. Big, posh and boisterous David, sitting in a booth with other suited men, ordering brandy and champagne, his blue eyes sparkling, his wallet stuffed with notes. Not her usual type at all.

'You are absolutely stunning!' he'd said as she'd walked past to the loos. 'No, no, don't walk away, you'll break my heart. Promise me now that you'll marry me!'

Later they'd had a slow dance but he hadn't tried to kiss her. Instead he'd handed her a business card and she'd thought that was it, relieved, but a little disappointed too.

He'd walked away, then come back. 'By the way, where do you live?'

She was no longer living in the council house, thank God; by then she was sharing a flat in West Didsbury with two girls from work.

'West Didsbury . . .'

David had grinned. 'I might need more clues for tomorrow.'

'Tomorrow?'

'At noon? Not too early?'

A date on a Sunday at noon. That was something new. She couldn't help but smile.

'Is that a yes?'

'Yes.'

That day she does remember.

Anticipating accusations of being 'on another planet', she

turns her attention back to Sophie. 'You've just got a bigger brain than me, Soph. That's why you remember everything.'

'And boobs.'

'Yes, Sophie, you always beat me on the boobs front too.'

Antonia looks at her watch. She's stayed far longer than she intended. 'Look at the time. I must go. David will be home from work soon and I want to make something nice for dinner.'

Sophie doesn't move. 'Defrost something. You must have a hundred "little delicacies" you made earlier.' Her feet are on Antonia's lap and she presses them down. 'Besides, the varnish on my toenails won't be dry yet. You don't want to be responsible for smudges.'

'I haven't seen David all day. He'll want to talk about Charlie. I'm going.'

She lifts Sophie's heels and stands, trying not to let irritation get the better of her. They've had a fun afternoon, but Sophie always has to push it.

Sophie stands too. 'Just a bit longer, Toni. You know you want to.' She places her body next to Antonia's, so close that they're almost touching. Pulling back Antonia's dark hair, she places cheek next to cheek, like a smooch, her breath warm in Antonia's ear.

The irritation spreads, but it's mixed with something else, a dark heat in the pit of her stomach, which Antonia recognises as lust. She's making a pass at me, she thinks. She's manipulating me and teasing me. She'll do anything to get her own way. Yet the desire is still there. She supposes it always will be, her baby Achilles heel. So she remains motionless, impassive and breathless as Sophie places small kisses on her neck from her ear to her shoulder.

Sophie pulls away after a moment, falls back on to the sofa, tugging Antonia down with her. She smiles, her face indolent, smug. 'I take it you're willing to stay. I'm sure that David can live without you just a little while longer.'

Antonia sits back, exhales the breath she's been holding and gazes at Sophie, wondering. Sophie's auburn hair is still magnificent, but she makes no effort any more. She's let herself go, and yet. What is it? Antonia muses inwardly. What is it that makes her so appealing? What is it that I want from her?

As though sensing some uncertainty in Antonia's face, Sophie leans forward, slips her hand under Antonia's jumper and strokes her back with soft fingertips before inching them forward.

'No, Sophie. No.' She gazes solidly at Sophie, seeing the girl in the centre of the photographs, in the centre of everything. It's your vitality, your confidence, your joy of life, she decides, wondering from the flash of surprise in Sophie's eyes whether the words have escaped.

'I really must go now, Soph. I'll collect you for tomorrow's appointment, I promise.' She kisses Sophie on the cheek and scoops up her handbag. 'Phone me if you need me,' she says. 'Love you lots.'

As she indicates right for White Gables, Antonia is surprised to see David's Land Rover in their drive. When she parks up the car next to his, she's even more startled to see the damage to the wall. The events of this morning feel like they happened a week ago. She had such an easy few hours at Sophie's it almost slipped her mind that she dropped David at the hospital in Macclesfield and that he went into work by train. They were in such a muddled rush to get to Charlie that she didn't notice the garden wall or the skewed position of his car.

She crouches down to inspect the damage to the wall. The dislodged bricks seem rather sad and pathetic, the soil around them saturated and spread. But it looks to Antonia as though the wall can be rebuilt fairly easily. She thinks she might try to do it herself, mixing a little cement can't be so hard, surely?

The wall tells the story as she stares. Drinking then driving. He's done it before, only the once. They had angry words. 'You'll kill yourself, David. Even worse, you'll kill someone else. Please don't. Never again.'

'I promise. Scout's honour.' A David smile. 'I'll never do it again, my darling Antonia. Promise.'

It's bad. Drink driving is very bad. David's nose was bloody and swollen. Next time could be so much worse. She'll have to say something, she knows, but it can wait. It doesn't seem important just now. After a disastrous start to the day, everything is fine. Charlie is stable in hospital, Sophie is settled at home and now it's time for David, her David. She glances at her watch and feels a jolt of disappointment. She has so much to say, but adding on the train journey time from Manchester, David won't be home for some time yet.

After leaving Sophie's house in Didsbury, she tried to hurry home in the car, driving as fast as she could within the speed limits. But the traffic lights conspired, each turning red as she approached. Still, it gave her an opportunity to practise the words out loud.

'Last night, David. When I . . .' How to put it? She still feels hot with shame when she thinks of the words she said. 'When I pushed you away.' Hardly the truth. She'd screamed at him, pummelled his head with her fists until she woke properly. Only then did she register it was David. Only then did she catch the look on his face, the crumpled sad face of a boy, before he covered it with trembling hands and cowered away.

'I was dreaming about my father. I thought you were him.' It's the truth, but it sounds so pathetic.

'He beat my mother.' She can say that. She can say those words, but not explain why. How can she ever explain the reason when she doesn't understand it herself?

'He was a racist, my dad. My dad was racist. That's why he beat her.' A racist who lived with her African-Irish mother for twenty-five years. It didn't make sense. She'd seen the photographs. He loved her then. And despite the beatings, they sometimes laughed, her mum and dad.

Far simpler to say, 'My father was a despicable drunk.' That covers everything.

She stands up and brushes the damp soil from her jeans. Dinner first, she has to focus. Her American-sized fridge is full as it always is. It's just a question of what will go with what. *Ready Steady Cook.* And sweet Rupert. What an age ago that was. She puts her key in the latch and pushes the door open, careful not to put her dirty hands on the clean paint. She smells the flowers before she sees them. A huge bouquet. Simple, stunning scented flowers, just the way she likes them. 'David!' she calls with the hugest of smiles. 'I'm home.'

'A failure, I said. And that isn't true. I was hard on David. Too hard,' Charlie sighs from his hospital bed.

Charlie has been sleeping on and off all day. He feels ill. For the first time since the whole diabetes debacle started he really feels ill, which is a good thing. He has no desire to pretend, to bustle about as though everything is fine and dandy. It's a relief, if he's honest, a relief to let go. He supposes this is how God designed illness, as a prelude to death. Not that he thinks he's dying, particularly, but he can see the very ill might welcome the alleviation.

'Mum says David's like a kid who never grew up. Peter Pan, she says. You took me once to see the play and I was scared of

Hook. And the hungry crocodile. Tick, tock! Do you remember?' Rupert asks.

'Did I really? That was jolly sporting of me.' Charlie frowns for a moment. 'Palace Theatre on Oxford Street. You were seven. Peter Pan looked like a girl.'

'I think it was a girl, Dad.'

Charlie closes his eyes. He was hard on David, definitely too hard.

He opens his eyes again. A thought has just occurred to him. Rupert must have been sitting in that chair for hours. 'Are you hungry, son?' he asks.

'Starving, Dad.'

'Did Mum leave any money? Do you have any?'

Rupert shakes his head.

'Then we must call the nurse!'

Rupert looks at the consternation on his father's face and laughs. He laughs so hard that it's infectious and Charlie starts laughing too.

Antonia is still 'in her head', as Sophie would say, as she pulls off her boots and massages her tired feet. How can you know someone when you don't really know yourself? she's thinking. She heard an unmistakable note of surprise in Helen's voice this morning on the telephone. As Rupert watched wide-eyed, she wanted to laugh at her own audacity and to say, 'You may be surprised, Helen, but not half as much as I am.'

She admires the flowers on the hall table and beams. It feels good to be someone who can make a difference, she thinks, however small that difference might be.

Running up the stairs two by two, she's careful not to slip on the limestone steps. Still smiling, she approaches the bathroom and knocks. Silly really, but knocking at any closed door is a habit from childhood. 'Don't you know how to fucking knock?' That was the first time she witnessed it. Her mother on her knees, cowering. Her father's open palm. She must have been nine or ten, older perhaps. Her mother had hidden it from her before then, had made excuses. 'I'm just clumsy, love. You know me, I'd walk into anything.'

The smile falling, she touches her arm as she waits for a moment, feels the scab, feels the irony. But that's completely different, she thinks. I hurt no one but myself.

'Only me!' she calls as she opens the bathroom door. Condensation has filled the room like smoke. The window and tiles are dripping in gleaming pearls, the floor is slippery, sodden.

'What happened to the extractor fan? Has it broken?' she asks. She knows it's odd. She knows David's stillness is strange. Yet she opens the windows and continues to talk, her back turned from the inevitable. 'What a day. Had a good soak? I'll get some towels. I bet you're hungry. I've got so much to tell you, love.'

PART TWO

CHAPTER TWENTY

It takes a few minutes to call, to steady her thrashing heart, to quell the urgent need to vomit. She's been here before. Seeing blood, pooling blood, her child's hands shaking uncontrollably as she phones the police.

'Ambulance, please. It's David, my husband . . .'

Paramedics and police arrive within minutes. Far more people than she expects, bringing in mud on their boots. And so impersonal, moving around her house and talking in low voices as though she isn't there.

'I'm sorry, Mrs Stafford. There's nothing we can do for your husband. He's been dead for some time. Is there someone you can call?'

Antonia longs to call Charlie, of course she does, he's the closest thing she has to a father, but he and his calm steady presence are not available. So she calls Olivia, although goodness knows why as she hardly knows her really. She realises there'll be trouble with Sophie once she finds out, but she can't face how Sophie will somehow make this all about her. 'This' being about David, her husband, who is dead.

They arrive soon after, Olivia and Mike, their faces pale and severe. She watches them park their car beside David's, leaving room for the ambulance and the remaining police vehicle with its lights still strobing into the silent night.

Olivia simply holds her at the open door. She puts her arms around her and grips tightly until the uncontrollable shivering calms down.

'You're still soaking wet,' Olivia says eventually. 'Let me find you some dry clothes – and a brandy.'

Wet? Yes, she's wet. She'd forgotten that. She looks down to her chest, expecting to see blood, but it's water, just water. She's wet from trying to pull him up. 'David? Please, David. Open your eyes.' But he was too limp and too heavy. A dead weight. Really dead?

Olivia dresses her like a doll in the lounge, then leads her to sit down. 'It's cold in here. I'll fetch Mike to make up the fire and I'll find you a brandy.' Then Mike comes in, sitting next to her on the sofa, opening his arms and just holding and holding, propping her up, saying nothing but preventing her body from dissolving. No digging, no questions, no probing, for which she's so grateful.

And then the police, a woman and a man, crouching down to meet her eyes. 'We know this is a difficult time, Mrs Stafford, but there are questions we have to ask. Do you understand?'

Questions, so many questions, one after another when she can barely breathe. Name, age, length of marriage, family. Work. Car. Today, yesterday. Illness. Broken wall. Broken nose. Texts. Charlie. And then more. The woman with such stony eyes: 'Antonia? Are you listening? Did David have anything on his mind? The telephone was on the bedroom floor and the casing was badly cracked as though it had been thrown violently. Was that David or you? Do you know who he might have been on

160

the phone to? Was anything worrying him? Did he say anything unusual or behave differently recently?' Just a breath and then more. 'Antonia? Are you still with me? Why were the contents of the bathroom cabinet scattered on the floor? Was David searching for something?' And even as Antonia was trying to work out the puzzle. 'Is this your diaphragm, Antonia? It was on the floor too, with the box. Did the electric shaver belong to him? Why would he have a razor blade?'

Mike's brewing up again, for Antonia, for Olivia, for the uniformed faces, coming and going through the open front door. He feels winded and helpless. He can't imagine how Antonia must be feeling.

The draught prickles his skin as Olivia comes through the kitchen door, closing it quietly behind her. 'Mike, I don't feel terribly well,' she says in a low voice. 'And I don't suppose we can expect Lydia to sit with the girls all night. I feel really bad about it, but . . .'

He studies Olivia's face; they've been glancing at each other all evening in silent communication saying 'shocking, tragic, unbelievable', but he hasn't been looking at her as such. She's paler than usual and there are violet smudges beneath her eyes.

'Sorry, love, you're right. This is just bloody terrible, isn't it? But it's hard to know what to do. We can't leave her alone. I don't think she has any relatives. What about Sophie? Should we call her?'

'God, no! If she's not here now, my guess is that Antonia doesn't want her.' Olivia looks around the kitchen for a moment. 'It seems huge without David in it. Busy with the drinks. Larger than life . . . You could stay, Mike. Would you mind?'

Mike ruffles his hair. He's surprised that Sophie isn't here, he's amazed at Olivia's vehement response to his suggestion that they call her and he's utterly astonished that David, of all people, has killed himself. He feels a sense of guilt. He'd always assumed David didn't have a care in the world. All things to all men, with a smile on his face, taking life in his large stride. A successful career, a huge house and a beautiful young wife.

A lucky man, he thinks. I thought David was a lucky man.

'Of course I don't mind. David was a mate.' Is that the right word? he wonders. A Friday night regular, dinner host, easy company and generous. The only person to call him Mikey. But it seems Mike hardly knew him at all. 'Of course I'll stay. It's the least I can do. You go home, love. I'll see you later.'

'Will you come to the clinic?' Sophie asks from the depths of the pillow.

It's late but Sami's still awake, his hands behind his head, staring into the dark. He isn't ready to close his eyes and anyway there's no point, sleep is so far away, dismissed by the tight ache in his chest. He's trying to work out whether it's his heart or just his pride that's dented. 'You have no heart,' Sophie once said to him, but that isn't true – he can be just as emotional as the next man if he lets himself. But he doesn't want to be emotional, that's the point, that's why he's so bloody frustrated.

Sami likes to be in charge, he knows it and everyone else does, too. 'You're a bloody control freak, you know that, don't you?' The criticism has been hurled at him too many times to remember. It always rankles, especially with his mum and his sisters when they know how he suffered as a kid, but he saw the humorous side with Mike in the Boot Room days. 'Ground control to Captain Sami' when he was pushing things too far. 'Sami Richards and his famous controlling power strikes again' when he notched up yet another conquest.

'Women like to be told,' Sami would inform an incredulous Mike and Pete.

'Don't tell Olivia. She'd cut off your balls,' Mike would reply with a grin.

They all laughed, but Sami's success rate with women was legendary. 'It works, I tell you. Be assertive and they go weak at the knees every time.'

'Bet your new shiny flat in town doesn't hurt,' Pete would retort.

'Nor this bloody beautiful face,' Sami would laugh, pointing to himself.

He turns his head towards Sophie on the pillow. 'I thought Antonia was going with you. It's only blood and urine, isn't it?'

He doesn't want to think about Antonia. He texted and called her mobile several times to clear the air, but she didn't pick up. So he resorted to leaving a message on her home answerphone this morning. 'It's Sami. Look, I'm sorry. Can we talk? I'll come over to yours.'

Sophie grunts. He assumes that's a 'yes' and turns back to his contemplation of old conquests. The sting of rejection is still there, but it helps to dwell on the bedpost notches. Maybe the dent is just in his pride . . .

'I'm off now,' they would say in the morning. Shelina, Joanna, Hilary, whoever. Their club clothes crumpled, their cheeks flushed with hope.

'Yeah. See ya.'

'Last night was really nice, Sami. I had fun.'

'Me, too.'

'Have a good day.'

'Yeah. You, too.'

'Oh, I'll just jot down my mobile number.'

'Yeah. Great. See ya.'

And that was that. Except once or twice when the offer of coffee at his place at the end of the evening was declined. That would be the start of a compulsive mission to hunt them, to catch them and to wear them down with telephone calls and flattery until they finally succumbed. He always succeeded. Almost always.

Antonia is huddled on the floor in front of the sofa with her arms around her knees when Mike comes back into the lounge, so he sits down next to her. He places the tray in front of them, lifts the teapot lid, stirs and then pours the strong tea into the cups. He wants to say that he feels like a fraud. Olivia suggested the teapot, the tray and the sugar before she left. He wants to say something light-hearted like, 'I've become my granny. I'll be wearing a cardigan next,' because that's what is usually expected of him in this house, a quip, some harmless wit. He wants to say, 'I'm so dreadfully sorry. I feel guilty, somehow. I should have known. I should have noticed. I should have helped.' Instead he says, 'I didn't think about sugar earlier, but I brought the sugar bowl in case.'

Antonia turns her gaze from the fire. 'David took sugar,' she replies with a small smile.

Mike nods, stuck for words, fighting the impulse to find a soft joke to smooth the edges of the silence. But he knows how unique grief can be. Some people want to talk about it and some people find it easier to withdraw. He withdrew after the miscarriage; it suited him, but looking back he realises it was selfish. It wasn't just his grief, he should have shared. He has no idea which camp Antonia falls into and he knows her hardly at all, but he senses a solitariness about her and wishes he could help.

She's still looking at him, her eyes not quite focusing. There's a rigidity about her, but she seems calm, she hasn't yet shed a tear.

'The razor blade was mine, you know,' she says quietly.

Mike nods, not sure if he's heard properly and, if he has, what point she's making. He vaguely understands that some women shave and that some women wax, armpits, legs and other places. He shifts slightly, wishing Olivia had stayed, wondering where the conversation is going.

She looks back at the open fire and the reflection of the flames dances on her solemn face. 'He must have found it in the bathroom cabinet,' she says slowly, as though speaking to herself. 'It was hidden with an old diaphragm I just kept for the box. He'd had a vasectomy, why would he look in there?' She gazes at Mike again. Her expression is blank, but her eyes seem huge. 'He didn't leave a note. I wonder what he was thinking. I wonder what went through his head.'

Oh fuck. I should say something. I really should, Mike thinks. He rakes a hand through his hair, squints at the fire and takes a breath. He begins to form meaningless words, but she stands up and removes her towelling robe before sitting down next to him again. She's wearing a vest top, her honey arms are bare, except for a gold watch and a plaster, a plaster he doesn't notice at first but which she peels away with care.

'You're the first person I've told. Ever.' Then she starts to cry.

CHAPTER TWENTY-ONE

'What's wrong, Mum?' Rachel asks. She's been standing in the doorway of the kitchen for several minutes watching her mother who is just sitting at the wooden table, a small paring knife in her hand, staring into space. 'Is Dad still in bed?'

'Nothing, love,' Olivia says. Then, realising she's replied on autopilot, she corrects herself, feeling guilty at having momentarily forgotten about the terrible tragedy of last night. 'Actually, something awful has happened, Rach. Come and sit down.'

Rachel's face blanches and she sits down slowly, her eyes fixed on her mother's.

'Oh, it's nothing to do with us, love,' Olivia says hurriedly, reminding herself that her eldest child is nearly thirteen, a bright girl who notices everything.

'Dad and I got a call when you were in bed last night. David Stafford has died. Poor Antonia found him. Dad stayed over to help out, which is why he's still asleep.'

'Oh Mum, that's so sad . . . What, what happened?'

Olivia touches Rachel's face and fixes a strand of dark hair behind her ear. 'I'm afraid he killed himself, love.'

'Grandma says that's a mortal sin.'

'Grandma says lots of things, Rach. I don't know what Dad thinks, but no one has a right to judge. Life isn't that simple. There are always reasons why people do what they do.'

Rachel nods. 'I know, Mum, but still . . . He's left Antonia all alone in that great big house. She must be so sad. It's her I feel sorry for.'

'Me, too. And such a terrible shock.'

Olivia stands and turns back to the work surface. She knows Rachel wants to ask more questions about David, but she can't talk just now. She's been preparing the school lunch boxes as usual but today the smell of the cheddar cheese makes her feel sick. Now that she thinks about it, she hasn't been feeling a hundred per cent for several weeks. The strange taste in her mouth, the inability to enjoy a cup of tea, the sharp reaction to certain odours. Looking drained. Tiredness too. They've all crept upon her unawares because she's always so bloody busy, because it isn't what she was expecting.

Sami wakes early to find Sophie's green eyes open and staring at him.

'Bloody hell, Soph, you gave me a fright. You're not usually awake this early.'

'How do you know? You're not either.'

Sophie's been awake for at least an hour, which is unusual, she admits to herself, but she has an excuse. It's the fertility clinic today, her stomach's in nervous turmoil and she wants to be sick. But she won't puke, she never does, which is a shame when she has at least a stone in weight to lose.

She continues to gaze at Sami's face. He'll be thirty-eight soon, but he looks exactly the same as the day they met. Black skin wears well, she thinks. Like Martha, like all his bloody sisters. But they don't have Sami's razor-sharp cheekbones, their faces are plump, their bodies are plump, thank God.

Eight years on and her need for him is as intense as ever. She tries not to show it, but at times it's difficult. Like now. She knows he was awake into the early hours, restlessly kicking the covers, an occasional sigh escaping him. Something's bothering him. She doesn't want or need to know what it is, she just wants it to pass without incident, without him looking at her and 'seeing you for what you are'. Her mother's words. So hurtful, so hateful and yet so true.

She first spoke to him at Tiger Tiger one Friday, at nearly closing time. She'd clocked him earlier in the evening, dancing with his mate Mo, and she pointed him out to Antonia. 'My God, that man is beautiful. Look at his face. Look how he moves. He's mine, OK? Mine!' she said. Then later, she'd just come out of the ladies' and he was there, near the bar where she'd left Antonia, all teeth and charm. By the time she made her way over to them, he was asking Antonia, or rather telling her, to go to his pad for coffee, there and then. 'Come on, woman, it's only around the corner. You know you want to. We would make such beautiful babies.'

She stretches out in the too-warm bed and sighs. 'We would make such beautiful babies.' She's thought about those words so often, too often. It was only a cheap chat-up line, she knows, but still, they hurt, really hurt.

Sami's eyes are closed again, but his breathing is shallow and she knows he's not asleep.

'Sami, don't forget my appointment at the clinic. It's at three.'

'What, me *and* Antonia? Isn't that overkill? You really don't need us both.'

His eyes flick open and Sophie catches the frown. 'Have you fallen out with her or something?' he asks.

168

'No. She was just acting a bit strangely yesterday and I'd really like you to come. Pretty please, Sami?'

The frown clears and he grins. Sophie is inching her soft hand up the inside of his thigh, higher and higher, her touch firm but yielding, just as he likes. 'So you want me to come, do you?' he asks, pulling her towards him.

Mike yawns and tries to focus on the room, on the work piled high on his office desk.

'You haven't been listening to a word I've said, have you?' a voice interrupts.

He looks up at Judith's round face. She's actually frowning, which is probably a first. 'Because I'm not having you call me every five minutes when I've got a baby to look after, Mike. One baby will be enough, thank you! Sue and Jane are covering for me, but no one will be as super-efficient and as wonderful as I am. Got that?'

'Got it.'

'Then listen!'

Mike nods, dutifully looks at Judith and pretends to listen. He thinks of explaining why he's late, telling her the shocking news about David. He tells her most things. She's a good listener and they share the same sense of humour. But effectively gossiping about a friend's suicide feels wrong.

He tries to keep his eyes focused on Judith's face, but his mind drifts back to Antonia. It was all so surreal that a fraction of him wants to share the events of the previous evening with someone just for a reality check. But then again, there are visual memories stored in his mind that he won't confess to another living soul. Not that he's done anything wrong. He most definitely hasn't.

As Mike silently looked on last night, Antonia peeled off the

169

plaster carefully and slowly, nipping her bottom lip with her even white teeth, her face entirely focused on the task. He wasn't sure what he expected to see, but it was simply a cut starting to heal. She gazed at him for a moment, her eyes large and luminous. 'You're the first person I've told. Ever,' she whispered. Then she dropped her head and tears spilled from her eyes, running down to the end of her nose where they gathered before dripping down on to her glossy chest. And it was all so fucking erotic that for a moment he couldn't move. But then he rallied.

'Tissues,' he said. 'Where do I find tissues?' By the time he returned to the lounge with a toilet roll, Antonia had put her robe back on and was sitting on the sofa, her legs curled up beneath her.

'I'm sorry,' she said, blowing her nose. 'You must think I'm nuts. I probably am.'

Good God, I've lived such a closeted life, was all he could think as the penny dropped that she'd cut herself, but then she smiled, letting him off the hook of a reply.

'Talk to me,' she said, closing her eyes. 'About anything. You have such a lovely soft accent. I don't want to talk or to think. It's nice just to listen.'

She fell asleep, eventually. He covered her in a blanket, added logs to the fire, then just watched and waited in the armchair opposite, not knowing what he was supposed to do. The doorbell awoke him eventually. He opened the front door and a gentle-faced, middle-aged family liaison officer was waiting patiently on the top step. 'Don't worry. You go home, I'll be here when she wakes,' she said and wafted him away.

Life goes on, Olivia thinks, pushing the trolley up and down the aisles of the huge supermarket. It's a different Tesco from the one she usually shops at, but looks identical inside.

A Tesco is a Tesco, she muses. Whatever is happening to the world outside, tragedy, anxiety, guilt and death, Tesco still heaves with shoppers, everyone oblivious to everyone else.

Mike arrived home by taxi at some point during the night without waking her. When the dawn chorus alerted her to morning, she gazed at his sleeping face for a while before slipping out of the bed. His dark hair was curling slightly and stubble shadowed his chin.

He'd had long hair when they met at university, so dark and handsome. 'Irish exotic,' she described him to her sister, thrilled to be the sole object of his affections.

'Daddy looks like a pirate!' the girls laughed when they saw an old photograph and they were right. Serious, dark looks which masked the sunny, funny person inside.

She gently kissed his cheek and sighed, remembering those long and terrible weeks when she'd convinced herself that she'd lost that sunny, funny person. Waking him gently at ten, they hugged in silence for a long time. 'How did it go?' she eventually asked. 'Was it awful?'

'No, it was fine. Antonia fell asleep and the next thing I knew was the arrival of a female police officer. I suppose she's still in shock. It really is so dreadful. Thank God we have each other, Olivia.'

She thinks of his words as she shakes herself back to the present. While he slept she'd called his office at nine to let them know he'd be late. Judith had come on to the line and she was as lovely as ever, friendly, interested, funny, talking about her maternity leave which starts in two weeks, so excited about becoming a mum.

The forgiven but not forgotten exchanges between her and Mike pierce Olivia yet again. The thought of him and Judith having an affair now seems so preposterous. Oh God, what had she become? What had she been thinking?

She tries to concentrate on the task of her shopping. She doesn't have a shopping list, which isn't a good idea when she's so distracted. But the one thing she has to buy is already in the trolley, waiting furtively beneath the *Guardian*. She tries to put that thought to one side as she gazes at the green leafy veg. Fruit isn't a problem, but how to sneak in just *one* veg a day with a fussy five-year-old child feels beyond her.

As she anticipates, the toilets are behind the cafe, but there's a queue. One of the three cubicles is out of order. She vaguely wonders if the other women suspect as she waits. Can they tell by the way she holds her handbag tightly under her arm? Or by the loud thrashing of her heart?

Perhaps I've got it wrong, she thinks as she pees on the pregnancy testing stick. Perhaps I've just wasted a fiver.

She stays in the cubicle far, far too long. 'Are you all right in there, love?' someone eventually asks, tapping at the door.

Olivia dabs the tears at the corners of her eyes with toilet roll and takes a deep shaky breath. It's shock, she thinks, that's all. Just shock. She'll get her head round it. Everything will be fine.

CHAPTER TWENTY-TWO

The chilled bottle of wine and the empty crystal glass are sitting on the coffee table, staring at Sophie. They've been there for a good ten minutes, untouched.

A debate is raging in her head as she studies the dribbles of condensation pooling on the shoulders of the bottle. To drink or not to drink; to call Antonia or to call Sami; to cancel or not to cancel the clinic appointment. Those are the questions.

The answer is usually straightforward, but Sami has put a spanner in the works. Ready for work that morning, he was at the door when he spoke, a parting shot as usual. 'She asked me to visit her, you know,' he said, looking at his nails. He was wearing a new shirt and tie, lilac and matching, Sophie noticed. He glanced up and caught her eye. 'Antonia, that is. She phoned me at work and asked me to pop over.'

'Really? When?' She said it casually, with a shrug, but her insides were burning.

'I don't know, a week, maybe two weeks ago.'

'What for?' Her voice was a little too shrill.

'She wanted to talk about you, of course. She said she was

173

concerned. Thought that I was putting you under too much pressure to have a baby.'

'Why didn't you tell me before?' Sophie asked, quietly, afraid of the answer. She felt winded, dizzy, shocked. What the fuck was going on?

Sami shrugged. His hand was on the door handle. 'I wasn't going to mention it, but you said she'd been acting strangely, so that might explain it . . .' He hitched up his double cuff and looked at his watch. 'Look, I'll be late. I'll come with you to the clinic this afternoon if you want me to. Give me a ring later, yeah?'

Now she shifts in the armchair and sighs. She's thought of nothing else since. What the hell is Antonia playing at? It's so unlike her to interfere. She doesn't have the confidence, the intelligence, the courage, surely? But only yesterday, she walked away from Sophie's caress, the first time ever. She was tempted, Sophie knew, and still she left.

She looks down at the pile of soft carpet pushing between her toes. Pulling the rug from under her feet. Shock, alarm, uncertainty, fear. That's exactly how it feels. She rubs her eyes and tries to focus. Antonia keeps secrets, she's good at keeping secrets. Surely to God that hasn't changed?

To make herself busy, she grapples with a clean duvet cover, whips the towels off the banister, scrubs grime from the shower and it helps. Her feverish mind eventually slows. She's still livid with Antonia and will be giving her a mouthful when she's worked it all out. But whatever has gone on, Antonia hasn't told Sami about the infection, the fucking pelvic inflammatory infection she hates to think about. That much is obvious. What bothers her more now she's calmed down is why Sami mentioned his visit today. Sami, her match, the one man who can give as good as he gets. He never does anything without

174

thinking it through. He has a master plan for life, never mind each day. A typical Sagittarius, she believes, shooting his arrows out high, galloping after them with determination until he gets what he wants.

'We'd make such beautiful babies.' The thought clenches at her heart. Sitting down on the loo seat, she lowers her head to her arms and starts to cry.

The Tesco bags are in the red hallway, eggs on top, ready to be emptied. This can't be happening, Olivia thinks with a sigh. I have no energy to do it. Already. I have no bloody energy.

She looks at her watch. It's nearly time to collect Hannah from school. She stops for a moment, deciding to bring down the toy till from Hannah's bedroom and let her beep the barcodes on the shopping when she gets home. It's Hannah's favourite game, but one which goes on too long and rarely without incident. The ice cream melted the last time and the yoghurt pots dropped, splat, on to the kitchen floor. Olivia was cross, but that's no surprise. She's painfully aware she's always bloody cross these days.

'Shit, shit, shit.' Putting her head in her hands, she wants to scream. The shock has worn off and reality has hit her. Just as life had got back on an even keel, here she is, bloody pregnant again with no prospect of being a person, rather than just a mum, for another decade. She's an awful mother as it is, she spends most of her life shouting. That person is horrible; she doesn't want to be her any more.

'No one said it would be easy,' her mother opined when Hannah was a baby. 'Some say it's the hardest job in the world.'

'Rachel was easy!' Olivia wanted to retort, but it seemed too disloyal to say the words out loud. It had taken years for her to conceive again after Rachel was born. She wanted the new baby so very badly, but Hannah didn't sleep. She was a loud, demanding, clingy baby and moved on to being a loud, demanding and clingy toddler. She never allowed Olivia out of her sight, even at birthday parties or at playgroup. It got to the point where Olivia had no choice but to give up the job she loved.

'You're such a talent, Olivia. Bright, witty, opinionated and highly valued. Why on earth would you throw it all away?' the editor had asked when she told him she was giving up the newspaper permanently.

'I have an albatross around my neck,' she almost replied wearily. Yet she felt guilty too; she loved Hannah dearly. She just needed space, time away from her demanding personality, which ironically she'd no longer have.

'I never knew something so small could be so much trouble,' she once said to Mike, but he just smiled lovingly at the little angel who slept in his arms. 'But she's worth it,' he said, the inevitable reply.

That's the trouble with Mike, Olivia now sighs to herself. He's a great dad, he loves his daughters and he plays with them endlessly when he's at home, but he gets the good bits, at the beginning and at the end of the day when they're docile and sleepy. Then weekends are different, there's no time limits or supermarkets or lunch boxes. What he sees then isn't a true reflection of the grind of daily life as a stay-at-home mum.

She picks up the *Guardian* and hurls it on to the kitchen table. 'I was important once,' she declares. 'I was respected, I was valued. My opinions counted. For God's sake, just look at me now.'

Mike knows he won't be able to knuckle down to work until he's spoken to Antonia, to check that she's OK. 'I don't want

176

to talk,' she said last night. But there are things to be done, surely? Perhaps she's spoken to the police, perhaps they're making calls on her behalf and are sorting things out. Nobody close to him has died, so he doesn't know how these things work, but he doubts it. As far as he's aware she doesn't have a family. There's Sophie, who's very close. He needs to tell her, or to tell Sami at least. But Olivia was insistent about not telling Sophie, and Olivia is generally right.

He doesn't like to think about his blarney to Antonia last night. He rarely speaks for so long, at least not unless it involves sport, football preferably. He talked a lot about his sister Harriet and how she died unexpectedly after a routine operation to fix a squint when she was fourteen. She just never woke from the anaesthetic. That's when the black dog first arrived at his heels. 'Her little heart gave up. A blessing really. Down's isn't easy,' people said. He heard those words so many times as a boy that he wanted to scream and shout, 'Fuck your fucking blessings! A blessing for who?' But his mother always nodded at the platitudes and it's only as an adult and a father he realises that perhaps it was a blessing for her.

He glimpses his face in the mirror as he washes his hands. Not very tactful, Michael. She needed cheering up and you talked about death. But perhaps there was an exaggerated tale or two which brought a small smile to her lips. 'God, Michael, you know how to tell them,' he says to the mirror before going back to his office. At another time and in another life, it would be a funny story to tell. That the first woman who listened to the story of his life fell asleep.

Sami is back in the office. He stretched out the site inspection for as long he could, charming the client and offering to buy him a Friday pub lunch. It's best to keep busy, he knows, when he has something on his mind. He's trying hard not to think of the dent in his heart-pride, but it's like a dent in his car, it niggles and gripes until it's tapped out and spray-painted, good as new.

'Dent Master,' he doodles on the pad.

If only it was that easy, he thinks.

There's a knock on the door and one of the trainees glides in without waiting for a reply. 'That report you asked for, Mr Richards,' she says coyly in a high-pitched Home Counties voice.

He usually grins, enjoying the tease and says, 'It's Sami to you, Jemima.' But today he just thanks her and goes back to his doodle. He knows she's an attractive girl and not afraid to show her attentiveness, but he can't summon up any interest just now.

He glances at his watch and wonders if Sophie will call about the clinic appointment. He didn't tell her the full story of his heated discussion with Antonia at White Gables. The truth was that he told Antonia it was none of her fucking business if Sophie drank too much, that she should look at her own marriage and stop interfering with his. She didn't push it then, but dropped her head and withdrew into herself, as she so often does. It still makes him feel like a shit. He dislikes himself for it intensely.

Sami rubs his head and groans. He doesn't want to think about Sophie's drinking. He likes control, there's no doubt. He likes to be assertive too. But he hates confrontation. Confrontation never ends well, especially with Sophie.

'I think you should cut down on the wine,' he'll say to Sophie when he's particularly exasperated with her louche behaviour.

'Why? I only drink it when you do.'

'That isn't true. You drink in the day when I'm not here.'

'Just a glass before you get home.'

'Several glasses, Sophie.'

'So, you spy on me do you, Sami? How terribly charming of you.'

He prefers it when she shouts back, it finishes sooner. Then of course when they're out, he's stymied by etiquette. As his mum taught him well, 'It doesn't do to wash your dirty linen in public.' So in company Sophie can drink steadily all night, downing two glasses of wine to everyone else's single glass. He's aware of her eyes on the bottle at the start of the night. She waits politely for someone to pour it for her when her glass is empty at first, but by mid-evening she doesn't care, she'll pour it herself, calling for the waiter to bring another bottle. Then at the end of the meal she'll buy cigarettes, even though she gave up years ago. She'll stagger outside and flirt with somebody, anybody, her guttural laugh wafting in to pound Sami's ears.

His private line rings. He snatches it quickly, stupid hope still tingling the end of his fingertips, but it's only Mike.

'Sorry to bother you at work, mate. I'm not sure how to put this,' Mike starts.

Sami listens, stunned. 'Bloody hell, Mike, that's terrible. My God . . . I don't know what to say . . .' But his mind is already sharp, analytical, working out how this new development will affect their lives.

Hannah skips home ahead of Olivia along the tree-lined street. A hug at the school gate and then off, happy and carefree. No clinging today. 'Stop when you get to the busy road and wait for me!' Olivia calls.

Another mum walks with Olivia and chats. 'So it's back to bags full of nappies, stains on my shoulders from puke. No sleep, no hair washing. No independence. Struggling with the split demands when you're finally back at work. Oh, and the

179

joy of feeding bras. Not that I ever managed to wear anything remotely sexy in between.'

Olivia stops and looks at the other mum's face. Her voice is smiling and so is she. 'But it's so exciting, isn't it? To create a new person. To guess whether it's a boy or a girl. To see what they look like, to get to know them as they grow.'

'Congratulations, Hazel, that's lovely news,' Olivia says, squeezing her arm.

I don't want another baby, Olivia thinks with sudden certainty as she catches Hannah's hand to cross the busy road. I don't want to be a mum for an additional five years. I need to get a doctor's appointment. Soon, get referred. I need to do whatever needs to be done. Before it's obvious. Before Mike notices.

Antonia sits at the kitchen table and accepts another cup of tea from Ruth, the police liaison officer. She'd replaced Mike in the armchair when Antonia woke up on the sofa, her eyes kind and watchful as she waited for the realisation of what had happened to dawn. The realisation that David was gone. Gone forever.

It had taken a few moments for Antonia to work out that she'd fallen asleep on the sofa. Reading poems as usual, she'd assumed, waiting for David to come home. She'd removed the blanket and sat up, searching for the slim volume, before noticing Ruth, and when the horrific recall of the evening before kicked in, she'd been grateful Ruth was there, calm and steady and kind. It had stopped the merging picture in her mind, the one she knows she'll see far too often. Of David, a white body, the red water, wet clothes, her desperate hands. But now she wants her gone. She doesn't want a stranger in her kitchen, in her cupboards, in her home.

She lifts her head and looks at Ruth. 'I have to go out in a while,' she says. 'Thank you for staying. It's been very good of you, but you can go now.'

'Are you sure? I can stay. Or I can come back later. You'll still be in shock. It takes time and support—'

'Thank you, but no. I have friends, friends who'll be around. In fact that's where I'm going now. A promise I made . . .'

Ruth eventually leaves with a nod, dropping her business card on the hall table and insisting that Antonia calls any time. Antonia picks up her mobile then, clutching it tightly, framing her words to Sophie. But nothing sounds right. She's certain that Sophie will be angry for not being told as soon as she found David's body. Before the ambulance, before the police. She's still not sure why she didn't. So she puts down the phone, deciding it's better in person; she'll wait until she collects her for the fertility clinic this afternoon as planned.

Giving the bathroom a wide berth, she walks through every room, checking for dirty footprints and disarray to fill the time. She'd never noticed it before, but her footsteps echo as she walks down the stairs. A dog would be nice, just for company, she thinks. But of course that would be wrong. David, who is dead, had offered her one, an orphan she could have given a home. But unprepared for his suggestion, she'd responded with a knee-jerk lie, telling him she was allergic. The thought almost makes her cry, but she doesn't, focusing instead on the visit ahead.

Driving the ten miles to Didsbury on autopilot, she's almost glad her anxiety about Sophie, and what to say, blocks out thoughts of David and why he felt the need to do something so extreme. But even before she opens her mouth at Sophie's front door, the reception she's given is shocking.

Sophie can barely stand. 'You can turn your fucking fake arse around and go back to the gutter where you came from.' Then, finger pointing, face sneering. 'Don't bother with that innocent gaze, it doesn't work with me, I know you too well. "Oh Sami, why don't you just pop over to my house without your wife knowing and I'll just flutter my eyelids and remind you of old times? Oh, and perhaps I'll just fuck you while you're here?"'

Sophie teeters, still clasping the door. 'You married that prat David, so we both know you'll fuck anything.'

'You've been drinking,' Antonia replies, stating the obvious. But she feels cold and detached, the harshness of her own voice surprising her. 'You have an appointment at the clinic and you're drunk. You're a disgrace. You don't deserve to be a mother.'

Sophie laughs, spittle flying from her mouth. 'Well, as it happens, I agree. I'm not going to the fucking hospital and I don't want to see your holy fucking face ever again.'

Sophie wakes at the sound of the front door but struggles to peel back her eyelids. She can hear Sami's voice. She can smell that bloody aftershave.

'Sophie, wake up.'

She eventually opens her eyes. It's dark beyond the open curtains. The television is shrill in the background. Oh, yes, she remembers. She drank all afternoon, all evening. The chilled Chablis won.

'What time is it?' she asks, closing her eyes and turning away from the harsh beam of the lamp.

Sami turns off the television. 'Nine o'clock or so. Wake up, I need to talk to you. Sophie? Are you listening? It's important. Mike called me earlier and it's bad, really bad. David committed suicide last night. He slit his wrists in the bath . . . Mike thought we should know.'

She doesn't move for a moment, but then his words sink in.

182

David's killed himself? Last night? Sami knew about it fucking 'earlier'.

'My God, Sami. Why the fuck didn't you tell me before now?' she says, sitting up and vividly recalling Antonia's earlier visit and the angry words they exchanged. She hadn't known that David was dead. Antonia didn't tell her. More to the point, she didn't give Antonia the chance.

Sami holds out his palms in a conciliatory gesture. 'I couldn't get away from work and I'm telling you now.' He sighs. 'Look, I thought it would be better to tell you in person, Soph.'

'So I'd be the last fucking person to know. You bastard!'

She scurries to her feet, grabs a crystal whisky glass from the sideboard and hurls it at Sami's head where it shatters on impact, leaving a small cut on his forehead which immediately pulses with blood.

Sami stands for a moment, his face frozen with shock, then he puts his fingers to his forehead before bringing them down to his eyes and bolting to the bathroom.

'Poor precious Sami and his beautiful face,' Sophie yells up the stairs.

She picks up her discarded wine glass lying on the floor, thumps back on the sofa and sloshes in more wine, but after a few moments, regret seeps in through the fog. She wants to hear more about David's suicide. She needs some detail to feed her sedated sluggish mind so she can absorb what he's said. David can't possibly be dead, can he? Not David, of all people. Antonia was here earlier, they argued. It's ludicrous, a joke, surely? She hears Sami's footfall on the stairs and lifts her head as he appears. His jaw is clenched, a pale plaster looks stark and accusing on his dark skin. She takes a breath to speak, but he shakes his head silently. Then he opens the front door and walks out.

CHAPTER TWENTY-THREE

It's a cold Saturday morning in early October, but the Turners' lofty old home is warm, busy and bright. Olivia and Mike are smiling and chatty, appreciative of each other, helpful. But in the silences, there are unspoken words, Mike naturally assuming hers are the same as his. 'What a terrible thing to happen. Thank God it wasn't us. Thank God for all this.'

'Are you sure you don't want to come with us?' Mike asks a second time.

'Sure, love. I've really got so much catching up to do. Send my love to Margaret and Liam.'

Mike contemplates Olivia as he drives in the balmy lull of the car towards Chester. It's his monthly visit to see his mum and dad. Hannah is asleep on the back seat, Rachel sits next to him in the front, gazing out of the window. Olivia doesn't always come to the monthly visits, so that's fine, though Mike idly wonders what she'll do all day. He would like them all to be together as a family today. Safely together. When death's been so close, it haunts, makes you appreciate what you have, and realise how lucky you are. But it's frightening too. Life can change in a moment and you might not be looking. And David's death was so lonely, leaving Antonia lonely too.

'Why did he do it, Dad?'

Rachel's small voice interrupts his thoughts. He smiles, squeezes her hand and looks back at the road. Why did David do it? Why did an apparently happy and successful man take his own life? He hasn't asked the question, nor has Olivia, but he's sure it's what everyone is thinking. Especially Antonia. 'I wonder what he was thinking. I wonder what went through his head,' she whispered that night. He can still picture her face, her huge perplexed eyes.

Mike clears his throat. 'I really don't know, love. Probably best not to mention it to Grandma.'

Rachel rolls her eyes. 'I'm not stupid, Dad.' Then after a moment, quietly, her blue eyes troubled as she looks at him. 'You wouldn't . . . you wouldn't do that, would you?'

'No, absolutely not, Rach.'

He takes her hand, but she's turned her head and is staring at the yellow countryside through the passenger window. She's wearing her new boots, pressed neatly together in the footwell where the black dog used to sit, the black dog he hasn't seen for days. His happiness seems wrong. Unfair. David is dead. There's nothing more final than death. Unless you believe.

He squeezes again. 'Love you lots, you know, Rach.'

'Dad!' It's said with embarrassment, but he can tell that she's smiling.

Helen says goodbye to Antonia, replaces the telephone receiver carefully and stands in the cold conservatory looking out to the garden for several moments, thinking.

She's shocked to hear the news of David's death, but she isn't surprised. 'Little David' the Proctors always called him, even when he became an adult. He'd been there at the Proctors' the first time she was introduced to her future in-laws, not long after meeting Charlie on a blind date. 'And this is little David,' Charlie's mother Valerie had said, glancing indulgently at a good-looking, exceedingly tall youth. She assumed David was Charlie's gregarious younger brother. She assumed there would be a big David too, but wasn't put right for some considerable time.

Helen had liked the young David well enough, but there were times when he'd got in the way of her budding relationship with Charlie. It wasn't David's fault. Charlie insisted that he came along too, to the theatre, or the cinema, then later to the pub, like an overgrown poodle. She often wondered if the relationship was healthy and at one time it troubled her sufficiently to put her foot down and insist that they left little David out of the loop. Charlie looked hurt. 'He's not as strong as he looks,' he said in a low voice, though no one else was there. 'You know . . . emotionally.' Of course when she quizzed him, Charlie clammed up immediately. An early indicator of his truculence, Helen now muses, twenty-two years later, as she thinks how best to deal with the dreadful news.

A tiny part of her mind dwells for a moment on her last conversation with David at the hospital, but only a tiny part, which she quickly dismisses. People who commit suicide are selfish, she thinks. A final act of spite. They don't hurt themselves, but everyone else around them. They're cowardly, that's the reality. She knows it isn't very politically correct, but that's how she feels and she's not afraid to say it.

'What was that all about, Mum?'

Rupert's voice makes her flinch. He's been in the dining room all morning with his school work spread out on the table. He's had an aura of determination about him since seeing his father in hospital. But here he is in the doorway of the conservatory with a frown on his face.

'That was Antonia. Uncle David has killed himself,' she replies, pushing back her glasses, her voice matter-of-fact. She nods, her mind already made up. 'But we won't tell Dad. Not until he's well enough to come home.'

Rupert sucks in his breath, lowers his head and slaps his hand against his forehead. For a moment Helen wonders if he's crying, but he lifts his head and stares, his eyes blazing from beneath his fringe. 'What are you like? Uncle David is dead and you couldn't give a fuck, could you?' he roars. 'You get things so fucking wrong, Mum. I'm calling Dad now. He needs to know. You can do whatever you want.'

He lifts the phone and they wrestle with it for a moment, before Rupert stands back with folded arms and starts to shout. Helen stares, feeling breathless. Perhaps she shouldn't be surprised at Rupert's rage, after all he is Charlie's flesh and blood, but still she is shocked. Not so much at his use of a whole host of expletives (some of which are surprisingly new to her) but at his truculence. He's usually compliant, in a taciturn way, with her directives. But Rupert argues fiercely that Charlie needs to be told about David's death now.

She almost laughs at the stony set of his face, so very unusually like his father's for once. 'Not found under the gooseberry bush after all,' she mutters as her heart slows. But Rupert brings her back to reality with a 'Gooseberry bush? For fuck's sake, Mum. Don't you ever just listen?'

She sits down and pats the side of the wicker sofa. 'I know you think I'm an old witch,' she says, 'but let's give Dad another night of rest. He'll be devastated, of course, but you know what he's like, he'll want to be up, sorting things out and there's nothing he can do at a weekend anyway.'

Rupert flops down next to her. 'What's to sort out?' he responds, his posture showing defeat. 'Uncle David is dead. I just can't believe it.'

She wants to open her arms and pull him close, but she can't. He's too tall, too old to be hugged. Both of those could be her excuses. But the truth is she's not a demonstrative person. Or emotional. Even though she liked David, she doesn't feel any urge to shed a tear for him and doubts that she will. It's Charlie she worries about. Since their first blind date at the Science Museum cafe, Charlie's the only one who's ever really mattered and she has no idea how he will take this dreadful news.

Sophie's in bed, the duvet over her head. She's woken on and off throughout the morning, but has no intention of getting up ever again. She can smell her own breath. It's rancid and bitter, disgusting. She was actually sick at some point. *Alleluia!* But of course she'll feign memory loss about that. And the rest.

She doesn't want to think about last night when Sami came home. The whisky glass and the cut. She lost it, really lost it. But why didn't he telephone to tell her about David? Why didn't he come home sooner? Other husbands would have. It's his own fucking fault.

The modern bedroom is warm. Sophie is sweating and her head throbs. She turns on to her stomach and spreads out her arms and legs, starfish-like. She can still picture the look of horror on Sami's face when he examined his fingertips and saw the blood. Pathetic really. The cut bled out of all proportion to the injury or to the offence. That's all. But her heart is thrashing loudly. Sami didn't sleep in their bed last night. She has no idea if he slept in the spare bedroom, or downstairs, or whether he came back home at all. She's too afraid to look.

*

'Cry as much as you want, Chinue. It's good to cry. There's no shame in it.'

They were her mother's words when she was young. Candy always said that everyone had a reserve of tears and that once they were done, they were done. Like Baby Annabelle: Antonia's dad bought her the doll and the pram when she was very small, or so he said.

'I bought you that dolly, you know. And clothes to match. From a toy shop in London,' Jimmy said from time to time.

They must have had money then, Antonia muses as she sits in her kitchen and steadies herself for the next telephone call. Or perhaps just money that for once wasn't squandered on booze.

She's been going through the address book and making calls all morning to advise those she supposes need to know that David has died. 'Passed away', she's put it. It has been surprisingly easy. And quick. Astonished and embarrassed, she supposes. Only Helen has asked for further information, asking for specific details, her questions bordering on rude. But this is a more difficult call that has to be made, and she has to do it.

Taking a deep breath, she picks up the telephone, dials the number for The Ridings and asks for Candy. She knows she'll be disappointed with her mum's response even as she waits the five minutes for her to reach the office phone.

'Chinue, is that you?'

'Yes, Mum, it is. I've some terrible news, Mum.' She tries to steady her voice but there's an involuntary quaver. 'David has passed away.'

'Oh, love. I'm so sorry. I'll come straight away.'

The ache in Antonia's chest almost prevents her from speech. 'That would be so lovely, Mum. But don't worry, I'll see you on Sunday as usual.'

A pause and then Candy's voice again. 'All right, love. Was he a friend of Jimmy, this David fella?'

Antonia's tears haven't come. Instead she's consumed by an overwhelming chill of loneliness. Her reflections are jumbled and random, punctuated by poetry. She sits in the lounge reading from *Poem for the Day*, though she's studying them half hourly rather than daily.

She tries to float above the image from the bath, but other thoughts jump in with no pattern. Perhaps I should've called for Sophie when I found him. The razor blade. Oh God, the hidden razor blade. What did he think? Perhaps that's why he did it. Realised about the cutting. Thought it was his fault. Helen was so cold. I shouldn't have interfered by taking Rupert to the hospital. But what a sweet boy. Will she tell Charlie? God, Charlie, poor Charlie. Sophie, so horrible. Never seen her so drunk. But why did he do it? Was it my fault? The cracked telephone on the floor. Who was David calling? I never told him I loved him. I never told him. Never told him.

Trying to push the thoughts away, she stands abruptly, walks to the hall and picks up Ruth's calling card. She seemed to be a nice lady, solid and sympathetic and not too intrusive, but still just a stranger. She seemed satisfied by Antonia's assurance that friends would be around, almost constantly, to see her through the shock and the grief, for some time to come. But the truth is she only has one friend, a friend who spat insults at her face. She shakes her head at the memory, Sophie's face, her shocking words. 'You married that prat David, so we both know you'll fuck anything.'

Going back to the sofa, she wraps the blanket around her legs, but the lonely chill is still there as she turns the page of her book. She's on February 8th, 'One Art'. She's read the poem before and likes it very much, but this time she studies the editor's notes, not surprised to discover the poet was an alcoholic and her mother was confined to a mental hospital. What a small world it is.

'Call any time you need us,' Mike Turner texted earlier today. She lifts up her mobile and scrolls through her list of contacts. Finds his number, and Olivia's too. But she pictures Sophie's face and then shakes her head, knowing she won't do it. Help is like a crutch; once it's there you cling on, never regaining your own balance. Besides, she's never asked for help in all her life. Now isn't the time to start.

Olivia finally sits down. She's been absently tidying and cleaning but hasn't been able to focus on anything else but her pregnancy all morning. 'You don't mind if I skip Chester this time, do you?' she asked Mike earlier. 'I'm sure Margaret and Liam won't mind and I really need to catch up.'

She held her breath as she waited for Mike's reply. He looked thoughtful. 'Course not. But how about a bit of "you time" rather than catching up? You look tired.'

'"You time" eh? Been reading *Cosmopolitan* again?' she laughed, deflecting his comment.

He hugged her then. The type of hug they used to have, which almost became a dance. Oh Mike, I do love you, she thought, though she didn't say it. It wasn't something she said as often as she should and she didn't want to seem odd.

The internet is the obvious source of information. A Google search first: *how to arrange an abortion*. She turns on her laptop. It was once state of the art but now it's huge, heavy and takes an age to get going. Like me this morning, she thinks wryly as she stares at the screen.

It occurs to her that she'll have to carry out another search before the search: *how to delete your search history*. Rachel would know, Hannah too, probably, but she's never had the need to hide anything before now.

She has many questions for Google: *Does your GP have to know? Can you pay privately? How long does it take? Does there have to be a medical reason? Am I the worst woman on earth?* Staring at the ceiling, she sighs. Mike and the girls will be at the in-laws' house in Chester by now. They'll nod to crucified Jesus on the wall and say grace before lunch. She wonders if their god is laughing.

CHAPTER TWENTY-FOUR

Rupert shakes the rain from his head and follows his mother along the stifling hospital corridor. There's a strong smell of disinfectant, mould and urine, not unlike the sports hall's changing rooms and bogs in his school.

His mum turns and looks at him before they enter the ward, the nose twitch hitching up her spectacles the only sign of her anxiety.

'It's David, isn't it?' Charlie says immediately he sees their pale and strained faces.

'Yes, Charles. I'm afraid it is,' Helen replies. She goes on to tell him clearly and concisely what Antonia told her, as Rupert listens and waits and watches near the door. His father pays heed and nods, like he pays heed and nods to his clients, a finger of concentration on his lips. His parents are silent then, before his dad clears his throat and asks Helen about the garden and the house, the news and the weather. It's only much later that Charlie abruptly puts his hand to his mouth. 'Dear God, say it's not true, Helen, say it's not true,' he sobs, and Rupert is so relieved.

Rupert runs to the bed and holds on to his father tightly for a long time. His father's whiskers are white, he notices, and he smells strangely of pear drops.

Helen leaves eventually, saying she has essays to mark for Monday morning. But Rupert stays. He's anxious about his father, who looks so grey. 'I've brought money this time, Dad,' he says, waving his wallet. 'For us both.'

Charlie sleeps intermittently. The hospital staff come and go. They glance at Charlie, examine the monitors, pick up the chart at the end of his bed. Then pull out a bitten Biro from a top pocket and scribble something. Rupert sits and observes, wondering what they're writing. He's too afraid to pick up the chart for a peek, let alone ask. The thought that his father might die was always a vague possibility, like the iCloud facility for his iTunes. There but not defined. But David's death has given it shape and breath and it frightens him enormously.

'They died when he was twelve,' Charlie mutters.

Rupert pulls off his headphones and leans forward. His father has done this all morning. Waking up and recalling snatches of conversation, or moments with David, before nodding off again.

'He was due a weekend leave-out from school, but his parents never arrived. He was the youngest in my study and we teased him about the scarf. We were all a little jealous, I think. His mother was so exotic. Yes, exotic, that's the word. The scarf was red, silk I should imagine, and someone caught him putting it to his face when he went to bed. Smelling it, I suppose.' He pauses for a moment, then starts again with a sluggish voice. 'But they were in Singapore then and he deflected all the ribbing. With humour of course. Even then, the great deflector, never really showing how he felt about anything negative or sad.'

There's a plastic container slowly filling with his father's urine by the side of the bed. Rupert doesn't want to look, but finds it helps to stare at the steady flow of yellow drops as they drizzle down the tube. It stops the tears which stab at his eyes, threatening to explode.

Struggling to clear his throat, his father speaks again. 'When the news came that they'd died, he curled up into a ball on his bed and wouldn't move when they told him to, when they chivvied. You know the sort of thing, "Moping around won't do any good, you're a young man now, not a baby." Then eventually the matron lost patience. She tore the scarf from him and never gave it back. As if that would have made a difference . . .' He stops, his eyes drooping. 'I did what I could. I was nearly eighteen, almost an adult. So, I tried to be there for him. A big brother, I suppose . . .' he finishes, closing his eyes again.

Rupert replaces the headphones, waiting and watching, but after a time he turns off the music and stands. His father's mouth is open and he's sleeping solidly, so he decides to look for a shop or a cafe, anything that sells food. He's starving.

Charlie is on his side, facing the window, when Rupert returns, but he isn't asleep. His chest is heaving up and down. Rupert knows that he's crying.

'Dad?' he asks, collecting a wad of green hospital tissue from above the sink. He puts down the carrier bag, his appetite clean gone. 'Dad. Dad. Don't cry.'

'"Get out of my sight," that's what I said. You were there, you probably heard. My last words to him. I was so angry. He was my friend. My best friend, Rupert. How could I? How could I?'

Rupert sits back, not knowing what to say, but wanting to say something, anything. As though he is the adult, the one with all the answers. He takes a breath, but his father holds up his hand to stop him.

'But that isn't the worst of it, son. At school . . . David went missing one night from the dormitory. His bed was empty.' He covers his face with his hands. 'I found him in the bell tower, ready to . . .' Parting his fingers, he stares without focusing. 'I was an adult. I should've said something to the matron, the housemaster. But I didn't. I talked him down, took him back to House and it was all forgotten. Suppose—'

Rupert interrupts quickly. 'Don't. Dad, that was years ago, years ago.' Then after a moment. 'Look, I don't know what happened the other day, but you were ill, you are ill. And David wasn't angry with you, I'm sure of it. He came here to see you, he visited the morning you came in, when you were asleep. Mum told me.' He trails off, realising too late that he's mentioned something Helen thought best not to tell Charlie.

The clock ticks. Then Charlie sits up, blows his nose and nods. Rupert breathes again.

'He was a good man, Rupert. A good man. Don't let anyone ever tell you otherwise.'

'I think I might go to church today,' Mike mumbles, crouching at the cereal cupboard, searching for something that doesn't involve bran, chocolate or charms.

'I thought you might,' Olivia replies.

He glances up at her face. Her voice sounds impassive, but he wonders if she minds. Olivia was fiercely atheist at uni, but mellowed as their relationship got more serious, eventually agreeing to the Catholic wedding Mike wanted (for his parents, of course). 'Just because I love you so much, Michael Turner.'

'Can I come too?' Rachel asks from the kitchen table.

'You don't have to.' Olivia's words come out sharply, but Rachel doesn't seem to notice. 'I know,' she replies lightly, before leaving the room to get dressed.

Mike gives up on the cereal quest and puts a crust of bread in the toaster. Then he sits opposite Olivia. 'I just feel grateful, that's all,' he wants to say, but he doesn't really understand it himself, so he says nothing.

'Is the church usually this full, Dad?' Rachel later whispers, pushed up next to Mike along a dark wooden pew.

Mike nods. St John's is heaving as usual on a Sunday and there's that familiar smell. Of candles, he supposes. How has he forgotten? Wishing he'd removed his jacket before sitting down, he shifts in his seat. He's burning up, his collar feels tight and his throat is clogged. Olivia would chortle if she knew. 'The symptoms of Catholic guilt,' she would say and smile.

He leans towards Rachel. 'Wish you'd gone to the party with Hannah?'

'With a load of babies. No thanks. Besides, this is quite—'

'Long and boring?' He laughs quietly. 'Remind me to bring you on Good Friday.'

He feels for his mobile. He knows it's bad form to send a message in church, but he's ruminated on texting Antonia since the start of the service and doesn't want to back out of the idea. The words and the prayers have come automatically, like he's never been away. But he suddenly realises he isn't the one who's in need. Which, he likes to think, is what the teaching of Jesus is surely all about.

'I thought I'd text Antonia. See if she's up to a visit,' he whispers to Rachel. 'Is that OK with you?'

The sandwiches are already prepared and waiting. Their crusts are removed, they're cut into triangles and covered in cling film by the time Mike and Rachel arrive at White Gables. Antonia ushers them into the kitchen, feeling nervous. It's the first human contact she's had for more than twenty-four hours.

Over the years she's spent many days in the large house on her own, but not at night, not without David's huge presence. Yet bizarrely, last night she didn't feel alone. She dreamed pleasant dreams and felt David was near. It was in the morning when she awoke so very early and without a purpose. That's when the desolation and the emptiness really dawned.

They all look at the sandwiches. 'Sorry,' she says with a shy smile. 'It seems rather desperate to have it all ready, doesn't it?'

'Not at all,' Mike replies, looking at Rachel with a grin. 'The truth is we're starving. I dragged my poor little girl to church.'

'Hey. Not so little, Dad.'

'That's child cruelty. I should know!' Antonia declares. 'St Hilda's in Northenden. Every Sunday and Holy Day, come rain or shine.' She looks at them both looking at her, their faces open and inquisitive. 'My mother is Irish too. Well, African-Irish, actually. Oh, go ahead, sit down and tuck in. Drinks! What can I get you both to drink?'

'I'm really very sorry about your sad news.' A nurse stops Helen in the hospital corridor. She's oriental and exceedingly pretty, but Helen doubts that Charlie will notice, even if he's well. 'Was he a close friend, Mrs Proctor?'

She replies in Charlie's words, 'The best friend anyone could have.' Though Helen wonders. It seems to her that Charlie always did the giving with David. Isn't friendship supposed to be reciprocal? She'd challenged Charlie on the subject a few times over the years, especially when David let them down, which was far too often. 'I do love you, Helen, very much,' Charlie would reply, 'but you are utterly incapable of seeing the grey area.'

Friendship or not, there'll be a massive hole in their lives with David gone, Helen muses as she readies herself at the ward door to see Charlie. She feels unsettled as she stands there. A hole that will need filling, she thinks. She's ill-equipped for the job. Charlie knows that, surely? Besides, she already has a job of her own, an occupation which comes very close in importance to her love for him.

She shelves her agitation and pushes open the door, the smell of illness assailing her nostrils. Glancing at Rupert, she expects his face to be blank or bored, moody even, but it's pink and blotchy and his eyelids are swollen. She's always thought of Rupert as having been a little changeling baby, planted in error in the Proctor household. That baby grew into a small boy who adored her, an emotion she's never been able to reciprocate, even though she tries. She watches him for a moment as he leans forward, his eyes on his father's as he listens intently to something Charlie is saying. The expression, the one with silver linings, has always puzzled her. Most idioms do. But as she looks from father to son, she finds herself thinking it anyway.

CHAPTER TWENTY-FIVE

Norma Jeffries sits in the dank garden despite the cold breeze. She hates Sundays at home, they're long and empty. Her two sons, Matthew and Simon, have been over for a roast lunch, one with his girlfriend in tow, the other without, but they never stay long enough to fill the void.

'Isn't Tavia around today?' Norma enquired of Harry, as casually as she could muster over lunch. The boys looked at each other with the silent communication they always have which makes her feel ridiculously left out. Like a silly schoolgirl at fifty-five. Yet that only happens when the boys are together. When she's with Harry or Simon alone, they talk to her and confide about their lives and their worries. They even hug her occasionally and these moments make everything worthwhile. She's needed. Maybe alone and lonely, but still she's needed.

Of course there's her daughter Sophie. She telephoned on Thursday, out of the blue after months of silence. 'I've missed you, Mum,' she said. Such lovely words to hear. She should've accepted them, welcomed them with good grace, said she missed her too. But Norma was immediately defensive, remembering

Sophie's hurtful words the last time they met. 'I suppose that's the closest I'll get to an apology,' she snapped. Brisk words. Hard-faced words. But at least they've broken the ice, Norma thinks as she stubs out her cigarette. And for the first time she can remember, Sophie has made the first move.

Sophie rises from her sweaty bed eventually and wraps herself in the thick towelling robe she left to dry on a radiator days ago. She supposes it was days ago. The last few have merged into a bedfest of loathing: loathing of Sami, of Antonia, but mostly of herself. She's slept a fair amount of the time and when she hasn't slept, she's tried to float above her thoughts with music and songs, or nursery rhymes almost forgotten. But it isn't easy. She's contemplated phoning her mum again and saying, 'You'll be pleased to know that I did it. Just like you said, I showed Sami the real me and it wasn't a pretty sight.' But she knows Norma will reply, 'I told you so,' and Sophie doesn't need telling. 'Selfish, manipulative, fat, ugly, stupid, stupid, stupid . . .' Round and round the houses, like a teddy bear. It's the stupid that gets to her the most. She's allowed herself to lose control, to completely lose control and Sami has seen her 'for what she is'.

It's Sunday now, she supposes, but she gathers from her silent house that Sami isn't there, that he hasn't been there since storming out on Friday night. Yet as she pads down the stairs, she's hopeful, pathetically optimistic that, by some small miracle, Sami will be in the lounge. That he'll be sitting in his leather armchair, his feet up on the pouffe and pointing the remote control at the flatscreen television, channel hopping.

The lounge is empty, the broken whisky glass on the carpet accusatory. Sophie slumps down in Sami's empty chair, picks up the remote and flicks, only stopping at an advert in which an actress assures her in treacle tones that a delicious-looking roast dinner with all the trimmings 'isn't just food'. She thinks for only a moment, reaches for the telephone and punches in the number. She isn't just hungry, she's starving. She's bored too, she needs a distraction. Norma answers on the third ring as always if she's in. 'Brilliant, you're not on a shift today, Mum. Please say you've cooked a Sunday roast for the boys and have some meat left to make a sandwich for your baby girl?'

It's cold and lightly raining outside. Sophie doesn't know why that surprises her, but she trots through the gate to the residents' car park, climbs in the car and puts on the radio. The journey takes less than ten minutes, yet still she flicks through every channel before finding a tune that she likes. When the song finally ends, she takes a deep breath and puts on her brave face. She's covered it in thick make-up. Her teeth and hair are brushed and she's wearing a T-shirt without her boobs on display and black leggings that are actually clean.

'Hello, Mum!' she says, bright and breezy at Norma's front door, as though she visits every week. 'I'm ravenous. Where's that sandwich?'

She sits on the pub stool at the tiny breakfast bench like she did as a girl, her legs plenty long enough not to swing these days. 'Stop kicking the wall, Sophie. It makes marks,' she recalls her mother saying, over and over when she was a child. She wonders vaguely if the scuff marks are still there, hidden, like she's hiding the thrust and the race of her heart.

Eating quickly, she bolts down the sandwich. It must be over a day, more even, since she ate anything and she wonders if she's lost any weight. Every cloud. Then she looks around, taking in her surroundings, noticing for the first time that her childhood home hasn't changed at all. There's only Mum these days, Dad long departed to his bachelor pad in Preston. Her hairy brothers outstayed their welcome by a few years, but left home eventually. She supposes her mum must get bored, lonely, even.

'Another?' Norma says, her eyes on Sophie's face, sandwich already prepared.

Sophie nods and takes the plate. The floury bap has been dipped in pork dripping, replacing any lost weight, but she doesn't care. The food tastes sublime and by the time she's stuffed full, she feels as though she's been plugged in and charged, high almost, ready for the next challenge.

Norma pours a second mug of tea – 'Tea so strong you could stand your spoon in it,' as Grandma used to say – and then adds half a spoonful of sugar. She pulls up the other bar stool and sits, looking far too top-heavy. Weebles wobble but they don't fall over, Sophie thinks, just managing not to say it.

'Now, Sophie,' Norma says, eyes still on her child. 'Time to tell me what's wrong.'

Claustrophobic is the only way Sami can describe it as he picks at the Sunday newspapers. He's had two nights under Martha's roof in Yorkshire, two days of being overfed and too many hours of not-so-subtle inquisition.

'It's Friday night, Samuel,' Martha said when he turned up unexpectedly. 'You always go to the pub. Why aren't you there?'

'One of the guys. Well, he's dead. Long story, Mum.'

'Why aren't you at home, then?'

'Sophie's away for a long weekend.'

He looked at the face his mum always pulls when it comes to Sophie. A face of disbelief and distaste, combined.

'What've you done to your head, Samuel?'

'Got bumped with a squash racquet.'

The same face from Martha but her eyebrows at a slightly less incredulous angle.

'You look too thin. Is she feeding you?'

He was unbelievably angry as he accelerated from home towards the motorway on Friday evening. He pulled over in a petrol station, sent a few texts to people, which he immediately regretted, then drove on to his parents' house in Yorkshire. But as the evening drew on, his anger abated just a little and then by the morning he was willing Sophie to text or to call.

Sami now looks up to the mantlepiece clock his dad winds every evening and sighs. He doesn't want to know why, he doesn't want to go into it or dwell on it, but he understands that Sophie is putting herself under pressure. As usual she's snapped, exploded, burst. It's what she always does, eventually. But she's never thrown a glass at him before. That's worrying. Worse, he's left her alone and she's probably still boozing. Perhaps he should telephone, but he's firmly decided that she must call first.

He goes back to the newspapers. He wanted to leave immediately after the full English breakfast Martha put under his nose first thing this morning, but his dad's silent eyes implored. 'It's raining heavily,' they said. 'There's no escape to the garden! Please don't go.'

Sami had hesitated. He was itching to get into his car, back into the driving seat to sort out his head. But then two of his sisters appeared at the front door, kids in tow, and he was struck by the noise they all made. Happy noise, it may have been, but even he might have been tempted into gardening if he still lived there. So he stayed for lunch. Moral support for his dad.

Sophie hasn't texted or called. Throughout yesterday and again this morning he's fingered the Elastoplast on his forehead, a reminder of resolve. But Martha has fussed, unbearably so.

'There's a spare inhaler in the cabinet if you get chesty, my boy. What do you fancy for your tea? I'll wash your shirt and trousers while you're here. I'm baking a chocolate cake. With fudge, just as you like it. You just relax and let your Momma spoil you.'

He's so stuffed, he can't move, like the fat little boy who used to lie on this very sofa and be fed food 'to cheer you up, my boy'. It was food as a cure for unhappiness. Temporary sweet comfort from bullying. As though making him fatter would help. And here is Martha, still watching him with little glances, just like she did back then.

He turns the page of *The Times* Sunday supplement and sighs again. Claustrophobic's the word. He'll talk to Sophie, he'll even forgive and forget. He touches his plaster. But she has to make the first move.

Still perched at the breakfast bar, Norma waits for Sophie's reply. Her daughter is pacing now, opening a drawer and examining kitchen utensils randomly, before moving on to select another drawer or cupboard.

Norma understands that she and Sophie are a little too alike, too ready to impose an opinion, too fond of being right about everything. She tried to let Sophie win their frequent stand-offs as she was growing up on the basis that she was the adult and Sophie the child. But it was difficult to do, not only because Sophie drove her to distraction at times, but because Norma fundamentally believed in strict parenting. Unfortunately, Barry didn't particularly agree. He was ambivalent on the point. It all depended on how he felt at any given time. Which made him the good cop, Norma the bad.

She's never worked out how Barry's 'seeing the bigger picture' works when both parties are adults, which is why she and

Sophie don't speak for months at a time. Unfortunately the strict parent part is still there, as important to Norma as ever. It's a desire, she always reasons, to help your child, to stamp out the bad bits, make room for the good. But as she watches Sophie's distracted look and as she examines her heavily made-up face, she understands that something is seriously amiss and it distresses her. She should have noticed, she should have known. She's been a nurse for over thirty years. She's seen that look before.

'Nothing's wrong,' Sophie answers eventually, stooping to examine the wall under the breakfast bar. 'I feel great, actually. Buzzing. I might go out for a drive. Stop at a pub for a drink.'

'OK, love,' Norma carefully replies. 'Fancy watching some TV first?'

'Put that blessed thing away,' Martha grumbles, glaring at Sami's iPhone. 'If you can't sit still, do something useful, like helping your dad.'

Sami strolls outside to the cold drizzly garden and proffers a hot drink to his father before putting his hands in his pockets. 'Just here for moral support, Dad.' He points at his shoes with a grin. 'Not got the gear for gardening.'

They chat idly about the cricket, Sami resting on a garden bench, his father digging, turning over the rose-bed soil methodically. He's a man of few words, though more words for Sami than he has for 'all those bloody women' in his large home.

Sami feels the vibration from his iPhone and the immediate acceleration of his pulse. He waits patiently for his dad to finish a story about his Uncle Josiah's farm in Antigua, one which he's heard many times before. Then pulls it out of his pocket, turning away from his dad, a combination of anxiety and excitement in his chest. He looks at the screen. It's an iMessage, but not from Sophie. Bloody Sophie. 'Sod her then,' he mutters, frustrated and angry.

'What's up, Samuel? Want to tell me about it?'

Sami looks at his dad, his lovely lopsided dad who deplores all the women in his life.

'Nothing to tell, Dad. I'm going to get off now. I'll catch you soon.'

His dad straightens slowly, lifts his maroon cricket hat to scratch his shiny head, then nods.

'Fair enough. Come back soon, son. And next time, if any of your sisters knock at the door, don't let them in!'

'I shouted at Sami. Well, screamed,' Sophie mumbles eventually from the sofa, her eyes fixed on the television. 'And threw a glass at his head. I had a good reason, though.'

Norma knows she's only been told half a tale, but it doesn't matter, half a tale is better than none. Sophie has swung from a spirited agitation in the kitchen to a near silent malaise in the lounge. She nods, saying nothing, her eyes on the screen too. I'm wearing my nurse's hat, she thinks. It's easier than my mother's hat and makes me a much nicer person.

'Plus I've sort of fallen out with Antonia. I can't be bothered explaining it all, but you know . . .' Sophie trails off.

Norma nods again, seeing mouths moving, brows furrowing, teeth that need fixing on the television screen, but hearing nothing but the rush of her own thoughts. Sami, handsome, charming and selfish Sami. But Antonia, that's a surprise. Loyal to a fault. Quiet, timid, too timid, she thinks. Norma was on the PTA and over the years there was gossip about the Farrell family, but nothing concrete, nothing to justify a call to Social Services. Yet still, if she's honest, she always thought young

Antonia's impassive face masked something, something dark and unhealthy. She felt guilty when it happened. Barry did too. The child was a constant silent presence in their house and they hadn't noticed anything amiss, not really amiss. 'Do you know what really happened?' they asked Sophie when it all came out, but Sophie shrugged, as teenagers do, and they were none the wiser.

'David's dead,' Sophie now blurts. 'He slit his wrists and bled to death in the bath. Which doesn't help.'

Norma looks at Sophie then. Someone's just walked over my grave, she thinks, as she shakes off a shiver. Sophie's face is wet and her nose is streaming. This isn't a joke.

'I realise that's terrible, obviously, I'm not a complete bitch. But it doesn't stop me from feeling, God, I don't know. Betrayed? And angry, really angry. Does that make any sense, Mum?'

Norma leans over, takes Sophie's hand and squeezes. Her little girl, who only ever had eyes for her daddy. A daddy who barely bothered to hide his night-shift infidelity with men, as well as women, before leaving home for good. Betrayal and anger. To Norma Jeffries it makes perfect sense.

Sami comes off the motorway, but instead of taking a right off the Parkway towards Didsbury, he indicates left. He drives past the crematorium towards Beech Road, realising with a jolt that he's not so far from Mike and Olivia's house.

Fancy some company? his text said, a text sent impulsively from his dad's garden.

Yes please! The flat above the craft shop, Jemima immediately replied. *Can't wait!*

She's an attractive girl, particularly her long wavy hair which looks incongruous in his poker-straight-hair offices, and they've been flirting for some time, but he's never really thought of taking it any further. But this evening it makes sense. He couldn't stand being suffocated at Martha's a moment longer and Sophie hasn't been in touch, so he's not ready to go home.

Blanking out any thoughts of betrayal as usual, he focuses on what he knows is in store. Jemima wants him, he knows that. It evokes memories from the Boot Room.

'There's no bigger turn-on than someone wanting you. Begging for it! Come on, guys, you know what I mean,' he would say when the Boot Room boys eye-rolled at the news of yet another conquest.

'Masturbation, in short,' Pete would drily reply.

'Well, who can blame me,' he would smile, a finger pointing to his own face.

He finds the craft shop and presses the intercom. Bounds up the stairs two by two. The flat door is already open and Jemima pulls him in, her fingers unbuttoning his shirt before he has the chance to put down his keys. Masturbation maybe, but the rush of exhilaration's still there.

She pushes him back on the bed and then strips off her clothes. No foreplay required then, Sami thinks with a grin. Fine by me.

CHAPTER TWENTY-SIX

'Housewife' Antonia always wrote on forms when David gave her something to sign and it asked for her occupation. She knows that some women hate the title, but she liked it, same as she liked 'Antonia, David's wife' whenever she was introduced.

'Well, I'm neither now,' she sighs to the four walls of her plush bedroom, a gaping day before her. The funeral isn't until next week. Ruth, the family liaison officer, telephoned to explain the delay, but Antonia didn't really listen. She doesn't want to think about David in that way. As a body in the bath. As a cadaver on a slab. Spirit gone.

'How are you?' Ruth asked on the telephone.

'Fine thanks,' she said, the automatic reply.

'There's often a delay, Antonia. You know that, don't you?'

'A delay?' she asked, thinking Ruth was referring to the funeral again.

'Grief. It might come much later. I'm here if you need me.'

Antonia now looks towards the window and wonders what she usually does on a Monday. She's never analysed it before, it's always been automatic. Cleaning and washing, tidying up after the weekend, probably. Tidying up after David, collecting kit and clothes and cups where he'd left them. Seeing Sophie too, perhaps. But of course Sophie dates were on Sophie's terms at Sophie's instigation.

Antonia doesn't want to think of her right now. She was drunk when Antonia called at her house on Friday. She said some outrageous stuff. Even if Sophie didn't know about David then, surely she does now. Surely that warrants an acknowledgement, some regard. Some love and sympathy, even if not an apology.

She sits at her dressing table and brushes her long hair, waiting for her hair straighteners to heat up and beep. 'Irish-African,' she had said to Mike and his daughter yesterday. Just like that. She offered the information easily. She saw no disgust in their faces, not even surprise.

She leans forward, closer to the mirror, and drags her fingers through the thick waves of her hair. She wonders if 'Hair by Aaron' is still going strong, whether Aaron would have her back as a stylist. She doubts it. Their last meeting was excruciating. She's kept the memory hidden for years.

Strolling along with David in Alderley Edge village, not long after they married. There was Aaron, walking towards them on the high street. He'd been holding hands with his boyfriend and smiling a warm 'Hello, Gorgeous, long time no see!' type of smile. But she'd panicked. A sudden clash of her new life and old which she didn't know how to handle. So she immediately looked away, grasping David's hand and propelling him across the busy road, her heart beating furiously. 'You wouldn't believe she was my best mate once,' she heard Aaron declare behind her to anyone who might be listening. 'Look at the posh bitch now. She wouldn't even give me the dirt under her finger-nails!'

She sits back and raps her manicured fingernails on the glass top of the dressing table for a few moments. She can still hear the words, her father's ugly words: 'Black hair. Fucking black hair. Are you black, then?' Nodding her head, she leans down to turn the hair straighteners off at the plug. Irish-African, she smiles inwardly. Today she'll leave her hair curly.

Sophie knows how to cook, everyone knows how to cook. The trick is to open a cook book and read. If you can be bothered. She finds it's much less grief and effort to phone a friend and ask for a recipe. Today, however, she doesn't have a friend to phone and is bothered. She wants to cook for Sami, properly cook, to show herself that she can. Without wine. Definitely without any wine. She's already searched through some recipe books, never before opened. They were bought as birthday, anniversary, Christmas, and any-bloody-excuse-to-drop-a-hint gifts, over the years. By Martha, of course.

'If somebody from your family buys me another bloody cook book I'll divorce you.'

'Idle threat, Sophie Richards, you'll never divorce me. I'm just too good looking!'

She stayed at her mother's house last night. It was the first time in eight years and she felt snug against the white wall in her single bed. The teddies watched her from the teddy-shelf and the floral duvet cover was the same as when she last slept there, but smelt fragrant and fresh as though newly washed.

Norma had left for work by the time she woke. Her head didn't hurt, but when she turned on her mobile, somewhere in the vicinity of her heart did. There were no texts and no missed calls. She hadn't expected Sami to get in touch, but she desperately wanted him to.

She padded around Norma's house with a mug of tea for a

while without wearing her contact lenses which were sitting in two egg cups by the bed. She hadn't got her glasses with her and rather liked the sensation of blurred edges. Sober blurred edges, she thought to herself, that's a novelty. But even though she'd found an old pair of her pyjamas in the pine drawers and a candlewick dressing gown on the back of the bathroom door, she was too cold. The central heating wasn't on, blasting out warmth day and night as it does in her modern townhouse. So she decided to come home 'just to get warm' she told herself.

The first surprise was Sami's car in the residents' car park on a Monday morning. The second was Sami, in his leather chair, feet up and channel hopping, when he should have been at work.

Her reaction as she gazed at him was heart-thrashing and overwhelming shyness. She hadn't expected to see him and she'd made no effort with her appearance. But she was relieved, happy and incredibly nervous.

'What are you doing here?' she asked, her voice a husky croak.

'Waiting for you.'

He took his feet off the leather pouffe. 'We need to talk,' he said and her heart sunk, even as she noticed that his socks didn't match.

Olivia hasn't had time to think, which is a good thing. On the other hand, she hasn't had time to do anything else either. She committed to the NCT breast counselling malarkey years ago. *Breast Is Best*, as the slogan says. It seemed important to Olivia at the time, but everyone is so bloody right-on in Chorlton that every mum breastfeeds their precious offspring.

'It's a sin to cross the Beech Road border and feed your baby formula milk,' she laughs with her sister on the telephone. But this means she is very busy with numerous new mums who are struggling to feed their babies with engorged breasts, cracked nipples or even mastitis, and who are racked with middle-class guilt.

'If I had my time again,' Olivia recently confessed to her sister, 'I'd go for formula milk or employ a wet nurse! Don't you dare tell anyone. They'd shoot me.' Only she is having a 'time again' right now, a time again she needs to do something about.

'Daddy! Daddy's home!' she hears Hannah shout from the bay window.

Blusher, she thinks, glancing in the mirror in the downstairs loo, I should've used blusher. But Mike is already through the front door, smiling and relaxed.

Happy, she thinks. Mike is happy.

'You're early. I haven't put on the pasta yet. Anything up?' she asks, trying for a light tone.

Mike shakes his head. 'Not at all. Thought I'd pop to White Gables later. Do my ten K around Mottram for a change. Thought it only fair to see you girls properly first.'

'You are good.' She feels vaguely guilty that she hasn't yet made the effort to visit Antonia herself. Antonia is nice, she undoubtedly needs support, but Olivia just doesn't have the time to drive all the way to the sticks at the moment. Or the energy.

Hannah reaches up to Mike for a hug. 'Mummy was sick this morning.' She looks at Olivia with narrowed eyes. 'You closed the bathroom door, but I saw you.'

Olivia doesn't miss a beat as she scoops up Hannah to hide her blushing face. 'Yes, thank you, with a bug you brought home from school, young lady!'

She can sense Mike's eyes on her. 'Are you OK? I don't need to go out. I could go running tomorrow.'

'No, I'm fine. Absolutely. You go.'

Her fixed smile is exhausting.

It's dark outside but Sami is still at work, trying to catch up from his late start to the day. There's a slight quibble at the back of his mind about the interlude with Jemima yesterday, but he hasn't glanced at his private line even once. His predominant thoughts are of Sophie.

He didn't stay long with Jemima. As soon as they were done he was itching to get home. He suddenly felt overwhelmingly apprehensive. He had no idea what to expect. Sophie drunk, Sophie dead, Sophie hurling abuse?

'Take a firm line, man, it's the only way,' he repeated to himself as he drove the short journey home.

The townhouse was silent as he let himself in. The kitchen lights revealed a shambles of empty bottles and crisp packets, dirty dishes and cluttered work surfaces. No discernible difference to how he'd left it two nights before. He looked quickly into the empty lounge and saw the splintered whisky glass on the carpet where it had landed. He felt the heat of the radiators, his heart pounding, only now really focusing on what he might find. He bounded up the stairs and took a deep breath before pushing open the bedroom door. Then he looked. The bedroom was empty. Thank God, thank God.

The disappointment set in then. He missed Sophie, he wanted to talk to her, to listen to one of her comically spiteful observations about Claudia Winkleman's fringe, or the lesbian neighbours, her mum or Princess Kate's eye make-up. He lay down on the jumbled bed to reinstate his resolve, and slept deeply until morning. It was light when he woke and to his surprise he was fully clothed. He squinted at his watch, realised it was Monday, then muttered, 'Sod it. I'm not going into work today.' He peeled off his sweaty clothes, showered for a long time, then sat in the lounge, waiting.

He resorted to turning on the television but didn't like the invasion of sound, so turned it to mute. He searched the cupboards for chocolate and biscuits, but they were too sweet and too dry, even washed down with a pint glass of Coke. Nothing seemed the same without Sophie. Then finally he heard her key in the latch.

'We need to talk. This drinking has got to stop,' were his first words. Whatever he expected to do or to say, it wasn't that.

'I know,' Sophie replied.

It was as easy as that.

Antonia's been engrossed for some time in the rhythm of kneading dough for some brioche and the sharp rap of the knocker in the silence makes her jump. She rubs her hands together to remove most of the flour and then washes them under the tap in the centre of the island. It seemed decadent when the plans were originally drawn up: two sinks, four taps, all in such close proximity. But the kitchen designer from Knutsford knew his stuff. One sink for washing up, the other for everything else. Like the two ovens and the integrated coffee machine, it all added to the huge cost of the renovation, but David had been firm. 'Pick the best. Let's do it properly. We have the money, my darling. Besides, you're absolutely worth it.'

She takes a breath, lifting her chin before answering the front door. It's silent and dark outside. A small thick-set man with red hair and cheeks to match is at the top of the steps. 'Colin. Colin Green, from the office?'

'Yes, of course, Colin. Hello. Come in.'

'Charlie called me. From the hospital. He asked if you

wouldn't mind me collecting a couple of files. Just work stuff, obviously. I did call, but there was no answer.'

He's looking above Antonia's head, to the side and even at the ground. Anywhere but at her, she notices. 'I haven't got the clap,' she's tempted to say, which surprises her. It's such a Sophie comment. 'The files are in the study, second door on the right. Can I get you a coffee? Or a sandwich to keep you going until supper?' she asks instead.

Colin Green demurs without eye contact and scuttles away, emerging an hour or so later with three boxes full of papers, one of which she helps carry to his car. The same Colin Green who all but pinned her to the photocopier with hot breath at the last partners' social in the office. The tarnish of death, Antonia muses.

She remembers it well.

CHAPTER TWENTY-SEVEN

Sami suggested the Lead Station after work because Jemima lives virtually opposite the wine bar. And after all, that's the point of him sitting here: a quick drink, then to her place for another shag before going on home to Sophie. The trouble is that Jemima seems to have different ideas.

The last interlude was nice enough. An easy conquest, a bit of astonishingly rapid intercourse and a lot of flattery, just when he needed it. She stripped in front of him without any coyness almost immediately, revealing a great physique. Slim, toned and athletic, like a man, almost, but softened by her hair. Perhaps that's why he noticed her in the first place. Or perhaps it's because her coffee cup says 'Posh Totty' on it.

He still isn't sure why he invited himself over on Sunday. It was frustration at Sophie's lack of contact, rather than having any particular desire for sex. He wasn't sure as he raced along the M62 back towards Manchester, but when he arrived at her flat, she had wanted him immediately and the compliments had flowed. 'So handsome, so fit, so big!' Followed by a crescendo of repeated 'Oh, my God!' Then it was all over remarkably quickly. Before he even caught his breath, she was up and in the bathroom, taps hissing, toilet rumbling. She sat on the side of the bed with her slim naked back towards him, raking her hair up into a tight high ponytail. Then she put on a sports bra and rooted around in a white chest of drawers for 'matching panties' in readiness for her 'cool down run'.

'You can take me out for a drink next time,' she said in her slightly lispy way, standing over him with her hands on her narrow hips. 'I'll send you a text and let you know when I'm free. Or maybe I'll just pop into your office.' Which she did at noon today, at the very moment Sami was at a low point, staring at his private line and willing it to ring.

So here he is on a Wednesday evening, sitting opposite Jemima at the Lead Station wine bar, realising far too late that her voice is really going to get on his pip. She's talking, she has been talking since they arrived. Sami has no idea what about, but he gathers from the movement of her eyebrows and hands that he's supposed to be impressed with whatever high-minded opinion she's espousing. Posh, attractive *and* intelligent, she wants him to know.

'So, not just a pretty face,' he finds himself saying at some point. Even as he cringes at the sound of his clichéd words, he knows it's a poor shot at encouraging her to shut up and suggest they go back for 'dessert' at her flat. Not that she looks like the sort of girl who ever eats it.

'Thank you for asking for me,' Antonia says, holding Charlie's hand at the side of his hospital bed. 'I would have come earlier but I didn't want to—'

Charlie pulls his hand away carefully, conscious of the cannula in the back of it. He hates feeling such a dependent fool. Even more he hates the fact that he hasn't the strength to

219

be anything other than that. When he tries to get up, he feels legless (an obvious joke he and David would have laughed at), but for all the wrong reasons.

'—make my condition any worse,' he says. He finds he's completing Antonia's sentences already. He knows that he should let her answer for herself, but it's a habit he has difficulty breaking. 'Oh don't worry about me, these pretty nurses will sort me out soon enough. It's you we should worry about. Has everything been all right at home? Has Helen been round yet?'

Antonia shakes her head. He thinks she looks nervous, her eyes remarkably calf-like.

'Oh, she will. With lots of sensible advice. So now you've been warned!'

Charlie tries for a chuckle. Antonia tries for a smile. He knows what they're both thinking, what they both want to say: 'David's dead. It's unbelievable. It doesn't feel real.' But neither of them do. Instead there's a silence, a very long silence. He clears his throat eventually and speaks. 'Did Colin Green call?'

Antonia nods, her gaze far away. 'Yes, he visited on Monday. He took—'

'—some files. Yes, nothing to worry about. You know, business matters.'

Another silence, then a Charlie cough. 'Ah, money. Are you all right for money? Enough in the bank? You must let me know if you get short.'

Another calf reaction, Charlie observes, as Antonia's eyes seem to widen. This isn't easy, not at all. But he continues stoically. 'You see, the thing is that David had life policies, as you would expect. Policies providing for you in the event of his untimely death, but some policies don't pay out in the event of, of . . .'

Charlie coughs again and clears his throat. 'Well. Some

insurers just like to be bloody difficult. But it's not something you need to worry about. So, promise me you won't?'

He feels quite winded by the time Antonia leaves. He pulls up the thin cotton sheet, then lies down quietly with his eyes closed, hoping that he'll be left alone for five minutes without someone in hospital uniform prodding him. Or talking as though he's invisible.

It isn't just imparting bad news that has made him feel dizzy, not that he's done so in any effective way. He feels breathless because he was dreading the 'why' question he thought Antonia would certainly ask. She hasn't asked why, which he thinks is slightly strange. But then again, he doesn't know the girl that well and who can predict how someone reacts to death? He isn't even sure how he's reacting himself, it's all so surreal, which isn't a word which often pops up in his vocabulary.

'Do you know why David did it, Charlie?'

'No, absolutely no idea.'

That's how it should have gone with Antonia, but the question wasn't asked. Indeed, the conversation didn't head remotely in that direction. He should feel relieved, he knows. If Antonia was going to ask why, that was the moment, when she and Charlie were alone. She didn't ask. But Charlie doesn't feel relieved or reprieved. He lies in his NHS bed, a pathetic figure who requires a nurse and a tube to help him to piss. What he really needs, he realises with irony, is purgation. Not of the body, but of the soul.

He closes his eyes and recalls his harsh words to David. 'I can't believe it. I just can't believe it. How could you be so bloody, bloody stupid? Why the hell didn't you tell me sooner? Do you realise what you've done? Has your thick head any idea of what the consequences will be?'

221

Charlie squeezes his eyes but the tears seep out anyway. David's face. He can still see it clearly. The boyish surprise, the confusion, the dismay.

'For crying out loud, David. You just don't get it do you? I'm not going to sack you. It's the Law Society who will sack you! You'll be struck off and if I don't report you, I'll be struck off too. You've taken client money without permission, for God's sake, and that is called stealing. It doesn't matter that you intended to replace it at some indeterminate time. It's theft and it will have to be reported. To the Law Society. To the police. You will no longer have a job because you will no longer be entitled to practise as a solicitor. Do you understand? You'll be prosecuted, imprisoned, disgraced. Has the penny finally dropped?'

Of course Charlie didn't ask the 'why' question then either. 'Why did you have to "borrow" client money to pay the firm's indemnity premium, David, when the money should have been in the designated insurance account you opened, duly earning interest?' He didn't ask because they both knew the answer was theft and frivolity with money, deeply humiliating and embarrassing for them both. It was easier to say, 'A failure, David. Again. Just get out of my house. I can't stand the sight of you.'

His very last words. How they hurt.

Helen's having a productive week without Charlie. Her marking is up to date, as are her lecture plans and paper research. Charlie isn't especially demanding to have around at home, but he's a distraction. Aimless chatter, the garden in summer, the conservatory in winter and of course their long-winded meals.

She hasn't particularly looked forward to visiting Antonia, but she knows that paying one's respects has to be done and in fairness she does have the time. As she drives to White Gables in the dusky evening, she wonders what on earth they'll find to talk about and how she'll stretch the visit out to a respectable hour. But when she arrives, Mike Turner and his daughter are already there, sitting at the enormous breakfast bar on the (rather tasteless, in Helen's view) gleaming chrome swivel stools. They're drinking hot chocolate topped with whipped cream from tall glass mugs, chatting and laughing together. Despite Charlie's grief, she still has no sympathy for David or his selfish actions, but she isn't sure laughter is appropriate the week after a death.

'I might get a job,' Antonia says after serving Helen with an acceptable espresso and a rather tasty brioche bun.

'Do you have qualifications?' Helen asks, trying, but not succeeding, to keep the scepticism from her voice.

'"Qualifications" sounds a bit grand for hairdressing, but yes, I suppose I do.'

Mike's daughter, Helen notices, is big-toothed and wide-eyed as she gazes at Antonia adoringly. 'Open a salon, Antonia. In Chorlton, near us. Then I could be your Saturday girl!'

The conversation flows easily, Helen thinks, surprisingly so. Until she mentions the wake at the Royal Oak and asks what plans have been made with Seamus and the caterers so she can tell Charlie. There's a silence then. Antonia's face flushes and Mike's seems to darken.

'Oh, I thought it would be here. I've already started to prepare,' Antonia says eventually, motioning towards what Helen calls The Tardis.

Helen glances at The Tardis too. It's still the size of a bloody wardrobe. Ridiculous, she always comments to Charlie. Who could possibly need such a large freezer? Especially for only two people, one of whom eats like a bird.

She turns back to Antonia's flushed face. 'Don't be ridiculous.

You can't do the catering, you're the widow,' she begins. Then she goes on to patiently (extremely patiently, she later tells Charlie) explain the facts. Perhaps Antonia doesn't fully understand that David was friends with the Royal Oak's landlord, Seamus, and his wife for years. Since he was a student at Manchester Polytechnic, in fact. That he even lodged with them at some point and they treated him like a son. So it's entirely appropriate and expected that the wake should be there.

Watching the girl's expression, Helen knows her careful reasoning has hit home. So she nods encouragingly and smiles, opening her mouth to say she'd be perfectly happy to sort the arrangements herself. But a voice interrupts. 'The wake will be here. It's Antonia's choice and she has decided, Helen. We'll hear no more about it.'

They all turn and stare at Mike Turner in surprise. He's raised his voice, which isn't really necessary, Helen later tells Charlie, and his unshaven face looks like thunder.

'What's up, Dad?' Rupert asks from the bedside. 'I mean, I know it's awful about Uncle David, but is there something else? You seem . . .' His voice trails away.

Charlie stares through Rupert with vacant eyes for a moment before answering. He's been working out how best to deal with 'the insurance problem' all day, without any solution. Cooking the books is the obvious way out, but that's too blatantly wrong. Besides, it would involve too many people, even if Tony from accounts were willing to doctor the statements, as he would be, for Charlie.

'How does one escape when there's no obvious way out?' he asks, finally focusing on Rupert's inquisitive face. It sounds like one of the riddles he posed on long journeys to St Ives when Rupert was about eleven or twelve.

'Bribery or blackmail? And if that doesn't work, then fall on your sword,' Rupert immediately replies with a grin. There's no need to mull it over for fifty miles or so on this occasion.

Charlie puts a thoughtful finger to his lips and his grey eyes focus on the too-short curtains of the hospital room before eventually looking back at his son. 'Yes, or perhaps a mix of all three,' he says slowly. His face brightens and he chuckles. 'Well done, Rupe. Good thinking! Got your mother's brains, you have.'

'And my father's good looks?'

The family joke. It's nice to hear Rupert say it. It's usually Helen's line.

'You can't ignore Antonia forever,' Sami says when he finally arrives home from seeing Jemima, feeling vaguely dissatisfied. 'She's been your best friend since you were a kid. David's dead. He killed himself, Sophie. That's really bad. She must need you. And the funeral's coming up soon.'

Sophie is lying on the sofa in the dark, without even the television for company. He glances around the room for a wine bottle or a glass but finds none. Then he apologises for being so late, explaining that the client prattled on over a drink and that it was difficult to escape.

'That's fine,' she replies. He's surprised at her mood. It's muted and she's quiet. Far too quiet.

He lifts Sophie's head and sits on the sofa, feeling the warmth she's left there through his fine-wool suit trousers. It was a crap evening with Jemima. He wishes he hadn't gone. The sex was perfunctory on his part and her compliments left him cold this time. He should have resisted. He should've come straight home.

'She didn't love David.' Sophie's husky voice interrupts his thoughts. It sounds flat, disinterested.

'Love's a funny thing,' he replies, bending down to stroke back her hair and plant a soft kiss on her forehead.

'Do you love me, Sami?'

His hand stops its rhythmic stroking for a moment before starting again. He can't remember her ever asking him that question before.

'Of course I do. Very, very much.'

'Even though I'm getting fat.'

'No you're not, I like you just as you are. Hey, what's all this?'

Thoughts flash through Sami's mind. Has he been sloppy? What does she know?

Sophie shakes her head, turning it into his body so he can't see her face. But the tears he can feel, as they slowly seep through his shirt on to his skin.

CHAPTER TWENTY-EIGHT

It's gone. The black dog has gone. At least for now, Mike thinks to himself repeatedly. He doesn't want to tempt fate. Fate being a bad thing. Like new shoes on the table. Like ladders, magpies and cracked mirrors. Just some of Olivia's superstitions. He laughed with surprise the first time they became apparent on a day trip to Blackpool not long after they started dating.

'Buying heather from a gypsy, Olivia? You of all people can't possibly believe in all that rubbish.'

'I don't. She needs the cash. Anyway, better safe than sorry. And stop laughing!'

'Sorry, but, spells and bad omens. Really?'

'Don't look so smug! It's not so different to your blessed religion, Mike. Remember that Old Testament God? Divine retribution and wrath?'

Mike sits back, his hands behind his head as he gently swivels his office chair. It's difficult to describe how he felt for all those months, but he no longer feels hollow. He's content, happy even, and more importantly, Olivia is too. They've survived the blip and he feels closer to her than he has in a long time. Life at home feels good.

Then there's Antonia. He's been to White Gables most days since David's death, taking Rachel with him after work. She's thrilled to go, tapping her foot with impatience as she waits for him to finish his dinner. He can tell from the way she holds herself at Antonia's kitchen island that she's pleased to be treated as a small adult, but it's more than that. Her eyes study Antonia. They gaze at her clothes, her make-up and hair. They follow her every move. Then when Antonia isn't in the room, they drink in the surroundings. The colours, the curtains, the lamps and the rugs.

'She's so beautiful. Like a footballer's wife,' he heard Rachel declare on her mobile phone, presumably to one of her school friends. Olivia heard too. She raised her eyebrows at Mike and smiled one of her secret smiles of mutual understanding. Olivia had said those very words many times before in the early years, and Mike had agreed with the superficial assessment. But now he knows Antonia properly, the words feel dirty. They suggest something expensive but cheap. He wants to tackle Rachel about it, to tell her not to use the expression, but knows she won't understand. She regards it as a compliment.

He looks at his desk. It's already a muddle even though Judith has only been gone a few days. He's surprised himself by how much he's missing her. Not just because he has to tell the temps what to do every two minutes. Not even because of the lost banter. He's missing her most because Judith understands him. Or if she doesn't actually understand him, she puts on a good show.

She's phoned him every day so far. 'You're still my baby until the new one comes along,' she says. 'Have you pined for me?'

'What do you think?'

'Ha! Told you so.'

This morning they chatted about David and Antonia and

228

the upcoming funeral. He mentioned Rachel. Not about the footballer's wife comment, which is still festering away, but the fact that she is temporarily star-struck by the whole White Gables thing.

'Why do you always take Rachel?' Judith asked. He gave the expected answer. That Rachel loved to go, that he enjoyed her company in the car and so on. But Mike knows Judith was doing what Judith does best. She was posing the question he's secretly asking himself. Not that he'd admit to the answer. He wouldn't admit to feeling an attraction, or to waking in the night and contemplating that erotic moment he and Antonia were last alone together.

He looks down at his diary again and taps his Biro on the page. He has a rare appointment out of the office today. It's at the Macclesfield Planning Department, so it seems sensible to pop in on Antonia afterwards, since she's only down the road. They can have a proper chat about the funeral, he reasons, something he doesn't want to do in front of Rachel. He can ask Antonia if she's OK, really OK. He hasn't asked her since she cried the night of David's death. He feels that a good friend should.

'I can't seem to get rid of you this week,' Norma says as she hands a mug of tea to Sophie. 'Would you like a Hobnob with that?'

Sophie takes a biscuit from the stripy tin and places it on the arm of the sofa. She tucks her feet under her bottom and holds the mug with both hands.

'You look cold, love. I'll put on the fire,' Norma says.

Sophie gazes at the stone cladding wall and at the gas fire with its wooden-look surroundings. It makes her think of sherry and artificial Christmas trees. It takes her back to board games with Dad: Cluedo, Monopoly or Frustration on Sunday afternoons. Mum being strict with the rules, Dad soft. 'She's only a kid, Norma. Come on. Let her have another chance.' She hasn't seen him in ages. She misses his handsome face and his relaxed view of the world.

'Preston's too far away, Dad, don't go,' she said when he left.

'Only thirty miles, love, we'll see each other loads,' he replied. Of course they haven't.

'To think it was state of the art when we had this gas fire put in,' Norma says, turning the switch repeatedly to fire it up. 'But even I think it's time for a living flame.'

'Living flames died out years ago, Mum. You could always put on the central heating. If it still works.'

'Not worth it just for me,' Norma starts. She sits on the footstool, slightly breathless from bending down and smiles. 'Guess you've heard that a few times. Mum on repeat. Again.' She pauses for a moment, looking over at Sophie. 'Is Sami OK?'

'Yeah, he says hello. And before you ask, no I haven't spoken to Antonia, so don't bother giving me a lecture.'

'I wasn't going to. Look, love, I don't know what she did to upset you, but you're entitled to feel whatever you're feeling.'

Sophie turns her head and stares out of the window towards the soggy back lawn. 'I don't know what I'm feeling, Mum. I'm so tired. All I want to do is sleep.' She looks back towards Norma with weary eyes. 'But what I do know is that I don't want to go to the funeral. People will think I'm a selfish bitch, but I don't want to go. I really don't want to go.'

'Then don't, love. You don't have to do anything.'

'For fuck's sake!' Sami hisses under his breath. He's sitting at his desk thinking about a woman. Again. For a moment he visualises his father limping into the garden. 'Bloody women! God, make me better, please. Get me back to work!' There's an iota of empathy for a moment, but Sami likes women and this particular woman is his wife.

He doodles on the pad, killing time until some building plans arrive. He likes to be methodical, to complete one task before moving on to the next.

He counted the wine bottles this morning and checked the level of the one in the fridge. Sophie doesn't appear to be drinking. Maybe she's improved her hiding technique over the last few days, but there's no doubt that she's retreated into herself. She isn't talking. There's no general chit-chat, sarcastic comments or shouting. Yet on the other hand, she isn't being unfriendly either. He doesn't think she knows about Jemima, but her behaviour is decidedly odd. He puts his pen down and sighs. The truth is that he doesn't know how to handle it. Sophie has always been Sophie. Sophie being something other than Sophie isn't a problem he's encountered before.

There's a banging noise and some laughter through his open office door. It interrupts Sami's doodling, his neat sketches of three-dimensional boxes increasing in size. It's unusual to hear the buzz of the office. He's objected to the suggestion of open plan many times, valuing his private line and his privacy. But he's having a hot-under-the-collar moment, a rare feeling he doesn't like. Jemima has strolled into his office three times today. Each time she closed the door behind her, her face proprietorial. Then she perched her neat bum on his desk 'for a chat'. Too cosy, too comfortable, too near. It makes him feel trapped.

'No need for that. I'm on the pill, I won't get pregnant,' she said the last time they met, as he carefully rolled on a too-tight condom. No need? Don't I bloody know it, he thought. But he always uses condoms with casual conquests, he always has, he doesn't want an STD. He could catch warts or chlamydia, get discharge or worse. The thought brings him out in goosebumps.

'This has just arrived for you, Mr Richards.' The sweaty office junior inches into the office, handing Sami a large beige cylinder. Sami nods his thanks. Now he can get on with the task in hand, put the women aside.

'Should I close the door, Mr Richards?'

'No, that's fine,' Sami says with a grimace. 'Definitely leave it open.'

Olivia's small hands are shaking as she punches the number into the telephone. Actually shaking. It's ridiculous, the whole thing is ridiculous.

'Can I make an appointment to see the doctor, please?'

She's met with the usual bored inquisition from the surgery's receptionist. For whom? Date of birth? Postcode? Usual doctor? Hold the line while I complain to my colleague about some random biddy who didn't say thanks. 'Probably because she's traumatised, deaf or dying,' Olivia wants to yell, but manages to hold her tongue.

'Dr Culcheth on the twenty-sixth at four pm?' Finally.

Olivia thinks of today's date. 'That's in three weeks!' she says far too loudly.

'Well, you didn't say it was an emergency. Is it an emergency?'

Is it an emergency? Olivia has no idea. She was on the pill. She took it late once, maybe twice. In her head, though, it's definitely an emergency.

'Yes. Yes, it is.'

'Then you should have called before ten.'

'What if the fucking emergency occurs after ten?' Olivia wants to ask. But she's using her reasonable voice. It takes up the rest of Olivia's yearly supply. She says, 'please' and 'I would be so grateful' and 'that's so kind of you to make an exception'.

'Just this once, Mrs Turner. A doctor will call you back later today or tomorrow to arrange an appointment.'

'Oh, for fuck's sake.' She doesn't say it out loud, at least she doesn't think so.

She clock-watches for the first hour, not listening to *You and Yours* on the radio, not emptying the dishwasher or sweeping the floor. Then she gives up doing nothing, leaves the oppressive house and walks up the cul-de-sac towards the shops. Hannah has a party at the weekend. Olivia needs to buy a gift for a child who has everything. Inevitably, as fate would have it, the callback from the surgery comes as she stands at the counter of the sparse and expensive local toy shop in the precinct.

It isn't a doctor she knows. He hasn't read her notes. He sounds very young. His first question is, 'Have you done a pregnancy test?'

Olivia manages to resist the inevitable 'What the fuck do you think?' but the conversation goes badly anyway. There are dates she can't give. Details she doesn't want to share with the other lunchtime precinct shoppers. When was her last period? How long has she known? Has she spoken to her husband? And other pointless questions. Olivia finds herself shouting outside the cluttered fruit stall and by then she knows that she's lost the argument.

'I don't think you're ready to see me yet, Mrs Turner,' the doctor says smoothly. 'You need time to talk to your husband, to reflect. Let's make an appointment for a week's time. Then we can have a calm and reasonable chat.'

Olivia throws her mobile into her handbag and stamps her foot, much like Hannah in a tizz. 'Unctuous bastard,' she shouts. A couple of elderly Chorlton-born-and-bred shoppers release their tartan trolleys and stare at her with open mouths.

'Sorry, ladies. Call centres! Makes you lose the will to live,' Olivia explains. The shoppers nod sagely and move on.

CHAPTER TWENTY-NINE

Sophie is still asleep upstairs, at least Sami thinks so. She's been so quiet over the last week that it's difficult to judge. She's been right next to him in their bed all night, available to speak to and to touch. Yet his mind has been swamped with dreams and thoughts of her as though she isn't there. He misses the Sophie he knows. He wants her back.

It's Friday today. Black Friday. The day of David's funeral. He hasn't thought about David much. When he does, it still feels unbelievable, like a bad joke or a lie. He wonders if the penny will ever drop. If he'll ever *feel* it.

Opening the wooden kitchen cupboard, he removes his favourite bowl and pours out the muesli. He likes his morning routine: muesli for breakfast, sugar free with skimmed milk. But today it looks dry and uninspiring.

He leans on the worktop, his mind propelled back to his night-time reminiscences of eight and a half years ago. He was at his pad in town, pacing. He was expectant, excited. His breath and aftershave were fresh, the cushions were plumped, wine uncorked on the side unit, the lights on dim. A new conquest was at the tip of his fingertips. The best feeling ever.

His doorbell trilled into the soft music. But when he'd opened the door, there was Sophie.

'Antonia isn't coming, so you've got me instead,' she'd announced, pushing past him and into the lounge. Her sharp eyes surveyed the room, her hand on her hip. 'Nice place, Sami,' she laughed. 'But fur throws. Really?'

He was extremely irritated. He'd barely noticed her at the club. She wasn't his style, not the more conventionally pretty type of woman he liked. But he could hardly throw her out and so she stayed. She sashayed around his flat, opening cupboards, gazing at pictures and stroking a finger along the spines of his books. Then she helped herself to the wine and drank greedily, her scarlet lips wet and glossy. Sami found himself watching her every move with fascination until he couldn't bear it any longer.

'I think you'll find there's more to see in the bedroom.' He grinned.

'I'm sure there is. Leave the wine in a cooler next time, Sami. Bye,' she smiled and then she left.

Sami opens the fridge and studies its contents. It's colder than it needs to be, but Sophie always did like her wine very chilled. There's milk, butter, yoghurt, a sausage of chorizo and some out-of-date ham. Then at the bottom, the phials of hormone drugs and unopened syringes. The remains of his last failure. He pulls back the foil on the Greek yoghurt and sniffs, then spoons it generously on top of his muesli, adding a dollop of honey from a jar in the cupboard. It's as close to comfort eating as Sami gets these days.

Sophie fended him off just with kisses. For weeks. He thought he might burst and he resorted to pleading, which made Sophie laugh. Until a summer's evening at a pub in the Lakes.

'You can have me now,' she said, draining the glass of wine.

'But we're miles away from home, in the middle of the countryside.'

'So?'

They made love in a field, in the shadow of an oak tree. The breeze caressed their naked skin which was dappled by soft sunlight peeping through the leaves. It was the most exhilarating moment of his life. Then afterwards Sophie sat up, the evening air cool on her pale pink nipples and he picked out the dry grass from her hair.

'Will you move in with me, Soph?' he asked.

She looked at him for a moment, her green eyes bright in the pale retreating sun and for a pulse of a second he thought she was going to say no.

'You'll have to catch me first.'

Her russet hair flew behind her like a kite as she ran. He knew then that there was no turning back as he pulled on his boxer shorts and hurtled after her.

Sophie waits for the click of the front door before opening her eyes. They're wet. She who never cries is crying all the time. Without reason, without warning.

Sami popped his head around the bedroom door before he left. 'I'll be back at twelve to collect you for the funeral. Think it would be best if you wore black, Soph. Love you.'

She can still smell his aftershave. The 'love you' catches her breath.

Her mother didn't say 'I told you so' as she'd thought, when Sophie confessed about lying to Sami. Instead, she took Sophie into her warm fleshy arms, kissed her hair and said, 'Oh, love.' Sophie cried and cried; she couldn't stop.

'I never told Sami about the chlamydia and stuff. I mean,

why would I? Why would anyone?' she sobbed to her mum.

'You were very poorly, Sophie. And brave. Nobody else would have put up with the pain for that long,' Norma replied, still holding her close.

'Stupid, you mean. I knew something was wrong. I was just a coward.'

As Sophie wiped her stinging face with shaking hands she pictured the doctor's frowning face from all those years ago. 'You have PID, Pelvic Inflammatory Disease. A very severe case of it,' he diagnosed, after she was admitted to hospital in horrendous pain. 'You really shouldn't have left it so long, young lady.'

But it didn't matter then, she was poorly and she recovered, life moved on.

'You could tell him now, love. Sami must know that you don't go for IVF unless there's a major problem,' Norma said, pulling gently away.

Sophie looked at her mum, an older reflection of herself. Her eyes were wet too. It was time to be honest. 'I told Sami that he was the problem, Mum. Low sperm, no sperm, whatever. I took Antonia to all the consultations so he wouldn't know the truth. When I told him that he was to blame, he just looked appalled but accepted it. He never mentioned it again.'

'So, Antonia knows . . .'

Sophie nodded.

'Ah,' Norma replied.

Antonia brushes her floury hands on her apron. She's been up since five, glad of something to do. Filo pastry from scratch isn't what most sane people will do on the morning of their husband's funeral, she knows, but she finds it therapeutic. It takes her mind off the terror of a funeral. The faces, the eyes and the inquisitiveness. The pity, especially. Still fresh from her dad's burial, even after all these years.

Last night she asked Mike how many people she needed to cater for, but he looked apologetic. He said he had no idea. But then he grinned, saying he'd be more than happy to pop out to Netto for some decent nibbles if the need arose.

Mike's friendship and his humour keeps her afloat. So it isn't so bad. Then all the scary stuff like the undertakers, the police and the coroner have been taken out of her hands by David's partners under the direction of Charlie, still seething in his hospital bed. She only really has Helen to impress.

She cuts the butter into thin slices and dots them carefully on to the dough. What she couldn't ask Mike was whether it was considered to be a *faux pas* to attend the funeral of someone who'd committed suicide. She can see it could be embarrassing for people who aren't close friends. Or for people who judge. But then she understands that a funeral is meant to celebrate someone's life and to pay respects to a person they admired or loved, however they died.

That's precisely why so few mourners attended her father's funeral, she thinks, as she tools the pastry. Sophie was there, though. Sophie was there to hold her hand.

Sophie has been standing still under the shower for a long time, thinking. The water is hot, almost scalding her skin. She can still smell Sami. It's the soap, perhaps. He'll be back soon to collect her. She has to think straight, to decide.

'Antonia doesn't know everything,' she eventually said to her mum.

'Oh?'

'She doesn't know . . .' She trailed off and started to cry again

238

then. She hadn't let Norma see her tears since she was very, very small and look at her now.

'She doesn't know that I got fed up of waiting for Sami to propose. He seemed to be losing interest.'

Norma shook her head, her eyes still bright with tears. 'Oh, Sophie, I doubt it.' She paused for a moment and then nodded. 'Let me guess. You told him you were pregnant?'

'Yes. Then of course I had to "lose" the baby. He was devastated, Mum. I think he'd told his family. Martha, anyway. She's hated me since.'

Sophie could almost see the cogs of her mother's mind, working it all out. The pregnancy and then the miscarriage, a lie that had snowballed. 'So, if you confessed to Sami now about the PID or if he finds out you were always infertile . . .'

'He'd see me for what I am.'

The central heating's still blasting out its heat in Sophie's bedroom, but the air feels cold against her hot and damp skin. She sits on the end of her bed, her hair in a towel, struggling to put the contact lenses in her eyes without looking in the mirror. She's fearful of what she might see. What her face might reveal.

It had been going so well, the time with her mum. Sophie had confessed it all, the lies and the deceit and Norma didn't judge or flinch. She didn't shout or say, 'I told you so.' She gave Sophie just what she needed, a tight hug of love. But after pulling away, she took Sophie firmly by the shoulders and looked her in the eye. 'I don't think you're well, love. You've been under so much stress for so long. I really think now is the time to go to the doctor and ask for some help.'

A punch to her stomach couldn't have been worse. It was the thing she really feared; the suggestion of some kind of mental weakness or instability. She stood and loomed over her

239

mother, her mind and her body consumed with sudden uncontrollable hurt and rage. 'You labelled me as a teenage slag and now I'm a fucking nut case? I should have known you wouldn't understand.'

Sophie has screamed those words, or similar, countless times to her mother over the years. But never before had she slapped her mother's face before stalking out of the house.

Antonia yawns as she studies her handwritten list. She's slept fitfully over the past week, waking up in the early hours but feeling too lonely to get up. Her mind has wandered, roaming from funeral food to the messages left by the insistent journalist, from hazy childhood to Sophie and to David, but not staying in one place for long. She expected to feel more. More grief, regret and guilt. Especially guilt. It's buried, she supposes, with everything else.

The Ridings called during the week. It was the manager herself, Mrs L Jones. Antonia held her breath as Mrs Jones introduced herself, wondering if she had a breaking point and if it was near. 'Candy would like to come to the funeral,' Mrs Jones said. 'I have no objection.'

'My mother has no idea whose funeral it is, you fool,' Antonia wanted to say. But the manager continued to speak in a syrupy voice that she had never heard before. 'It must be a terrible thing to lose your husband, Mrs Stafford. I'm very sorry. I hope having your mum there will give you some comfort.'

Antonia wanted to cry at that moment, but only for a moment, as anxiety set in. No one knew her mother here. No one knew about her history and her illness. The way she looked, the way she acted. Except Sophie.

'Of course a carer will come too, drive her over, keep her company and bring her back. You'll have other things to worry about,' the manager continued. 'I hope in some small way that helps.'

There's good in everyone, Antonia now thinks. Candy's wise words. Perhaps she's right.

There is a tremor in her hand as she scrutinises her list of finger foods yet again. She feels slightly nauseous. Like the dinner parties of old, she wants to impress. She knows Sophie will laugh at her for doing the catering herself. That she'll sneer and say no one appreciates a 'bloody martyr'. But what Sophie doesn't understand is that some things in life are a labour of love. Antonia didn't enjoy the dinner parties, not one bit. They were for David. Today is for David too.

'What are you doing, Sophie?'

Sami's frame fills the bedroom door. He's home earlier than Sophie expects. She has stuffed some clothes into a holdall, but she's found it difficult to concentrate on the task. Her mind only goes so far down her mental list of things to pack, toothbrush, knickers, glasses, before it bounces back to the beginning.

'What does it look like?' Sophie replies, but not in a challenging way. She just doesn't have the energy to explain, even if she tried to understand it herself.

'The funeral starts in an hour, Sophie.'

'I know. I'm not going.' She stares at the holdall. It looks deflated. There must be more she should pack. But her mind feels like jelly.

She glances up at Sami. His jaw is clenched. His knuckles are prominent on the metal bedstead.

'What am I supposed to say? To Antonia, to Mike and Olivia, to Charlie. To our friends, Sophie. What am I supposed to say?' His voice is tight, controlled.

'That I've gone away for a few days, of course.'

She can feel his anger like a hot burning coal in her chest. She doesn't want him to be angry. She wants everything to be OK. Only it isn't. She turns and looks at Sami's beautiful face, then lifts her trembling hand to touch the small scar on his forehead. 'I'm sorry, I really am. I just need to get away.'

She knows Sami will flinch from her touch, even before he jerks away and stalks from the room. 'Don't you want to know where I'm going?' she calls after him.

'I don't give a shit,' he shouts. 'And this time, don't bother coming back.'

CHAPTER THIRTY

The day of the funeral is like flash photography. It gallops by, leaving only a few mental images. An album of moments and snatches of conversation stored temporarily in Antonia's mind.

David's coffin is brass and mahogany, an elegant dark box covered in an exquisite wreath of white lilies that someone has chosen. Today is surreal; his death doesn't feel real. She didn't see him after the bath. She declined when they asked if she wanted to. A dead David wasn't David. Even to say goodbye.

The weather is wrongly dressed for a funeral. It's bright, far too bright for October. But unusually chilly too, there's a thin covering of frost on the gravestones. Grace, Elizabeth, Ethel, Margaret. Names she might have chosen instead of Antonia.

The church is her local Anglican. A proper old stone church with a steeple, an archway and a choir. A kind place, she senses. The pews are scratched and worn, the hymn books are tatty and the sun shines colour through the stained-glass windows. It feels warm and welcoming. Not the cold and impersonal crematorium at Southern Cemetery with one in and one out like a take-away shop. David deserves far better than Jimmy. Thank goodness for that.

There are many people in the small crowded apse as she walks to the front. People she knows, people she doesn't, faces she recognises but can't name. She sees a row of young lads at the back, their heads bowed as they whisper. Two of the girls from the book club. Then little Rachel in a hat, squashed between Olivia and Mike, her eyes huge in her small face.

David's work partners and their wives sit to one side. They're chatting. Too much chatting, she thinks, and too loud. Charlie isn't there but his mother and her brother sit solemnly. Valerie has a violet handkerchief to her face and the uncle looks ashen and frail. A slim, attractive older woman with red ginger hair sits on one side of Helen. A huge man on the other. Then there's Rupert, lovely Rupert, tapping his leg, his fringe in his face.

She glimpses Colin Green and his wife, plain and pregnant, next to Candy and her carer. Does her mum look bewildered? She said hello and gave her a reassuring kiss earlier, but it's difficult to tell. There are too many faceless hands and cheeks to know what anyone might be thinking. Their words are murmured and instantly gone. But Sami is there. Solid Sami, his face set. He's waiting for her on the front pew and he holds out his hand to take hers. He's alone.

Antonia doesn't think she'll cry, but the burning at the top of her nose starts the moment Rupert rises and walks to the front of the church. He stands next to the coffin holding a sheet of paper, his face white with nerves. He's wearing a too-short school suit. She had no idea he would speak.

'As many of you know, my father is still unwell in hospital. He tried to escape, but they caught him.' There's a small tremor of polite laughter. 'But he asked me to read a few words.'

The few words are many, which Rupert reads with shaking

244

hands but in a loud clear voice. Loving words, warm and funny. Tales of school and sporting achievements, stories she hasn't heard before. An explanation about David's parents too. Loving parents, Rupert reads, who tragically died together in a car crash, when David was so young. He's at peace with them now.

Black ice, Antonia thinks. Like so much in life. You can't see it but it's there.

'David was loved,' Rupert finishes, his tears soaking the paper. 'Loved very much.'

Charlie's tender words from the voice of his boy.

The Anglican hymns and prayers are so similar to hers. Not a priest, but a vicar, with a kindly booming voice. 'A popular man,' he says. 'A generous man. Much loved by all.' He offers David back to God.

Antonia turns her head, then. To Candy and the carer. Is this the same God that her mum adored but forgot, she wonders. Does Candy remember him now?

Then it's over, so quickly. Her limbs are automatic as she stands. But she's grateful for Sami's firm hand under her elbow as he guides her down the aisle to an open world without David. 'I'll drive you back to White Gables,' she hears him say. 'I'm so sorry Sophie's not here. It's unforgivable.'

Sophie's car has a sat nav, but she hates the female voice. It's smug and satisfied. Sophie is well aware that's what people think of her too; they've said it enough times. She knows she can appear that way, sometimes even feel that way. But what she's not, she's absolutely not, is unstable, depressed, bipolar. Or whatever her fucking mother might think.

She glances at the AA route planner on the passenger seat, still damp from her earlier tears. She feels fine now, absolutely fine. In fact the rush of adrenaline she felt when she drove out of Didsbury is still with her after thirty fast miles, goading her on.

It's a right on to Meadow Lane and then first left. She's sung along with Madonna the whole way, belting out the lyrics through the open window even though it's so cold. 'The Immaculate Collection' CD, bought by her dad when she was a kid. They used to sing it together. She still knows every word.

She pulls up the car, flips down the mirror flap and presses the lipstick on her mouth to get an even full spread. Then she fluffs up her hair. She grins at herself and nods. Here goes.

The door is answered eventually. 'Yes?' The girl is young, certainly no more than twenty-five. She's not conventionally pretty but has a stunning ponytail of thick blonde hair down the back of her petite frame. A T-shirt barely covers her thighs. The girl puts a hand on her hip and examines Sophie with luminous eyes, her lips in a dismissive slant.

Sophie pushes past her into the warmth of the flat. The aroma of sex and dope fills her nostrils. She didn't expect it to be so small. The bedroom door is ajar, the bedcovers rumpled and the curtains closed.

'I take it that you know Baz.' The girl has a high-pitched southern accent. Essex, Sophie guesses. 'The sort of accent that makes her sound stupid,' she would laugh with Antonia.

'I do. Where is he?'

The girl falls back on to the sofa and folds her arms. 'I'm not sure if that's any of your business.'

'I'd better wait then.'

Sophie sits down in the armchair opposite, her chin high and her eyes on the girl. She folds her arms. Smug and satisfied, she thinks, don't desert me now.

*

Sami holds Antonia's hand in the car. He squeezes tightly and silently as she closes her eyes. She understands they are friends again after their spat about Sophie. Warm and dependable once more, like the big brother he's always been, which is such a relief. Then suddenly they're back on the large driveway at White Gables. Antonia shakes herself and turns around to look through the rear window. Cars have followed. People are climbing out. They're milling and chatting. Hungry and thirsty, no doubt.

She strides from Sami's car. There's a job to be done; she has a purpose now.

Like a wedding, she thinks, as she opens the fridge, turns on the ovens, peels away cling film and foil. Nibbles are heated, drinks are poured, time flies and Antonia floats above it all.

'We're here to help, remember. Where are the tea towels?'

'I'll carry that tray, Antonia. Sami's opening the wine.'

'I'm Robert Smith. We met at law college. Such a great guy.'

'We're so sorry for your loss. The other girls send their love.'

'What a fabulous eulogy. Chip off the old block. Hope Charlie's on the mend.'

She walks from room to room with a bottle or a tray. Hearing everything. Hearing nothing.

'We heard you were stunning, Mrs Stafford. Dave had a great left foot!'

'A hundred not out, and a hat trick if I remember. Should have gone into sport.'

'Sorry I've left all the visiting to Mike. Thank you for being so sweet to Rachel. She adores you, you know.'

'Dad sends his love. Hopping mad he couldn't come. I hope I did OK.'

'You look really pretty, Antonia. Can I help?'

From the lounge to the kitchen, she offers snacks from silver trays. Hears snatches of conversation as she glides among the guests.

'Can I see you, Olivia? I really miss you.'

'They confiscated her scarf. I can see it now after all these years.'

'I didn't think people had mistresses any more. And look at her, she's so old.'

'You've done an excellent spread, Antonia. I'll make sure to tell Charles I was wrong.'

'No smoke without fire.'

People want to talk, but she finds it's easier to keep moving. There are glasses to fill and plates to collect.

'Should I turn off the oven?'

'No kids. I wonder why.'

'She's called Misty, apparently! No, really, that's her name.'

'Come on, one more time. It was great, wasn't it?'

The party is going well. She should stop and chat. But still Antonia drifts, not chatting, not speaking, but still hearing and seeing. Hearing things she doesn't want to. Seeing glimpses of David. She offers sweet treats. Checks platters and plates.

'It's very red, her hair. It must be dyed.'

'Please leave it there and let's stay friends.'

'Keep your voice down. She's just there.'

'Should I turn off the oven?'

'Antonia, love, should I turn off the oven?'

It seems to Antonia as though everyone leaves together, suddenly. The house is full one minute and empty the next. Just Mike, Rachel, Olivia and Sami are left. They're standing in the kitchen with twitchy feet, all eyes on her. 'Are you all right? Would you like us to stay?' said almost in unison.

Antonia looks around and shakes her head. The platters are

248

mostly empty, just cocktail sticks, flakes and crumbs remain. 'The food's all gone. Do you think everyone had enough to eat?' she asks.

Sami laughs and kisses her cheek. His eyes seemed distracted and she guesses the answer is Sophie. Sophie's absence. But Antonia is glad that she didn't come, the fine line between her kindness and her cruelty was one less thing to worry about.

'The spread was fantastic,' Sami says. 'You did David proud. Really proud. I'm going now, Antonia. Call me if you need me. Anything, yeah?'

'We'd better get back to Hannah,' Olivia says as Sami walks away. 'I'm sorry we can't stay longer, but my sister needs to get back to her kids.'

Antonia nods. 'Of course, thank you for everything. Especially you, Rachel. You were a star.'

The cold breeze blows in through the open front door as they leave. Someone has moved David's car and the loose bricks of the small wall have been stacked neatly to one side. Antonia didn't notice before. 'Who's Misty?' she asks.

Mike takes a breath, but it's Olivia who answers. 'She's married to Seamus, the really big guy. Isn't she, Mike? They own the Royal Oak.' She pauses for a moment, her eyes flickering to Mike's. 'Do you know, I don't like to leave you all alone so soon,' she says, putting a hand on Antonia's arm. 'I'm sure Mike won't mind staying for a while. He can just about manage to wash up the dishes, but I'd keep an eye on your best crystal.'

'That's true, Dad,' Rachel laughs. 'And maybe Mum will let me come round tomorrow for a bit. You could give me some tips on make-up and stuff.'

'Hey cheeky, you're only twelve,' Mike says with a smile, but he's looking at Antonia.

CHAPTER THIRTY-ONE

'Do you think Antonia will be all right, Mum? It must be so horrible for her. She's really nice, don't you think?' Rachel asks from the passenger seat of the car.

Olivia stares ahead through the windscreen, her body plugged into the miraculous autopilot she's used for days. Rachel is chattering, has been chattering since they left White Gables, pulling at a loose strand from the black ribbon on her hat. There's too much noise, it's too invasive. Olivia's mind is jangling, she needs silence to think.

'I was starving in the church, but the food was ace. You know those mini banoffee tarts? Antonia showed me how to make the salted caramel, so I sort of helped. Do you think Dad will drive me over tomorrow? Or you could drop me off if you're going to M&S. You said Hannah needed socks.' She looks over at Olivia. 'Mum, you're not listening.'

'Of course I am,' Olivia replies. She's holding on to her reasonable voice by a thread. 'Yes, that's fine, I'll take you. Stop pulling the ribbon, Rachel. You'll ruin it.'

Rachel is silent for a moment. Then another torrent of patter.

'What did you think of the funeral, Mum? How many people were there? Uncle Sami was on his own, wasn't he? Where was Sophie? That man was so fat! I thought that Rupert was really brave to stand up and read out Charlie's speech. He's so tall! But quite good looking. Is Charlie still in hospital, Mum? Is he going to get better? I really hope so for Rupert's sake. It was so sad when he cried. I thought that Uncle Sami looked quite cross. Do you know why Sophie wasn't there? Mum? Mum?'

The thread breaks. 'Rachel. Can you shut up, for just a moment! Stop asking so many questions.' Sharply, like a slap.

Rachel looks hurt and turns away, the hat sullen on her lap. The car jolts as it stalls. Olivia sighs. 'I'm sorry, Rach. I didn't mean to shout. It's dark and I'm just trying to concentrate on my driving. OK?'

'Have you broken any yet?' Antonia says to Mike's white-shirted back.

He's at the large sink with his sleeves rolled up. Suds are bubbling on to the drainer.

'Absolutely not, not a chip in sight. Though I might've used too much washing-up liquid.'

Antonia smiles. 'Don't worry, I'll give them a rinse in the other sink. That's the beauty of having two!'

Mike turns his head and grins. She notices his teeth. They look very white against his stubble. He's so darkly attractive and yet kind. His looks and personality don't match, she thinks.

'This feels like washing up at a friend's house when you're ten. Wanting to please and your mate looking daggers at you when his mum says how helpful you are.'

'Were you always a good little boy? Wanting to please?' she asks, her back to his at the sink.

'Well, the mums liked me! But in my own home, if I'm

251

honest, Mum did all the household stuff. Dad and I weren't expected to.'

'That's terrible.' Though as Antonia says it, she wonders why. David never lifted a finger in the house. She didn't want him to. The house was her job and she liked it. Being David's wife too. It made them both happy. But she hears Sami's words from a few weeks ago when she tried to talk to him about Sophie. 'Look at your own marriage,' he said. What did he mean?

'Oh, don't worry, Olivia soon had me trained,' Mike replies, turning back to his sink. 'I should have taken my tie off, shouldn't I?'

He flicks his black tie over his shoulder and continues with his chore as Antonia watches the soapy fingerprints on the tie disappear.

The washing up of the glassware has been a distraction. As has the sweeping of the kitchen floor and the emptying of the bins. Mike knows that the question will come at some point, but has no idea how he should or will reply.

He hovers near his jacket on the coat stand in the hall, debating on whether or not to call a taxi and escape, but Antonia appears from the kitchen. Her lips are slightly parted as she concentrates on carrying a full large glass of red wine. 'Your reward for being such a "good boy" seeing as you're not driving. Come on through and sit down.'

She's tied her hair in a large knot at the top of her head. Mike thinks how young she looks. Exotic too. Her neck is long and slim, but her eyes seem hidden somehow, though he can see them quite clearly in her serious face.

Cheers, Olivia. You've really put this one on me, he thinks vaguely. But it feels right. Antonia's shown him the cut, he's already involved.

She sits down on the sofa, curls up her legs and bows her head. 'I trust you to be honest, Mike,' she starts and he knows that he will answer truthfully.

'Was David having an affair with this Misty person?'

Mike takes a deep breath before answering. Seconds pass. His eyes reach hers, then he speaks. 'I never discussed it with him. I believe that he saw her from time to time, but it's not something I would describe as an affair.'

'How would you describe it, then?' Her question is immediate, her voice tight.

Mike rakes his hair. He finds it hard to explain what he thinks, but he wants to be honest. 'She's a fair bit older than David and it's not as though he was after women in general. To be honest, I don't think he particularly noticed them.'

'Did he pay for it?'

Her question throws him. 'No. I don't know. Does it matter?' he replies.

She stands from the sofa and stalks to the fireplace. 'It does, actually.' Then she turns and glares at Mike, her eyes dark and fierce. 'What about you? Do you go to other women for either paid or unpaid relief? Is that what married men do? Am I just out of touch?'

'No, I haven't ever . . .' His voice trails off. The conversation is going badly. He didn't expect such anger. 'Look, he adored you. You know that. I have no idea what their friendship was. It was just rumours. I'm sure it didn't mean anything.'

'Of course it meant something. Like his death meant something. It's me, isn't it? I'm cold and hard and unable to love.'

Mike stands too. He takes Antonia in his arms and holds her tightly. He wants to say that her words are ridiculous. He wants to tell her that she's beautiful and very, very lovable. To say the words out loud, but some instinct holds him back.

'Look, David's mother died when he was young, right?' he says instead, his head thoughtful but his body instinctively alert to hers.

Antonia pulls away slightly and searches his face with troubled eyes. 'So, what are you saying? That she was some sort of mother substitute?'

'Well, perhaps.'

She frowns and wipes the tears from her nose with the back of her hand. Then she looks at him straight. 'Like you're a father figure to me?'

Mike releases his arms and steps away. 'Well, I'm not that old!' His laugh sounds empty and his heart feels a stab. 'But yes, in a way, I suppose so.'

The girl with the hair helps herself to juice from the fridge in the small kitchen annex. She sips it slowly from a pint glass and glares at Sophie without offering her any. Half an hour or maybe more passes before she detaches her spaced-out gaze from Sophie's face, fetches some jeans and her mobile. Then another half before Barry turns up with a wry smile. He doesn't look much different, Sophie observes. A youthful tanned face with thick greying hair. Still slim and fit. She can see why men, women and too-young girls still fancy him despite his being in his mid-fifties.

'So you two have met, then?' he asks with a grin.

There's a flicker of emotion from the girl's eyes. 'Zoë,' he says. 'This is my daughter, Sophie. I hope that you've been looking after her.'

Zoë's mouth opens for a moment before she recovers herself with a shrug and says that she had better be going.

'She reminds me of you,' Barry says when she's gone.

They sit in silence for a while, listening to a muffled drumbeat from the adjoining flat.

'Are you going to talk to me now that you're here, Sophie? You could have phoned and given me some warning.'

'I thought you were on nights.'

'I was the last time we spoke. But that was a long time ago, Soph.'

Sophie looks at her father and sighs. It was a mistake to turn up unannounced. She feels deflated and tired. 'I thought you'd be pleased to see me,' she says, not able to keep the pique from her voice.

Sophie despises her own neediness. She badly wants a drink. An alcoholic drink. It took a great deal of effort not to shove the girl away from the fridge earlier and drink straight from the wine bottle she glimpsed next to the milk.

As though reading her mind Barry stands and opens the fridge door. 'Course I'm pleased to see you,' he says absently. 'Are you hungry?' He passes the wine bottle to Sophie. 'You crack that open and I'll make us an omelette.'

Olivia is sapped. She's fed up with putting on a face that isn't hers. She's tired of fighting the constant nausea and the brutal rounds of ugly thoughts in her head.

Bad, bad mother, she thinks as she lies on the soft double bed in the dark. Hannah was clingy after her bath. She cried and demanded another story. She wanted milk, she wanted Daddy, even Rachel. She wanted anything other than to close her eyes and bloody well sleep.

I want to bang my head against the wall. I want to scream! Olivia thought, but instead she asked Rachel if she wouldn't mind reading Hannah another story and Rachel nodded, her silent eyes still reproachful.

'I'm sorry about shouting in the car,' Olivia had said when they arrived home.

'Don't worry about it, I'm getting used to it,' Rachel replied. And there it was again. Bad, bad mother. Bad person, bad wife.

Olivia yearns to fall into an empty sleep as the pillow cradles her head. But her mind isn't that kind. It's still playing out the imaginary conversation she'll have with the doctor when she sees him next week.

'I've had time to think. I want a termination.'

'Why?'

'Because I'm at the end of my tether. I don't feel I could cope if I had another miscarriage.'

Olivia rocks her head. She doesn't look like a woman who can't cope, and besides, she's never sought help or medication for depression or stress. It's really a non-starter.

'I don't want a baby. I want a life,' her mind tries. That sounds much better because it's the truth, or at least part of it, but it's hardly grounds for an abortion.

'Have you discussed this with your husband, Mrs Turner?'

And Olivia will have to reply, 'No.'

Then doctor will say, 'Can I ask why you haven't told him?'

Ah, there's the rub. She turns and presses her face firmly into the pillow as her mind reasons and pokes.

'It might not be his,' her mind soothes.

'But if it is, there'd be no mistake,' it needles her in reply.

God knows what happened. God knows what insanity made her change her mind about Sami.

'What on earth do all these women see in him, Mike?' she used to ask.

'Good looking, confident, well off?' he'd reply.

'But he's so conceited and shallow. There's nothing beneath his pretty face. He really irritates me.'

'I think he's got that message, Olivia!'

She looked anywhere but at Sami during the funeral service.

She hung back with Rachel in the church, fearful of catching his eye, terrified that by some strange instinct he would look at her and know. Know that she's carrying his child. But after the church, when they congregated at White Gables, there was no escape. No escape from his hot gaze across the kitchen. No escape as he approached her with a smile. Tall, lithe and sexual. She'd been greedy and abandoned and she hated him for it.

'Can I see you, Olivia?' he said. 'I really miss you. Come on, one more time. It was great, wasn't it?'

She wonders what her face looked like as she said the words in reply. Did it betray her terror, her loathing, her regret? She touched his arm and tried to smile. To be the Olivia she used to be. 'Please don't, Sami,' she whispered. 'Please leave it there and let's stay friends.'

CHAPTER THIRTY-TWO

Mike bends down to tie the laces on his trainers. The old house is silent, unusually so.

'The girls are still out for the count,' he whispers to Olivia as she stirs. 'Go back to sleep. I'm off for a run. I'll wake you when I get back.'

The morning is misty and cold, a slight drizzle in the air. Mike stretches for a minute, then lifts his hood and starts to run past the other Victorian homes in his cul-de-sac and then on to the main street with its assortment of small cafes, drink houses and take-outs. It's strange, not having the black dog with him. A void, in a way. Perhaps that is why he needed to fill it, he thinks.

The notion that he was father-like was a blow, an unexpected blow. It wasn't an unfair suggestion, even if he is only eight years or so older than Antonia. It's what he intended, absolutely. Yet it hurt. Dreadfully. He drank the glass of wine quickly and made his excuses. Said he'd call for a taxi. 'What, already?' she said, her eyes looking forlorn. Then she recovered herself. 'I'll drive you. Of course. But before you go, I just wanted to show you . . .'

He feels his heart pumping in his chest with the effort of running. His pace is faster than usual. He wants to run down by the Mersey river to the water park, to sit on a bench and watch the birds at the lake.

She knelt in front of Mike's chair and unbuttoned the sleeve of her crisp white blouse. Then she rolled the sleeve up, layer by layer in neat folds until her slim arm was fully exposed. Her eyes were glued to his, expectant. 'It's healed,' he observed, conscious of her body, her exquisite face. 'I know!' she replied, beaming. Pleased. Like a child.

He was angry then. 'What the fuck,' he wanted to say. 'What the fuck do you want from me? Do you really not know what you're doing to me?'

She sat back and looked hurt. 'You're cross with me. I thought you'd be pleased that I haven't . . .' Her small voice trailed off.

'I am. It's great. It's just—'

'What have I done wrong?' she asked, her eyes still on his.

He wanted to stand, to escape, but if he stood at that moment it would be all too apparent what was wrong.

'Nothing at all. Really. You probably want some peace,' he replied.

She leaned forward again, her body between his thighs, her hand reaching up to his face.

'Your hair.' She smiled, running smooth fingers through it. 'It's going curly.'

'Perhaps you should trim it—' he started to reply. But by then the weight of her upper body was firm on his groin. He could smell her skin, feel her breath. Then her lips, her soft lips.

Lifting his hands to her face, he kissed her, deeply kissed, momentarily lost and unable to stop. Then summoning all that remained of his self-control, he pulled away, lifted her smooth hands from around his neck and held them firmly in his. 'I'm sorry, that was wrong of me. You're full of grief and confusion and unanswered questions and I'm . . .'

The drizzle has turned to rain. Mike's legs feel heavy. He's had far too little sleep. But his head is determined as he runs against the flow of the river.

'Coffee for you,' Barry says.

Sophie opens her eyes and sees her dad clearly. She stretches out a leg from beneath the blanket. Her whole body aches. The wine sent her straight off last night. A good thing, she notes looking down. She's considerably longer than Barry's black leather sofa.

He holds out the steaming drink. He met her wine glass for glass during the evening. Yet he looks fresh and alert, scrubbed and dressed in his nurse's uniform for work.

'You'll be gone when I'm back?'

Sophie sits up, pulls out the hair trapped behind her back and takes the mug. 'Is that a question or a command?'

Barry grins. 'Come on, Soph. You're all grown up now. You wouldn't want to spoil your old dad's love life.'

Sophie blinks, finally registering what's wrong. She fell asleep wearing her contact lenses. She's awoken with sight, which feels particularly ironic today.

'Why did you marry Mum?' she asks, looking carefully at his handsome face.

'We went over this last night.'

'OK. Then why did you betray her? It wasn't as though it was just the once.'

He turns his head towards a photograph of Sophie as a child. She's squeezed between her two smaller brothers, wearing the pink National Health glasses she hated. He shrugs. 'It's complicated. I never really analysed it.'

'Liar.'

He turns away, picks up a canvas bag and some keys. 'It was lovely to see you, Soph. Pull the door to when you leave. And call me in advance next time.'

Barry plays with the keys for a moment, his back to her. 'I always felt inadequate and blamed her. I needed the endorsement. Pathetic really, and self-perpetuating.' He turns and nods with a small smile, then blows Sophie a kiss and leaves.

It's so hard to judge. It isn't like the old days when Antonia didn't care. 'Take it from me,' Sophie always said. 'If you want to do it, they definitely want to.' She slept around, as did Sophie, if bushes and bus stops and bedsits counted as sleeping. Antonia liked the kissing mostly, the foreplay sometimes, but the intercourse rarely.

It was fine with David. He was always gentle and there were times when she almost came. At least she thought so. But David never seemed to notice. 'Say please,' he whispered. 'Tell me you want me.' So she said the words and David would orgasm and laugh joyously. He was happy, delighted, which made her happy too.

The mistake, long ago when they were teenagers, was to confide in Sophie. They were lying on Sophie's bed at her mum's house. They'd been with some boys drinking pear cider in Wythenshawe Park and she was tipsy, too tipsy.

'I don't really like it that much,' Antonia had confessed. 'It doesn't hurt or anything, but I don't feel . . . Well, nothing happens.'

Sophie propped herself up and examined her face with a grin.

'You need to practise. Haven't you tried doing it yourself? With your fingers. Everyone else does.' Her green eyes were mischievous and mocking. She slipped a hand down between Antonia's thighs, into her panties and touched. Soft but firm. 'Like this? And this? Use spit if you're dry.'

'Stop!' Antonia declared. But it was too late. Like static electricity she'd felt it and Sophie had seen. Sophie knew.

Antonia flips on to her belly on the king-sized bed, her body goosebumped, although she's so hot. The closest she ever came to feeling that frisson was with the razor blade. Her Friday night treat. Until the night of David's death. As inappropriate as it was, she had felt it then. Desire. Lust. Growing and swelling inside her. Mike had held her when she cried and she'd felt it then, like a spreading blaze. She wanted him to fuck her, to take her and fuck her. But it was only a craving, a thought, a feeling. She would never act on it. David was dead. Olivia was her friend.

There have been moments when she's caught a flash, a dark glint of connection in Mike's eyes when he's looked at her. But it's happened so fleetingly that she doesn't know, she isn't sure. He's always brought Rachel with him too. Which is fine, she is lovely. Mike is just caring and kind, like a brother, like a father. Isn't he? Then there's Olivia. Nice Mumsy Olivia. Olivia her friend who she wouldn't betray. Until yesterday, at the wake. When she passed Sami and Olivia in the kitchen. When she clearly heard their conversation.

Olivia isn't asleep. She was awake when Mike climbed into bed late last night. His breath became deep and slow the moment his head touched the pillow. The innocent sleep, she thought, as she continued to stare at images through her closed eyelids. 'Sleep that knits up the raveled sleave of care.'

She wonders if she's slept at all. The same pictures are still here this morning. That of Sami naked. Sami smiling. Sami declaring his love. But she feels cold and dispassionate. She doesn't recognise the woman in the images. The woman who's so gluttonous and uninhibited, the woman who fucked her husband's close friend in her marital bed for weeks. Moments of madness? On another planet? Frailty? Yes frailty, she thinks. That woman has succumbed to flattery and she despises her for it.

Olivia writes the newspaper article behind her closed eyes. 'Counsel for the defence argued that the respondent was at a low point in her life. She'd recently miscarried a baby. Her husband had become remote. She suspected him of having an affair. She felt unattractive and ignored. She no longer worked and felt she'd lost her identity. It was therefore inevitable that, subjected to a sustained onslaught of compliments and flattery, she would revert to the frailty of all womankind.'

Though hardly justification for what she's done, it's true. Yet if she's honest, it wasn't just a silly woman's frailty, it was also deliberate and vengeful. Like that Old Testament God. If Mike was having an affair with Judith, then why shouldn't she? Who better than one of his closest friends? Poetic justice, she thought at the time. Which was wrong. Wrong on any level, she knows.

Divine retribution and wrath. That woman tempted fate and must now face the consequences.

Sami is in the tiny walled garden of his townhouse, listening to the discordant peal of St James's church bells. A wedding, he assumes. A couple's happy day, a thought that he quickly dismisses.

The perimeter of the garden is lined with high red-brick beds filled with plants he can't name. They're bowed, losing their leaves or their colour, looking to Sami as though they're dying a slow death.

He rakes up the fallen leaves in his hands wearing Sophie's Marigolds, then snips off the protruding bare branches with secateurs, carefully picking up the spiky twigs and putting them in a black bin liner. Pruning makes him feel like his dad. 'Preparing for life after death,' as he puts it. Sami thinks he'll call him later and have a chat. 'Hey, Dad. Guess what I've been doing. How's the leg?'

He knows his dad's been lucky, really. A relatively small stroke, affecting just his left side. And only seven months ago, so still room for improvement. But his personality has changed from the gregarious successful barrister he was to a moody recluse stuck at home with too many women. Or maybe he's just depressed. Sami has never been depressed. Miserable as a boy, granted, but never depressed. He vaguely understands that it can happen with illness and stress, when life goes awry. But he misses the old dad very much. As a child he would go to him in his study, even when it was forbidden, to escape the smother of Martha's love. He'd sit there in silence, reading a comic or playing with a toy, while his dad read his brief for court the next day. Nothing was ever said, but Sami felt his father understood how difficult it was to sever the tie of Martha's intense maternal love. To grow from fat boy to man, when he really wanted to be a mummy's boy forever.

It could so easily have been Dad in that coffin, he thinks as he crouches down. He scoops up a fistful of soil, letting it slip back to the ground through his fingers.

Thank God David didn't have children. Losing a father must be unbearable, even when you're supposed to be a man. Sami has thought a lot about David since the funeral, more than he imagined he would. It's the end of an era. There'll be no more dinner parties at White Gables. Friday in the pub will never be the same. There'll be no more banter between them. No more soft jibes.

'They didn't mean anything,' he says out loud to the garden. 'They were just a bit of fun.'

Yet the jibes bother him now. 'You're putting weight on, Dave. You're losing your touch. You'd better keep an eye on Antonia. She's a stunner. Your hair's getting thin. Naughty boy, Dave. A taste for redheads, eh? You wouldn't want Antonia to find out.'

He remembers his last conversation with David. Only in retrospect does he realise it must have been on the afternoon of his death, perhaps even his final call. The thought makes him uncomfortable, a chill on his spine.

It was a telephone call out of the blue. 'What the fuck are you doing with Antonia?' David demanded.

'Nothing,' he replied, caught on the hop at work, surprised at David's unexpected call and his anger.

'I've just listened to your fucking answerphone message, Sami. The one you left for Antonia today. What have you got to be sorry about? You've been here, haven't you? In my house. With my wife. You've been—'

But Sami cut the tirade off. He'd tried to speak to Antonia and to apologise for upsetting her over their Sophie meeting at White Gables several times. He'd followed it up with the answerphone message. But the whole thing with Sophie's drinking and with babies was difficult. Personal. Embarrassing. Humiliating. He hadn't felt able to talk about it to Antonia, so he wasn't going to explain it to David of all people.

'She asked me to go to your fucking house, David. It was Antonia who started it. Stop giving me grief and speak to her,' he replied before ending the call.

Sami hadn't been kind to Antonia when she'd tried to talk to

265

him about Sophie's drinking at White Gables. 'Look at your own marriage, stop interfering in mine,' he'd snapped. He'd assumed David's angry call was because he'd upset her. But, thinking about it now, he feels David was suggesting something more about the visit. He might even have said, 'You've been screwing my wife.' But of course that's ridiculous; Sami likes Antonia very much, he's always felt a protective and brotherly love for her, not least for the connection of their skin colour. But he'd never dream of propositioning her, not even as a joke. He wouldn't put her in that position, she'd be embarrassed and shocked.

Sami shrugs off the memory of the conversation. They weren't particularly nice words to end on, but they had no bearing on David's suicide, surely? It's the thought of the occasional sniping that bothers him more. He knows he could have tempered that.

He stands and looks up to the sky. The drizzle wets his face. 'The quips didn't mean anything. You gave as good as you got, didn't you, David?' he asks. He feels abandoned and lonely and unbearably sad. 'I'm sorry, man,' he adds. 'I'll miss you. I bloody will.'

The geese are milling about on the banks of the lake at the water park. They're vocal, angry and loud. Or so it seems to Mike. But who can tell? He wonders if he's ever been able to read situations, or whether it's a recent failure. Olivia, Rachel and Judith. Even Sami. He asked Sami what happened to Sophie, where was she, when she didn't appear at the funeral or at the wake.

'Things are difficult at the moment,' Sami replied. 'We've tried for a baby for a while and I think it's getting to her.'

Mike nodded, thinking, these things happen, it takes time, poor Sophie.

But then Sami said, 'We've had the tests and stuff. It seems I'm a Jaffa, you know, seedless.' Sami laughed, trying for humour, but it didn't spread to his face.

'God, sorry to hear that, mate,' Mike replied, trying not to show his surprise that Sami had any problems, let alone that type of problem.

The surface of the lake ripples as the rain becomes heavier. Mike knows he should move from the wooden bench. His shorts are soaked and they cling to him, but his eyes are transfixed by a lone swan gliding silently through the water.

He squints through the rain as he stands. Aren't swans meant to swim in pairs? Don't they mate for life? He remains rooted to the spot, his eyes scouring the mere for another swan. He needs to know. Really know. The kiss with Antonia was unmistakable. It was too sensuous, too intense and too long to be anything other than mutual desire.

Mike starts to run. He can feel the water from his hoodie streaming down the back of his legs. He shakes the rain from his hair and increases his pace, searching for the swan as he heads for home.

CHAPTER THIRTY-THREE

'Come on Daddy, keep up!' Hannah calls.

The local park is crisp and cold, the wind sharp against their faces. Hannah runs ahead and wades through rusty-coloured leaves in her pink-spotted wellington boots. Rachel hangs by Mike's side, looking down as she kicks the autumn carpet. 'Everything all right?' Mike asks, putting a hand around her shoulder and kissing the top of her head.

Rachel nods and then sprints away towards Hannah. She has something on her mind, Mike guesses. But she's like him in many ways. She's not ready to talk. 'I wish she wouldn't do that,' Olivia occasionally comments. 'She needs to be more vocal. People will think she's a pushover.' 'But she isn't a pushover. And that's what counts,' Mike replies. But he understands Olivia's frustration. Olivia is assertive, strong and opinionated. Not in a bad way. It was one of the things that attracted him back at university. The paradox between how she looks and how she behaves. She's blonde, fine featured and petite, but she's the first to wade into the fray, to stand up and be counted for something she believes in. He admires her enormously for it.

Strength, not weakness, he sighs inwardly. As simple as that. Sometimes that's all it takes.

'Daddy's sorry. It's only a bump,' Mike says as he rubs Hannah's knee. She's still crying, though from the scrunch of her pretty face it looks like an effort to squeeze out any more tears. He can see Rachel in his periphery vision, desperate to laugh. And it was funny. Rachel and Hannah were on one side of the see-saw and he was on the other. He bumped them about and Hannah squealed with pleasure. Until she let go of the handle and fell off.

The highs and lows of life, he thinks as he wipes Hannah's face with a hanky. Just a breath in between.

'Will some sweets help, do you think?' he asks, offering up the miracle cure.

'It will have to be a *lot* of sweets, Daddy,' Hannah replies sagely as Rachel clenches her fist in a silent 'result!'

Hannah rushes ahead in the direction of sugar. Her cheeks are flushed with excitement. But Rachel hangs back again and takes Mike's hand. 'Dad . . .' she begins, her face looking uncertain.

'Yup?'

Rachel takes a deep breath. 'Is Mum pregnant again?'

Mike stops walking immediately and calls Hannah back from her race to the corner shop. 'No. I don't think so. What makes you say that?'

Her face flushes and her eyes flicker. 'Oh, it's just . . . She's like she was last time. She's biting my head off over nothing. She doesn't look normal and she's being sick.' Rachel looks down at her feet, then kicks away a ruptured tennis ball. 'Sorry, Dad. Have I said the wrong thing?'

Mike shakes his head. He takes Rachel's hand again and holds it firmly. 'No, of course not.'

He feels winded and foolish, but he tries for a smile. 'OK, sweet shop. I've got a fiver in my pocket. What damage can you girls do to it?'

'Sorry, Mum,' Sophie says with shivery teeth.

Sophie stands at Norma's front door rubbing her arms from the cold. She's wearing no make-up and her hair looks in need of a good wash, but her eyes are clear. She looks like Sophie this time.

Norma holds out her arms. It's strange, she thinks, it's strange how you mull over things and ruminate, waiting for a 'sorry' to come, a moment when, inwardly at least, you can crow and gloat and say 'finally!' But when it comes and you hear the word aloud, you only want to say sorry, too.

'Oh, I'm sorry, too, love. Come in and get warm. I'll call work and say I won't be in this afternoon.'

Norma hasn't baked a cake in months, but she's making one now, the chocolate roulade her kids always love. Sophie watches from the kitchen table, mostly silent but talking occasionally about Barry. She tells Norma that he has a young moody girl-friend, that he wasn't pleased to see her, that he didn't even ask why Sophie was there. That he only thinks of himself.

The crowing and the gloating should be even sweeter, but it isn't.

'Have you decided what to do? About Antonia. About Sami?' Norma eventually asks.

Sophie puts her hands to her face and shakes her head. Her nails are badly bitten, the tips of her fingers red and raw. 'No. I don't know what to do. Everything feels hopeless.'

'That isn't true, love. Believe it or not, I do understand.'

'Do you, Mum? I've messed up so badly.'

Norma sighs. She's messed up, too. When Sophie was only

270

just nineteen she was brought by ambulance to the hospital with severe abdominal pains. She had chlamydia, untreated chlamydia, possibly for years. Her daughter's pelvis was inflamed with a severe infection. Ironically, it was the same hospital where Norma worked. She was an experienced, respected nurse and was working on the geriatric ward when Sophie arrived. An experienced and respected nurse who'd seen nothing amiss with her only daughter, even though they lived under the same roof.

'You think I'm a slag, don't you?' Sophie accused her with angry eyes when Norma appeared at her hospital bed, breathing heavily from running and from fright. But Norma didn't reply. She was fighting the urge not to shout. 'Why didn't you tell me? Am I such an ogre? Do you hate me so much? I would have helped you, of course I would!' So she backed away, saying nothing, the words, 'You're her mother. A bad mother. You should have known, you should have known,' resounding through her head.

'How about sleeping on it?' she says now, placing a hand on Sophie's pale cheek. 'The sheets are clean, we have cake and I've even put on the central heating.'

Sophie smiles. Only a little, but it's still a smile and smiles are hard when there seems to be no way out. 'Thanks, Mum,' she says.

Sami has finally finished tidying the house. He hasn't cleaned or dusted, particularly, as he doesn't notice the dirt. But he hates untidiness. Sophie is untidy, very untidy. But he doesn't hate her. Well, not any more. The day of David's funeral was fuelled by anger and hurt. She had no regard for his feelings, for the obvious humiliation, the knowing looks, the prying questions and the whispers her absence at the funeral would cause. For Sami that's the worst: humiliation and shame. Even now he occasionally recalls the taunting and teasing at school. 'Fat boy, wheezy boy, blobby. Mummy's little pig.' That little boy still sits with him occasionally. He wishes he'd go away forever.

Sami slouches in his favourite chair, idly switching channels between *The Great Escape* and Sky Sports. He keeps glancing at the sofa, the sofa that's empty save for the fur throw still left as Sophie left it.

'Don't bother to come back!' Oh God.

Of course they'd rowed before. There had been many times when one or the other of them stomped out and slammed the door. But he'd never said those words before. Suppose she takes him at his word and doesn't come back? What then? He flicks to another channel. *Miss Congeniality 2*. Sandra Bullock. Now she is fit.

Mike phoned earlier, from his Sunday walk with his kids, said he was watching them play on the swings. 'Everything OK, mate?' he asked. Sami regrets saying anything to him about Sophie, about tests. It was a moment of self-pity and pathetic really. Which makes him think of Olivia. She politely but firmly turned him down again at the wake and on reflection he's glad. Even as he spoke to her, he knew he was trying to rekindle their affair for all the wrong reasons. He was pissed off with Sophie.

Sami rubs his head and sighs deeply. What the fuck was he doing? He never really loved Olivia, he realises that now. It was the challenge, the chase, the desire for that bloody, bloody ego boost. The need to erase the fat boy. It's Sophie he wants, he knows that now, now that she's fucking gone.

He leans to one side and pulls his iPhone from the back pocket of his jeans. He was determined not to look at it all day when he woke. Yet here it is in his pocket, his skin alert to its vibration, just in case she texts or calls. He peers at the screen. His screensaver photograph of the new version of an expensive sports car is there, but no message from his wife. 'For fuck's sake!' he declares, lobs the mobile on to the sofa where Sophie should be, then picks up the remote control and watches the football results.

'So, is everything OK, Dad? With you and Mum?' Rachel asks as they drive down the M56 towards Alderley Edge and White Gables.

'Absolutely!' Mike replies. 'Mum was going to tell me today, but you guessed first, clever girl. Another little Turner. It's great news, isn't it?'

The expression 'Be careful what you wish for' pops into his head.

As he drives, he thinks back to this morning. His initial urge to storm home from the park and confront Olivia wasn't possible. The girls were focused on sweets, selecting them with great excitement and care from the corner shop. Then there was the walking home at a leisurely pace so that Olivia wouldn't know quite how many Mike had allowed them to buy. But it gave him time to reflect. He had no doubt Rachel was right; he'd seen all the symptoms himself, but not registered them. Olivia was pregnant. He swung from feelings of angry irritation that she had kept the news from him, to an examination of how he felt about the prospect of being a father again. Of course there was no question about keeping the baby, but was it something he still wanted?

'Olivia, are you pregnant?' he asked after lunch as they cleared up the dishes. He'd thought of a multitude of ways to ask as he strolled home with the girls, but when it came down to it, there was only one way. Just to ask.

273

She flushed immediately, two bright patches of colour in her wan face. 'How do you know?' she breathed quietly.

He shrugged, standing away from her, conscious that this was not how it was supposed to be. 'You look pregnant, you've been acting pregnant,' he said slowly. 'Why didn't you tell me?'

She didn't speak for a moment, but her pale eyes flickered and then she sighed. 'I've only just realised myself. We've been so busy, what with one thing or another. I was just giving myself a day or two to get used to the idea. I'm sorry.'

He pulled her towards him then, the tea towel stuck between them. Any anger or irritation faded away. He could see the weary look in her eyes and he realised another baby wasn't what she wanted. 'Look,' he said, kissing her forehead. 'It's wonderful news. Another beautiful child. We simply need a little time to adjust.'

The sun catches the windscreen as Mike accelerates into the driveway of White Gables, momentarily blinding him. He hopes Antonia has remembered that they're visiting today. He doesn't want to turn up unannounced. But she opens the door before they knock, the aroma of croissants escaping, her face lucent and so very lovely. 'Hello, you two,' she beams. 'Hope you're both hungry, I've been baking. Come on in!'

'Mum's going to have another baby but we don't know when,' Rachel blurts out before they've stepped inside.

There's a pulse of silence before Antonia replies. 'That's wonderful news,' she says, giving Rachel a hug. 'You'll be a big sister again!' Then, 'Congratulations, Mike,' she adds.

She kisses him on the cheek, but doesn't meet his eyes. Instead she turns away, her back slim, elegant and remote. 'Now, what are we girls going to do this afternoon?' she asks Rachel. 'Shall we give Dad a call later when we're finished?'

CHAPTER THIRTY-FOUR

Antonia drives towards Stoke, still feeling unsettled from her nightmare this morning. She's had similar or the same for several days, waking in the early hours and crying uncontrollably until she nods off again. In the dream she climbs the limestone stairs and knocks on the bathroom door, but she knows David's just sleeping, nodding off in the bath. She approaches quietly, reaching out a hand to gently wake him, but just before she touches, he lurches upright, his eyes bloodshot and angry. That's when she wakes with a sickly jerk, shocked and fearful, taking too many moments to remember where she is; to remember he's dead.

Her visit to The Ridings is on a whim, Antonia tells herself, a rather long diversion from her planned trip to Waitrose. Even as she drives into the small car park, she isn't sure if she'll actually get out of the car, or struggle with a hurried five-point turn to retreat. But by the time she places her finger on the front door buzzer, she's praying that Mrs Jones, The Ridings manager, will be there. She doesn't want her resolve to fade.

'Hello, Mrs Stafford. We don't usually see you in the week,'

Mrs Jones starts to say with her practised smile. Then she pauses and Antonia notices a flash of embarrassment in her eyes. She's just remembered about David, she thinks. She wishes people would forget.

The taint of death. Again. She recently tried to read the novel *Heart of Darkness*, but struggled to get even halfway. She abandoned it for Sylvia. She always comes back to her. Chooses which poem to relish next by its title. 'Death & Co' it was last night, read over and over until she thought she understood.

Antonia stands at the office door of the care home, both hands clutching her handbag to keep them still. 'I've come to speak to you, actually, if that's OK.'

Antonia has decided to have a project for every day, no matter how small. It was letter writing on Monday, on the embossed notepaper she and David were bought as a wedding gift.

Just a note to thank you for your kind condolences.

She wrote them in her best handwriting, careful to check the spelling and hoping for the best with the grammar. She doesn't know if a thank you letter is the done thing, but it felt right. Then on Tuesday she took the long walk from White Gables to the village post office and the newsagents. There she scrutinised the postcards offering work, the ones randomly displayed in their dusty windows. She hopes for a shop job, but it doesn't really matter, anything will do if there are people. 'I long for workmates! People to talk to, to laugh with,' she would confide to Mike, knowing that he'd understand, but she hasn't seen Mike for days.

Of course her visit to The Ridings isn't on a whim. It's something which has pestered her since having coffee with Olivia all those weeks ago. 'They fuck you up.' More so since David's death. She didn't know him, her husband of five years, not really. The speeches at the funeral, the stories and banter at the wake and of course the Misty revelation were proof of that. What of her own flesh and blood? 'They fuck you up, your mum and dad.' She's grown up now, it's time to find out.

She continues to clutch the handbag as she waits for the manager's reply.

'Oh?' Mrs Jones says. She puts her hands in her lap, her face a polite blank.

Poor woman, my request could be anything, Antonia thinks. It could be a complaint, an argument or a demand she can't fulfil. It can't be easy doing her job.

'I just wondered if I could talk about my mum. Or, I don't know, look at her file or her records or whatever you call them.'

It clearly isn't what Mrs Jones expects. 'Oh,' she says again, her eyebrows raised. 'I'm afraid we can't do that. I'm sure you realise that under the Mental Health Act . . .'

Antonia nods, not wanting to listen today about Candy's mental health any more than she has previously. 'Mental capacity assessment; section one-one-seven; case conferences; mental health team; best interest meetings; social circumstances report.' They're words and phrases she's heard many times before, but she was too young, too scared and too powerless at the beginning. Then as she grew older, she both appreciated and resented having all the responsibility taken out of her hands.

Mrs Jones's small eyes are fixed on Antonia. She's struggling to hide her curiosity. 'If you don't mind me saying, why the interest now? Your mother's very settled here.'

'Oh, it's nothing like that.'

It suddenly occurs to Antonia that Mrs Jones might think she wants to take her mother home. To live with her now that David has gone. She doesn't know if it's possible in the circumstances, even if Candy hadn't been sectioned all those years ago.

'I was wondering more about my father, actually.' Antonia glances up at the woman before dropping her gaze again. It's hard, hard saying the words, even harder asking for help.

She can hear his words now, as though he's in the room: 'Eat your fucking food.' She shakes them away. How should she put it? 'Growing up. Well, he wasn't the best father in the world.'

Mrs Jones says nothing but waits, her chin resting on her hands, her eyes on Antonia.

Antonia tries to swallow but her throat feels too dry. She considers getting up from the clamp of a chair she's sitting in and leaving. But she's come this far, she's been very brave. She lifts her head and meets the cool, inquisitive eyes of the manager.

'He was a drunk, actually. Violent at times. That's all I really know about him.'

'That didn't come out at the trial.'

'I know.'

Mrs Jones's thin eyebrows shape a frown and she holds out her hands. 'There was a guilty plea from Candy and then silence. She wouldn't say anything further. The social workers were tearing their hair out, desperate for your mum to defend herself. At least to explain why. For mitigation, a reduced sentence.'

Antonia remains silent. She doesn't want to hear what she already knows. Her head is bent, but she can still feel the heat of Mrs Jones's interest.

'There must have been a reason why she refused to speak,' the manager says, still studying Antonia. She pauses. The room is stifling. 'You didn't give evidence at the trial, did you?'

Antonia pulls back the chair to stand. 'As I said, I was just wanting to know more about my father, but obviously . . .'

'Well, the file won't tell you anything.'

Mrs Jones sits back. She looks smug, what an absolute cow. Antonia sighs inwardly and turns to leave.

'But I think *I* can, Mrs Stafford. Shall we get a coffee?'

'I promised I'd drop by to see Judith's baby on the way home,' Mike said at breakfast.

'That's nice,' Olivia replied. 'Say hello from me, would you?'

Eggshells and explanations, forgiven but not forgotten, Olivia thought. Then she realised she hadn't even bought a card, let alone a gift. Judith's first baby too.

'Sorry, Mike. I should have sorted out a present for the baby, shouldn't I?'

'It's not a problem. You've had other things on your mind.'

He kissed the top of her head and then picked up his briefcase. 'I almost said I'd get Judith to sort it for me. Only . . .' He grinned. 'They're taking bets at the office, apparently. Name the father.'

'That's awful!' Olivia replied vehemently.

Perhaps a little too vehemently, Olivia now thinks, alone in the house. But it is awful, the uncertainty, the not knowing. It's fucking, fucking awful. Like a heavy stone in her chest. It's entirely her own fault too.

Perhaps she should've lied when Mike asked if she was pregnant. She was caught on the hop, sure, but still, she knew in that instant she couldn't lie to him. Not to his face, his concerned, lovely face.

She presses down the iron. It's a steam iron so she doesn't need to press, yet she can't escape the notion that clothes fare better with pressure, any creases totally obliterated.

Olivia sighs. She's aware that she likes to iron out all the blips in life, to tackle any problems head on and as soon as she

279

can. Yet with Mike and her suspicions about Judith, she not only hesitated, but ignored them completely and then hurled herself in the opposite direction. As *The Archers* theme tune wafts by her consciousness, she vaguely wonders why.

Hanging Mike's shirt, creases totally obliterated, on one of the yellow plastic hangers from the dry cleaners, she grimaces. She hates those hangers, but they always appear at the top of the ironing basket, disposable and yet very useful. She sits down for a moment, her cheek resting on her hand. When she was a teenager she swore she'd never wash a man's shirt, let alone iron it. She almost laughs at the memory. That girl was so certain.

The baby is suckling at Judith's breast so Mike can't see her tiny face.

'She's beautiful, Jude. Congratulations. How did it go?' he asks. He feels slightly embarrassed at being in such close proximity to a breastfeeding mother who isn't Olivia.

'Bloody awful, since you ask. It's a terrible conspiracy, isn't it? No one tells you just how painful it's going to be. I said to Mum that there was no way I was going to grin and bear it, but they wouldn't give me a flipping epidural. They said it was too late so I had to push her out cursing and screaming. Poor kid, the first words she heard from her mother were swear words.'

'Or square words, as Hannah calls them,' Mike adds with a small smile. He's forgotten just how little and fragile newborn babies are and he wonders how Hannah will deal with such an impostor when the new baby arrives.

Judith cocks her head. 'Anyway, why are you asking? Men usually shy away from the blood and gore sagas. You'll be asking me whether my nipples are sore next, which, by the way, they are.'

Mike smiles again. He misses Judith. 'Well, as it happens, it's topical. Olivia is pregnant again.'

'Wow, that's fantastic news. Was it planned, or was it a little surprise?' Judith asks.

Mike glances at the baby. He knows Judith is looking at him. Seeing into his soul. Bloody Gypsy Rose.

'A big surprise, actually. I'm still getting my head around it, if I'm honest.'

'Ah.' Judith nods. 'Best not be honest with Olivia, though.'

Mike gazes through Judith for a moment, his thoughts elsewhere, before coming back to her quizzical eyes.

'Best not be honest with Olivia about getting your head around the pregnancy, I meant,' Judith explains.

'Yeah, I know.' He pensively looks back to the newborn. 'Have you decided on a name yet?'

The baby is asleep. He watches as Judith inserts the tip of her little finger into the corner of the baby's mouth to detach her nipple. Then she looks at him carefully, a concerned frown on her face. 'What's up, Mike?' she asks.

Antonia clutches the coffee mug and watches the manager's animated face. She's learning a little about her father, the young Jimmy Farrell, a boxer from Wythenshawe with promise, real promise to make it big in the boxing world. But his career ended suddenly. He was beaten up badly by a gang of youths from the estate.

'Ironic,' Mrs Jones says sadly as she sips her coffee, 'with him being such a good fighter. But there was only him against six or so of them. He had no chance. He was lucky to survive. My dad was a huge boxing fan. I remember him saying that it was a terrible loss to the sport. I read about it in the local newspaper. Perhaps you should try the central library in Manchester, see if there are back copies.'

'Were they black?' Antonia asks, her eyes on the trees through the office window. 'The men who beat him up?'

Mrs Jones pauses, thoughtful. 'No, I'd have remembered. What a strange question. Why do you ask?'

'No reason,' she replies.

They fall silent for a while, then Mrs Jones leans forward, her voice softer than before. 'Have you ever thought of talking it through with someone? About your parents and your childhood. Maybe a counsellor? Perhaps I'm making assumptions, but I get the impression of self-imposed isolation, of hiding away.'

Her tiny eyes are kind, but Antonia's thoughts are elsewhere with her father, once a young man from a council estate, but with talent and hopes for the future. Hopes that were cruelly dashed. 'Thank you, but I'm fine. Really,' she replies, her voice choked with unexpected emotion.

'The only child of a mother who kills a father. I shouldn't think so. That alone . . .' Mrs Jones stares at Antonia, an intense sharp look. 'There must have been more. There must have been a reason for a religious caring woman like Candy to kill a man she obviously still loves, even now after all these years.'

Antonia stands. 'Thank you for telling me about Jimmy. You've been very kind. I'll pop and say hello, chat to Mum for a while.'

'Talk to someone,' Mrs Jones calls after her.

Ten minutes later Antonia is pencilling her time of leaving in The Ridings visitors' book and heading for the exit. She feels ridiculously rejected. After the coffee with Mrs Jones and on a high, she dared to peer into the patients' dining room. Candy was sitting at a round table with other residents. Her head was down and she was shovelling mashed potato into her mouth as though she hadn't eaten for a week.

She waited until her mother looked up, then smiled and lifted a hand by way of a greeting. Candy's eyes shifted. Then she looked back at her plate and continued to eat without any acknowledgement.

'Sorry, they like their routine,' one of the regular carers said, guiding Antonia away by her elbow. 'And of course their lunch! Best leave it until Sunday.'

The dismissal by both her mother and the carer stung. It still stings as she leaves. She doesn't really know why. Her mum is entitled to her life, just as she's entitled to hers. It's been a worthwhile visit too, to learn about another side to her father, one she didn't know. The recollections from Mrs Jones excited her, yet the high of discovering that there's more to her father than the drunk she knew has almost evaporated already. It's been replaced by the sting of rejection and by a memory long forgotten, triggered by just one word: routine.

'It's not religion, Candy, it's routine. You're like a thick half-breed dog with your bloody routine. Fuck off to church then. Go to your beloved God. Likes them black, does he?'

As she walks towards her car the cold November wind hits her hot cheeks. She's trembling uncontrollably, not just from the cold but from a combination of emotions and thoughts. Release and relief from tension, but a flood of memories too.

Talk to someone, she thinks. But there's no one, there's no one, and there'll never be David.

CHAPTER THIRTY-FIVE

There have been occasions, particularly when Sophie first moved into his flat, that Sami wished she wasn't there. That feeling continues to surface from time to time, but it's only a question of space. Sami likes his space. He was used to it when he lived alone in his flat, when he'd escaped from Martha and all his noisy sisters. And Sophie is big, not in terms of size particularly, but in terms of personality. Laughter and chatter, untidiness, hair. Like the colourful furniture and furnishings she likes to buy, she uses up a lot of room.

Sami keeps busy at work and tries to be positive. She'll come back and if she doesn't then it'll be like it was. I'll get a place of my own, he thinks. Space. I'll go walking like I used to, eat out, meet up with the lads, buy some new gear and a bike.

On Sunday he walks. Puts on his new trainers, flicks up the collar of his thick jacket and walks to Fletcher Moss park. Past the weathered tennis courts, the memorial benches and the cafe, past the winter peonies and pansies and down into the woods. He folds his hands in his pockets, kicking the rust-coloured crispy leaves, wondering what people might think of a man alone among the bowed trees, without friends or even a dog. He stops on the way home for coffee under the heated canopy of a cafe bar in the village to read the *Sunday Telegraph* and all its supplements. Talking to no one but himself.

At work it's easier to be distracted by clients and by colleagues and in quieter moments to think about food. I can do what I want, eat what I fancy! What do I fancy for dinner? So on the way home he stops at the village deli and buys chilled slices of meat, salami and sausages from the counter and freshly baked bread. The fridge at home is full of the delicacies one would hope for in a hamper: smoked salmon, potted prawns, pâté and dips. Treat food, weekend food. Only Sami realises too late that the crusty bread goes stale by morning and that he's buying too much food just for one.

He scrolls down his list of contacts and calls Mo, Pete and Salim. But the conversations are short. Their kids are going to bed or there's the washing-up to be done. Their promises to meet up very soon sound hollow. So Sami calls his parents' home to chat with his dad, but Martha intercepts. 'Why are you calling so often? What's going on, Samuel? Isn't Sophie at home?'

He ambles down the road in the evenings, strolls along the wet pavements lit by pretty street lamps and shops, looks into the windows of the bustling restaurants and cafe bars and sees people he recognises, but doesn't really know. Ends up nursing a pint alone in the front bar of a pub, listening to the highs and the lows of the football fans watching the match on a large screen in the back.

Sami has as much space as he could ever want. He has the whole of Didsbury village and Fletcher Moss park beyond. He has a tidy house, a high-definition television, boxes of bottled beer, his car magazines and Sky. But Sami is struggling, especially in the mornings when he first awakes. Even now, the realisation that Sophie isn't there feels like a punch to his stomach. Freedom aplenty, but aching emptiness everywhere.

Norma sits in the garden on a rusted metal chair, wrapped in her padded coat. She's drinking coffee and smoking her first cigarette of the day. Her eyes focus on the iron table top. It's rusty too, but nothing that a lick of enamel paint won't cure. The boys used to paint it, a different colour each summer, eager to have tea outside as soon as the weather permitted. 'Please, Mum. Can we have burgers on the barbecue? We'll clean it, we promise!'

Of course the boys never cleaned the barbecue. She loved her boys and still does. She misses having them around the house with their affectionate jibes, even if they leave the bath-room grimy, their bedrooms bedraggled and eat unbelievable quantities of food. But what do they say about sons? They're yours until they find a wife. Neither son has married, as it happens, but both live with their girlfriends, who seem pleasant enough.

Norma takes a drag of her cigarette and sighs; she gave them up for years. But she's put on weight that no diet will shift and so she's gone back on the fags in secret, berating herself each time she lights up.

A daughter's a daughter for all your life, she muses. It's lovely to have Sophie home. They've been talking, really talking. Probably for the first time ever.

My thirty-year-old baby, she thinks, feeling that she can, perhaps, forgive herself a little for somehow failing Sophie for all those years. Maybe she was just better with boys. Or perhaps she was envious, jealous of Sophie's devotion to Barry right from the start. 'Darling little Sophie, Daddy's princess.' She felt excluded, she supposes, and withdrew her demonstrative love to protect herself from that awful feeling of rejection. 'But you're the adult.' Barry's words. Her own words too, internally.

Norma stubs out the cigarette and stands up. OK, enough psycho-babble for one day, she thinks. Time for action.

She looks up at Sophie's bedroom window and sighs. The curtains are still closed. Sophie has slept most of the week or so she's been there. The initial camaraderie has faltered slightly into occasional bickering, mostly as a result of her attempts to chivvy Sophie along. To get up and get dressed. To brush her hair and her teeth. Even to eat.

Norma walks slowly up the stairs, a feeling of gloom making her legs seem heavy. She doesn't want to be the baddie, yet again, but someone has to do it. She opens the bedroom door, yanks back the curtains, expecting the inevitable, 'Mum! That hurts my eyes. Go away.'

'Come on, Sophie,' she says, trying for her nurse's best brisk voice. 'Time to get up. You've felt sorry for yourself long enough. I've made an appointment. We're off to the doctor's at ten.'

Three laps of the garden in the drizzle, three more to go. Charlie is dismayed at how shaky he is on his legs. Still, it's only day two, it's a very large garden and the walking gives him thinking time away from Barbara, the cook slash cleaner. Of her own volition she's taken on the additional chore of loitering. Wherever Charlie is, she is too. He suspects Barbara has orders from 'on high' to keep an eye on him. But if anyone's going to drop dead on the spot it's the octogenarian Barbara and certainly not him.

'Who were you talking to in the garden?' Rupert asked yesterday.

'Uncle David,' Charlie replied.

Rupert nodded. 'Fair enough.'

It does help, the talking out loud. It helps Charlie to cope with the intermittent spasms of intense grief and of guilt. Of culpability too. For not noticing David's overspending on White Gables. For not intuitively knowing that David was in trouble, for not seeing his dear friend had been brought so low.

'David, oh, David. Did we push you too hard?'

But Charlie is putting things right for David. For his reputation, his good name.

'Got that insurance business sorted, David, so no need to worry about that. Straightened it with the client on the QT, so there won't be any comeback. Money back with enhanced interest and a promise not to look too closely at the Money Laundering Regulations. An offer he couldn't refuse.'

Charlie chuckles as he strolls. He's said it aloud in his best *Godfather* imitation, which isn't terribly good, but David always appreciated it. He'd laugh and slap Charlie on the back. 'Not bad, Charlie,' he'd smile. 'But don't give up the day job.'

David loved that film. He liked to quote from it frequently. He was good at remembering lines from films and a talented impressionist too. Don Corleone, Dirty Harry, Indiana Jones and of course Sean Connery's Bond. Then the Jason Bourne films more recently. Not that Charlie has seen them himself. 'Shall we go to the cinema to see what this Bourne malarkey is all about?' he asked Helen a couple of years back. 'Good God, no,' she replied.

Charlie missed the funeral. His desperation to be there mucked up his blood pressure, which then upset his blood sugar and the doctors wouldn't let him out of the hospital.

'Tell me again,' he says frequently to Rupert, wanting every little detail of who was there and who said what. 'Robin Hudson, are you sure it was him? I thought he was in Nigeria. Trevor

Foster, really? He's MP for Plymouth. Simon Dunthorne? Bald? You're joking. We used to call him Sid.'

It brings Charlie back to thoughts of school and especially to the death of David's parents. One didn't cry at school. David didn't cry when he heard the news. He stayed in bed and refused to move but he didn't cry. Yet Charlie can still clearly recall finding him alone at the fives court, sobbing in a corner. Such a beautiful boy, with long tanned limbs and hair so blond it was almost white. David was a new boy then. His parents had recently been posted to Singapore and his aunt had taken his dog to the vet and had her put down.

'Lucky was mine,' the boy sobbed in Charlie's arms. 'My aunt had no right. She was mine.'

Charlie shakes the water off the umbrella in the porch and sighs. He loved that boy, the boy he held tightly in his arms until the hurt and the anger and the shaking subsided. The boy had grown into a man, a big broad man with many flaws, but he loved him dearly too.

There's the inevitable spat between Sophie and Norma. 'Go away. I don't need the bloody doctor. I need to be left alone. I'm tired,' Sophie sulks, turning away in the bed.

'Then you can tell the doctor that,' her mum replies firmly. 'As well as about the drinking, the anxiety and the mood swings. You've wallowed long enough now. It's time to make some decisions about the future. Staying in bed all day isn't going to cure anything.'

'I didn't think it would last long.'

'What wouldn't last long?'

'Nothing,' Sophie mutters. She can hear the quaver in her mother's voice. This has got to stop, she thinks morosely. I must stop blaming her.

Sophie pulls up the pillow and squints towards Norma. The room is warm and the teddies stare. She feels as though she's ten years old. 'Mum, I really don't want to go to the doctor's. Please don't make me go.'

Norma sits down on the bed, her face set. 'You know what to do. You put on a brave face and you go. It's as simple as that.'

'But I'm not brave, that's just the problem. People think that I'm courageous and confident, but I'm not.'

Norma sighs, her face wrinkled and worn. She smooths the duvet cover with her hand.

'I know that, love. Now more than ever.'

She still wears her wedding ring, Sophie notices. Does she miss him? Does she still yearn for Barry? Her husband, her lover. The man who betrayed her and not just the once? Like Sami, her Sami. Is he missing her now? Or has he shrugged her away from his thoughts as she fears? He hasn't called, he hasn't texted. 'Don't bother coming back,' he had said.

Norma is looking at her. Her green eyes are still bright, but her auburn hair is now streaked with grey. Like mother, like daughter, in so many ways. She reaches out and tightly grasps Sophie's hand. 'In life nobody is going to help you unless you help yourself. You're being self-destructive.' She gives a small smile. 'How can I put it? There's no point expecting CPR if you unplug your life support. That's what you're doing now, Sophie. You aren't helping yourself by lying here and feeling sorry for yourself. And you've alienated the people you love. It's time you got up and started building bridges.'

Sophie smiles despite her need to cry. 'You and your bloody metaphors,' she says.

*

290

'So, it's a return to school next week, now I'm back home, Rupe. Bet you can't wait to get back into the swing and see all your friends. You've been such a good lad. All this hard work.'

Rupert is sitting at the old dining table, his school books spread out. He's been there all morning, his fringe tucked behind his ear and his face taut with concentration.

'Yeah, but I'm not like you, Dad. It doesn't come easily. I'm not that . . .' His face colours and he looks down at his writing pad. 'Academic.'

'Of course you are,' Charlie starts to say, but something holds him back. There's a feeling of déjà vu, an echo of conversations gone by. Then there's that question too, always in his mind, that comes to the fore when he walks. Oh, David, did we push you too hard?

Rupert sighs, his head still bent. 'And they push you so hard at school.'

Charlie flinches at the repetition of the words, then pulls out a chair, sits down and stares at Rupert's scratchy left-handed scrawl. His initial reaction is to defend the school, his school and his father's school before him, but Rupert looks close to tears. It isn't what Charlie expects. 'I thought you were happy there,' he says instead.

Rupert's fringe falls forward. 'The sport's OK, but if you're not clever, it's just embarrassing,' he mutters. He lifts his head for a moment and he glances at his father. 'Sometimes I just wish I was normal.'

Charlie sits back, feeling slightly breathless. He wants to ask more questions, but feels that perhaps he should already know the answers. Should have noticed. Should have seen. He opens his mouth to speak but his son pre-empts him.

'It's OK, Dad.' Rupert shrugs and picks up his pen. 'I'm just glad I was here. You know, when you needed me.'

Rupert tries for a smile and reverts to his school work. Charlie stares through the window at the garden, his finger on his lips, thinking.

'Isn't it time you went home to your wife?' Jemima says, kissing the back of Sami's neck to wake him.

'She isn't there,' Sami replies, sluggish with sleep.

'Where's she gone to?' Jemima asks, her high voice loaded with interest.

Sami doesn't reply, but drags himself from the single bed and picks up his neatly piled clothes from where he left them a couple of hours previously.

'So, where's she gone, your wife?' Jemima asks again, sitting cross-legged on the bed as she watches him dress.

Sami groans inwardly. Fool. The more he tries not to be one, the more he seems to suit it. 'Her mum isn't well,' he fibs, but he catches a glimmer in Jemima's eye as he fumbles with the buttons of his shirt.

She lies back and stretches with a satisfied smile on her face. 'I'll have to pop by. Didsbury, isn't it? The townhouses just behind the shops. Might be exciting, making love in your bed.'

'Oh, she'll probably be back tomorrow,' he replies, searching for his socks.

He shakes himself fully awake, he needs to be alert. Like a fool he fell asleep. Like a bloody fool he weakened, weakened because he's lonely and sad and needs a boost.

Jemima places her long arms around his neck and kisses his lips with her eyes open. They're smug and proprietorial, he notices. 'Stay tonight if you like. Or we could go to yours now, make love and travel to work together in the morning.'

Sami's face feels hot. It's burning with irritation and with anger. At her, at himself. 'I have sex with you. I only make love to my wife,' he wants to yell.

He pulls away and tries for a relaxed smile. Then he looks around to see if he's left anything. That's it, he decides. Finito. He doesn't even like her that much.

He kept his distance at the office, cordial but cool. Until today, until tonight. There were leaving drinks at the office after work for one of the associates. Jemima ignored him completely. She flirted with all the men and with Andy Maher, the handsome office silver fox, in particular, her laugh a high-pitched tinkle.

Of course Sami couldn't stand the competition. He slowly made his way to her side of the room, asserted his presence and invited himself round to her flat.

Played like a fool, a bloody great fool.

Her finger now strokes the back of his hand as he opens the door to leave. Her nails, he notices, are long and sharp. 'Night night, Sami. Tomorrow then,' she says, her slight lisp struggling with the S.

Sami isn't sure what she means, but he doesn't like the sound of it.

CHAPTER THIRTY-SIX

Mike contemplates whether the smell of incense is real or imagined as he gazes at the paintings of the Stations of the Cross hung on the small church walls. He's taken to popping into the Hidden Gem behind the buzz of King Street at lunchtimes. He can't quite pin down the reason. It isn't for prayer, the silence or even the thinking time. The reason, he supposes, is that time seems suspended here.

'Don't go,' Antonia whispered on the night of the funeral. 'Don't go.' Two small words that changed everything.

They talked. Or rather Antonia talked and he gazed and watched and listened. He drank in her eyes and her mouth, the exquisite sculpture of her features, until the early hours.

'Perhaps you're right,' she murmured, her eyes dark and huge in her soulful face. 'About the parent thing. Childhood never goes away, does it?'

Antonia's account of her upbringing was shocking. It wasn't so much the episodes of her father's heavy drinking, not even the violence towards her mother that followed, but the hatred and the spite that went with it.

'He didn't hit me,' she said. 'But I had to watch, to learn my lesson. My mother is black and so she was beaten. He'd ask if I was black too, and I would say, "No, I'm not, of course I'm not, Dad."'

She cried then. Large tears tumbling from her chestnut-coloured eyes which she didn't bother to brush away. 'I did nothing, Mike. Nothing to help her. It's like I connived. Is that the right word?'

He held her in his arms, her face buried in his shoulder, her hair soft against his face.

'You were only a child,' he soothed, his body on fire. With anger. With lust. 'Not your fault. Just a child.'

Mike shakes his head and looks up at the statue of Our Lady of Manchester with her child. Weeks have passed since the funeral and Olivia is carrying his child. In a few months there will be a new life, a life that has to be protected, nurtured and loved. It's precisely what he wanted for so long. Yet more than anything now, he needs time to stand still, to work it all out.

'It has healed. Beautifully,' he said later, as he stroked Antonia's arm, feeling other bumps of scar tissue just under the surface. 'Why did you do this?'

She looked at him for a long time before answering. 'Perhaps because I'm not as flawless as everyone thinks.'

'But none of us are perfect,' he replied, wretched with desire.

'I know that now,' she whispered.

Mike stands, walks to the aisle of the church and genuflects. It's a mark of respect, nothing more. The black dog has gone, replaced with something else he can't quite define. A soft lament, perhaps. Something lost which was never his to lose.

He sees the marble face of Our Lady as he turns away. Just to chat, he explains to her inwardly. A small prayer that I'll see her. Just to chat. To see if she's OK. That's all it would be. I promise.

'Another day another dollar,' Sami says as he strolls on to a busy building site carrying his hard hat. He's trying to be upbeat. To talk the talk, to walk the walk and all the other stupid sayings that regularly pop into his head to mask the fact that he's lonely, pissed off, pining, angry, disappointed and hassled, to name but a few.

The hassled part is his mother, his bloody mother. He's stopped calling his dad to avoid her interrupting on the phone, but she seems instinctively to know when something's amiss.

Except when I was a kid at school, he thinks, still mildly resentful. When I needed it most.

Martha has taken to telephoning Sami at home at various times in the evenings. 'Doesn't Sophie answer the telephone any more? Could you put her on? I just wanted a little word.'

Of course she doesn't want a little, medium or big word with Sophie; she can't stand her. The fact that his wife and his mother loathe each other has always been best ignored. It's preferable to float above conflict, otherwise one gets embroiled. Embroiled isn't good. Embroiled means heavy discussions, angst, emotion and decisions. The sort of shit that's messing up his head right now.

'What's happening with the IVF?' Martha asked last night. He doesn't want to think about the bloody IVF. He agreed to it for Sophie. For his bloody wife who fucked off when she should've been there at the funeral. Who should be at home now. Fending off his mother's questions, preparing him questionable food and laughing with him. Just being there, keeping him happy.

'Call her! Just call her!' one inner voice cajoles.

'She was the one who walked out. She's the one who must beg to come back!' the other voice shrills.

He wonders what his dad would do. The latter, naturally. What about Mike? The former, definitely. But at least Mike will listen to Sami's point of view and talk it through. He decides to give him a call after this job and to arrange a pint before home.

There are times, like now, that Sami's self-punishing thoughts touch on what he's done to Mike, his friend, his good loyal friend. But if words like 'betrayal' and 'disloyalty' loiter, they're soon boxed away. 'What the eye doesn't see' has always been the rationale. 'Only guilty if you're found out.' And he's never been found out; he's lucky that way.

Wanting what he can't have has always been a problem for Sami, but it's sorted now, he's over that blip. Besides, things have worked out pretty well. Olivia seems happy, Mike's ignorant of it all and they have another kid on the way. So there's no need to let it peck his head like today, no need to go there.

Sami puts on his hard hat, as ever careful not to mess up his hair. He imagines having not just one but three noisy and demanding kids under his feet and he shudders. Sami likes his space. Rather Mike and Olivia than him any day.

'Guess what?' Antonia asks.

She can see Rachel's reflection in the dressing-table mirror. There's a frown of concentration on her pretty fresh face and her mouth is slightly ajar as she struggles to twist Antonia's thick hair into a French plait.

'I've got a part-time job in the village.'

She's been offered three mornings a week at Alderley Boutique, covering for one of the stylists who's on maternity leave and she's thrilled. 'At a hair salon. Maybe I'll have to practise on you, Rach!'

'That would be ace. You could dye it for me. Dip dye or red streaks. I'm not sure which.'

'I don't think so. Your mum would kill me.'

It's a teacher training day tomorrow, so Rachel has been allowed a sleep-over at White Gables. Though Antonia's grief is tainted by occasional thoughts of Misty, she still misses David enormously, often crying in her dreams, waking up with a wet face, so lonely, so lonely. So she's thrilled to have Rachel's company. Olivia dropped her off at the top of the drive after school, climbing out of the car, waving and shouting a thank you with a friendly smile. Not a huge bump, Antonia noticed, but Olivia's belly had a definite curve.

'Anyway, Rach, you have gorgeous hair. Don't ever mess with such a beautiful colour. It's dark chestnut, like your dad's.'

Antonia averts her eyes from her own face watching back through the mirror. It gives too much away when she mentions him. Perhaps Mike will collect Rachel tomorrow, perhaps he'll come in for a coffee and chat like they used to. But Antonia knows he won't. She messed up, she messed up badly the day after the funeral, the day Rachel broke the news about the new baby.

She was curt. She sent him away. Then she thought about him constantly for the rest of her day with Rachel, angry, disappointed and missing him badly. They didn't speak when he returned to collect Rachel. He waited for her in the car and then turned it around in the driveway to leave. Antonia stood at the door, waving them away. Then the car stopped and Mike climbed out and walked towards her, his face dark and obscure.

He stood at the bottom of the steps and looked down at his feet for a moment. Then he lifted his head to look up at her, a red stain of blush in his cheeks. 'On Friday, on Friday night . . .' He sighed, his eyes troubled. 'I didn't know about the baby.'

Antonia already knew. Rachel had told her the whole story

with pride. That it was a surprise for them all, but she was the first one to notice. Yet Antonia was piqued. She didn't know why. She didn't want a baby, she never had.

She glanced over Mike's shoulder. Rachel was in the front seat of the car, watching. 'Thanks for everything, Mike,' she said, turning towards the sheer drop of The Edge on the horizon. 'You were there when I needed somebody and I'm very grateful for all that you've done for me.' Like a formal thank you and goodbye, and from Mike's face, wholly and heartbreakingly effective.

'You OK, Antonia? You look sad.'

She comes back to Rachel through the mirror. She has a furrow of concern on her smooth forehead, just like her dad. Antonia nods, holding back the sudden urge to cry. She longs to see him and to talk. Most of all to feel his arms around her, tight, safe and solid. But she's messed things up. Or perhaps, if she chooses to be honest, she's put things right. Whichever it is, it hurts deeply.

'Sami says hi,' Mike calls from the hall as he takes off his jacket.

Olivia wonders if the goosebump feeling will be there forever when Sami's name is mentioned, or whether it will fade with time. She doubts it, even if the baby isn't his. She shoplifted once, she and her best friend, when they were still in primary school. She'd stolen a packet of Rolos, her favourite chocolate sweets her mother only allowed as a special treat at weekends. But she was caught red-handed by the shop keeper. 'I know where you live, young lady,' he had said, pointing his finger. 'Now get off home. There won't be a next time.' She got off scot-free, but absolutely forbade her friend to speak of it. She never ate Rolos again and from time to time she caught her mum gazing at her, as if she knew.

'That's nice,' she replies, her face hidden, busy at the oven door. The constant 'if the baby is his, if the baby is his' beating louder in her mind. 'Is he OK?'

Mike sits down at the kitchen table and removes his tie. 'Well, no, not really. Apparently Sophie still hasn't come home.'

Olivia suddenly feels febrile. Sophie wasn't at the funeral, but until that moment it hasn't occurred to Olivia that Sophie might know about her and Sami.

'Really?' she says. Is that what the Olivia of old would say in reply? She doesn't know any more.

Mike pours a glass of red wine and offers it to her. She shakes her head, aware of a cold bead of sweat on her spine.

'To be honest,' Mike says after a moment, 'I feel a bit guilty.'

Olivia sits down and looks at him questioningly. The hairs on her arms are beginning to settle as reality kicks in. If Sophie knew, Olivia would be stabbed in the heart by now, surely?

'Us on our third child and he hasn't managed even one,' Mike continues. 'He didn't say anything tonight and of course I didn't raise it either. But I'm guessing that's why Sophie has gone.'

'What are you on about?' Olivia asks, trying to smile. To sound normal and mildly interested.

'Oh.' Mike holds up his fork, looking slightly embarrassed. 'Don't say anything, obviously. I think he regretted ever mentioning it. They tried for a baby and when nothing happened they had tests. And as Sami put it, he's a Jaffa, seedless.'

Her heart is thrashing. 'You mean he can't have . . .' she knows she's pressing the point, but she has to know.

'Yeah. He's infertile. Awful isn't it? Of all the people we know, you'd expect Sami to have at least five kids. If I know Sami, not being able to be a dad will be doing his head in.'

300

CHAPTER THIRTY-SEVEN

Sami's lilac shirt clings to his chest. He can feel the drench of sweat down his back and under his arms as he strides over the puddles in the road towards his house.

The text he received half an hour ago is branded in his memory, he doesn't need to read it twice.

Looked at your diary and saw you're on a site visit. Just what we hoped for on a Friday. Sneak off ASAP. Meet you outside your place. PS I'm the one wearing stockings xxx

He takes a deep breath before lifting the latch of the door to the walled garden of his home. He wants to burst with irritation and anger, but he needs to stay calm, to handle this delicately.

Jemima is sitting on the wooden garden bench with her legs crossed, her suit skirt hitched high showing the stockings to good effect. A large bottle of champagne and a small bottle of water stand next to an overnight bag.

She follows his eyes and smiles. 'Early start to a long weekend, I thought. You're keen to get here so quickly,' she trills, much like a bird. A vulture, Sami thinks.

He wants to tell her to fuck off right there and then. Invading his office is bad enough, but this is his home and he's nearly broken his neck speeding the fifteen or so miles to get here. But townhouse gardens are not the place for any conversation, let alone a 'Fuck off, you fucking bunny boiler' type of altercation.

Be careful. Take it easy, he repeats inwardly as he tries to release the tension from his face. 'Actually, I'm out tonight with some mates. But there's time for a quick coffee, if you like.'

She follows him into the house and sits down. Her arms are folded and her chin is down, her shoulder to one side, her eyes on him. She's gone for petulant, he muses as he puts on the kettle. Posh girls think it looks sexy, but it doesn't, it really doesn't.

His tongue burns from gulping down the coffee so quickly, but Jemima sips hers slowly, like a kid avoiding bedtime. His hand is on his knee, moving in time with the tap of his foot.

Be patient. Take it easy, he mentally repeats. But she loops strands of her wavy hair around her fingers and pouts her lips, her eyes still on his. She seems to have rallied.

'So, yeah,' Sami says, rubbing his hands. 'I'm out tonight, for the weekend in fact. Better get organised.'

'OK. I just need the loo before I go.'

Sami sighs and waits, tentative relief overcoming the anger. He watches the clock, taps his leg and listens for the flush.

'What are you doing here?' Antonia asks at the door of White Gables.

'I've come to say sorry. I bet you never expected to hear that. It's freezing out here. Can I come in?' Sophie asks with a grin.

Antonia looks at Sophie for a moment before smiling. 'Come here,' she says, pulling Sophie inside. 'I've really missed you, you know. Are you back home with Sami?'

'Maybe later, who knows. I wanted to see you first.'

Antonia slides over the frothy cappuccino in the 'Sophie' cup, liberally sprinkled with ground chocolate, towards her best friend. She hasn't seen her for several weeks and yet it feels both like a year ago and like yesterday. Sophie seems slightly quiet and she's lost weight, but she's still Sophie. She just wonders if she's still Antonia.

'I have a job!' Antonia announces, amused by the look of surprise on Sophie's face.

She has enjoyed working in the salon. It's only been a couple of mornings, but already she looks forward to the company of the other girls and the customers, especially the older ladies, one of whom still comes in to have her hair set in rollers. She's been downgraded to Antonia, much to the other stylist's relief.

'You don't get any older on the inside,' the old lady said that morning, massaging her arthritic hands. 'I still feel like a girl, but then I catch myself in the mirror and I realise that I'm old.' She clutched Antonia's arm and looked at her sharply despite her milky eyes. 'Perhaps a little wiser, though.'

Antonia thinks that perhaps she's a little wiser. But the learning curve is slow and at times she's very lonely. Not so much being on her own, she's used to that, but not having someone to talk to intimately, to share her thoughts and discoveries.

She and David didn't talk, not deeply at least. They co-existed lovingly, their histories sealed away and preserved and it worked for them. But Antonia feels that her past is seeping out. It's both thrilling and terrifying.

'Talk to someone,' Mrs Jones advised. But she had talked to someone. Not just someone. She had talked to Mike. She'd told him things she hadn't told another soul and he didn't recoil or turn away. She misses that. She misses him.

303

Antonia turns her attention back to Sophie who's gazing at her with a puzzled frown. Of course Sophie knew Jimmy. She knew about his death and the trial but none of the detail. It's that detail which consumes Antonia now. She told some of it to Mike, but not everything, some things were too raw, too inexplicable. She omitted to mention that after Jimmy's violence, be it repeatedly slapping her mother, punching or kicking her, he'd lead Candy by the hand into their bedroom. Little Chinue would hide and cry and cover her ears, but still she could hear. Her mother's moans, loud and intense. It was only when she grew older that she realised the moans were not from terror or fear but from pleasure. These memories are surfacing and they trouble her.

'Isn't it a bit of a come down?' Sophie's saying, picking up the postcard from the journalist. 'You know. Lady of the Manor to sweeping up hair. I bet the girls are chavs too. It's in the job description. What's this?' she asks. She reads from the postcard. 'Young boxing champions of the past.'

Sophie settles herself on the sofa and tucks her legs under her bum, her face relaxed. She throws the postcard aside, forgotten already. Antonia smiles, she's missed Sophie too. 'Well, being an ex-chav myself, maybe I'm among friends.'

Sophie narrows her eyes. 'I've only been away for a couple of weeks and you've changed.'

'More like a month or more. It's probably because I buried my husband since the last time I saw you,' she says, looking pointedly at Sophie. 'Anyway, so have you.'

Reaching out her arm, Sophie's face looks genuinely contrite. 'I'm sorry about David, Toni. Truly sorry. He really loved you and I loved him for that.'

Antonia nods, the thought of Misty and David still colouring her grief. She's mostly shared with Sophie for as long as she can remember, but so much has happened, she doesn't know where to start. Instead she raises her eyebrows and looks at her fingernails theatrically. 'Well, your absence threw me into the arms of my new best friend, Helen.'

'Really? Into autistic hairy-chinned types?' Then rolling her eyes. 'Come on Toni, it's obvious to everyone but poor old Charlie that she's on the spectrum.'

Though she knows she shouldn't, Antonia laughs. 'Medical expert now? You are rotten. And there's me thinking you've changed.'

Sophie doesn't reply, but after a moment she smiles, her face lightly flushing. 'Perhaps I am and I have. I'm on the bloody happy pills, Toni. Can you believe it? Oh yeah, and Norma gave me a good talking to, so I'm being an angel.' Then she tosses back her head and laughs, her auburn locks shining as they bounce. 'But there's no need to panic, I'm sure it won't last.'

Sami's still listening to the flush of the loo when Jemima emerges into the kitchen. He turns his head and he looks. He should have known, he should have fucking known. The relief felt too sweet, he'd let it come too soon. She's naked, of course, save for the stockings. Her nipples are erect and strangely shiny. Her fanny has been completely shaved since their last encounter. Worst of all there's that look of entitlement on her pouty face.

He feels nothing but rage. 'I actually like fanny hair,' he wants to shout. 'My wife, who I adore, has lots of it. And she's witty and bright. She knows that she's not perfect and I love her for it. Don't you dare to come into her home and presume . . .'

But instead he leans back, his legs apart, his hands behind his head and smiles. You can smile and smile and still be a villain, he thinks determinedly. It's a line he remembers from school. It sums up the boy who bullied him the most.

'Hey, Jemima!' he says. 'You look great and I'd really like to, but I simply don't have the time.' He waits a beat. 'Or the money.'

He reaches for his suit jacket and removes the designer wallet Sophie bought him for their wedding anniversary. 'I realise that I've been a bad boy not paying before now. But it's always a little delicate discussing money, isn't it? What did the lads at work say, a hundred? So, I must owe you . . .'

He briefly glimpses her mouth gape as he thumbs through the notes in his wallet, counting the twenties out loud. 'Sorry. I'm a bit short. How about you get dressed and I nip to the bank?'

But by then the house is reverberating from the slam of the toilet door.

'Don't I have any say?' Helen says, clearly exasperated. 'I am his mother. I am entitled to an opinion.'

His mum is talking as though he isn't there, as usual, Rupert notes, but he's inordinately proud of his father. 'Go, Dad, go!' he wants to shout.

'In this case no, Helen, you don't have a say. You agreed to take up a post at New York University without consulting us and so you won't even be here next term. Rupert isn't going back to Staffordshire and that's final. He isn't happy there and we've been too pig-headed to notice. Cheadle Hulme school has a place, so it's a done deal, as they say.'

Helen puts down her huge quilted bag stuffed with books. Charlie has caught her unawares, on her way to the university, with little time to spare.

Dad knew she wouldn't want to be late for her student seminar, Rupert thinks. Sly old fox.

'I didn't think that *happiness* was the point, Charles. What

306

happened to *good education* and *family tradition*? Your words, not mine.'

'What's good for the goose is not necessarily good for the gander.'

Charlie pauses for a minute, his face rather red. Rupert wills him on. 'Gosling, maybe, Dad?' he wants to say.

'Besides, I'm not sending him to a state gangland, Helen. Cheadle Hulme is a perfectly good school. Gibson sends his children there, despite spouting his left-wing rubbish whenever he gets the opportunity. I shall be here to see that Rupert is watered and fed, so that's that.'

Rupert looks at his father's truculent face. 'So there!' it says. He glances at his mother. He can tell from her blank expression that her mind is already elsewhere, with her students probably, but that's the way it is.

Helen shakes herself, examines the watch she keeps on a chain around her neck and picks up her bag. 'Goodness. Look at the time.'

'Another thing before you go, dear. We feel that Barbara is getting a bit long in the tooth. That perhaps she needs a young assistant she can train up. An attractive au pair, we thought, didn't we, Rupert?'

'French would be good,' Rupert nods. 'For educational needs, of course.'

Charlie and Rupert laugh. Nice one, Dad, Rupert thinks as his mother nods absently. Whoever says his dad doesn't have an ace sense of humour is way off.

Jemima doesn't bother slamming the front door, she simply walks out with a stony face, clutching her overnight bag to her chest.

Sami sits at the kitchen table, the cold breeze from the open front door finding its way to his cheeks. He drops his head, a feeling of shame deep in his chest. He was brutal, horribly brutal, something he can't recall doing before. He doesn't like how it feels.

He scratches his chin. He hasn't shaved for a few days. It makes him look older and less chiselled. He's aware there are specks of grey in his fledgling beard but he woke up late and couldn't be bothered shaving. Sophie likes him clean shaved. Perhaps he's accepting the inevitable, that she isn't coming home.

He rests his forehead on his folded arms. His dad called him last night, his dad who never calls. 'Samuel, now you know I don't listen to women's talk,' he started and Sami knew what was coming. It was an echo of his own thoughts. Sophie was the one for him. He was a fool if he was letting her go. She was bright and charming, if a little rough around the edges. He needed to sort it out before it was too late. Even Martha was missing her. She had no one to complain about. She'd start on him next.

Sami takes a deep breath, trying to stifle the sob, but it's impossible. 'Fat boy, don't blubber or I'll give you a slap,' he remembers.

He cried too much as a boy, alone in his bed. But not as a man. Not since receiving the news of his dad's stroke from his sister, the one sister who isn't a clone of his mum. Ramona told him straight about what had happened to Dad. The man Sami appreciated it, but the fat boy inside fell apart, certain that his father would die. But he had Sophie then. She put her arms around him and she held him, keeping him together, keeping him safe.

He stays at the kitchen table for a while, playing out scenarios in his head. He wants Sophie back. More than anything he wants her to come home. It's pride, he knows, fucking foolish pride that's holding him back. He reaches for the kitchen roll, then wipes his face and blows his nose. 'What the fuck,' he announces to the room.

Please come home, he texts. *Missing you badly. Love you very much.*

He presses send, waits for the swooshing noise and then places his iPhone in the middle of the table. That wasn't so bad, he thinks, knowing the hard part is waiting for a reply, if ever. He stands up to close the front door, spots the champagne and the bottled water in the hall. He feels a last stab of shame, then opens the fridge door and places them inside.

CHAPTER THIRTY-EIGHT

Sophie sits in the car, breathing deeply and reflecting. Who would have thought it? Sophie Richards saying sorry without being asked, not once but twice. The old Sophie would laugh at the suggestion that saying the S word is therapeutic. 'A load of right-on church-loving bearded hippy crap.' Or words to that effect. But there's no doubt that the sorry feels good, a weight off her shoulders, if not her thighs. So easy too.

Her heart still races boom, boom in her chest. Without warning or obvious cause most of the time. But at least she has insight from an expert now. 'It's deep-seated anxiety, Sophie,' the therapist said. 'Think of how long you have bottled it up and allowed it to ferment. But you can beat it if you face it.' So Sophie breathes deeply, from her diaphragm. Which helps some of the time. Not all, but it keeps the panic at bay. It saves her fingernails from total annihilation.

The 'sorry's were easy, but Sophie understands that she's lucky. By some miracle her mum and Antonia made it easy. Because they love her, she supposes. The thought makes her want to cry. So many tears. She hopes the tough old Sophie will make a comeback soon.

She thinks of her morning with Antonia as the beat of her heart starts to slow.

'So, what was the sorry for?' Antonia teased with a grin. 'Shall we start at the beginning? Year Seven, maybe, and work up from there?'

'Don't push your luck.'

'Come on, it's like a life achievement award, I have to milk it for all it's worth.'

They settled on the sofa, just like old times, Antonia eating one chocolate button to Sophie's handful. Sophie glanced at Antonia's contented face and took a deep breath of resolve. She knew Antonia didn't expect a reply or an explanation, but Sophie didn't want to cheat. As the therapist said, 'You only end up cheating yourself.'

'I'm sorry that I didn't come to David's funeral. I should've been there for you, like before. I should've stayed with you and comforted you.'

Antonia nodded. It wasn't the usual shut-down cloud, Sophie noticed, but there was a strange reflective look on her face, almost a smile. But that was the easy apology. That part wasn't personal, that part didn't jangle in her chest with anxiety and fear. She took a deep breath. 'Also, I'm sorry I was so horrible. The things I said. I imagined some stupid things about you and Sami.'

'Paranoia, loss of self,' Sophie recalled as she waited for Antonia's response. But sometimes it was hard to know what was real and what wasn't. 'A step at a time, Sophie. A step at a time.'

'Bloody right they were stupid,' Antonia replied. 'You know

311

I love Sami, but never like that. Besides, I'm not a married man type. You're my friend, Sophie, my best friend. I wouldn't do that to you. People shouldn't do that to their friends.'

She studied Antonia's face as she spoke. Now there is a shadow, she thought. But then again, she knew that Antonia didn't tell her everything. The night of her father's death, for example. Antonia had never talked about it, not once to that day. Sophie knew not to ask. She never asked and never probed, as much as Norma and Barry had wanted her to.

There are some things one is entitled to keep private, Sophie mused as she sat snug with Antonia and ate another handful of buttons. Like the counselling sessions she'd had for the past two weeks. She couldn't hide the anti-depressants or keeping off the booze, but she could hide those, close to her chest. Sessions which were comforting and painful, brutal and honest. She didn't know why, but having them wasn't something she wanted to share with Antonia. At least not yet.

They were both silent for a while. 'And you knew too many of my secrets,' Sophie said eventually, needing to say it, needing to know. 'About the chlamydia, the PID, the lies to Sami.'

Antonia looked at her face and reached for her hand, held it firm. 'No need to worry about that, Soph. Those secrets are safe with me. I promise.'

Sophie continues to sit in the car, still not ready to move. Her breathing has deepened and her heartbeat has slowed but the anxiety is still there like a knife in her chest. Rejection, rejection, that fear of rejection. She tries to focus on her therapist's advice: 'Reality check, Sophie. What's the worst that can happen?'

She had loathed the therapist, naturally. She sat in stubborn silence for most of the first session.

'The only remotely good thing I can say about her is that

she hasn't got a beard,' she said to Norma on returning home. 'I'm not going again.'

But a combination of self-will she didn't know she possessed, and Norma's face, drove her back. Then once she started to speak, to explain it all from the beginning, she found that she couldn't stop.

'You say that you love him, you say you miss him. Why haven't you gone back to Sami?'

'I'm afraid.'

'Afraid of what?'

She thought about the answer for a long time. Where to begin? I'm afraid of losing him. I'm not as young or as slim or as pretty as the other girls. He'll hate me when he knows that I can't give him a baby, she thought. She settled on rejection, she supposed that was the crux.

'I'm afraid of rejection. Really afraid.'

'How do you know he'll reject you?' the therapist asked.

It was a fair point. Sophie didn't know, she didn't know anything. She assumed all sorts. Her mind had been inundated with assumptions for a long time now. Assumptions and paranoia and anxiety which she'd gratefully drowned in chilled Chablis.

'Would it be fair to say that it was only ever temporary drowning?'

Sophie started. She must have said the words out loud. Or perhaps the therapist was very good after all.

'What would be a more permanent death, Sophie? For all those assumptions?'

She shuffled in her chair, feeling like a school kid, afraid of getting the answer wrong. 'To know?' she ventured. 'To actually know?'

The beep of a text message rouses Sophie from thought. She

lifts her head and looks out of the car windscreen. A passer-by turns her head and stares. She looks confident, Sophie thinks. A young woman in a short suit with long legs, wavy hair, slim and young, without a care.

Sophie sighs, wondering what happened to the forthright girl she once was, the one who would head into battle, fearless, brave and strong.

'Perhaps it's because you care too much. Or perhaps you need good on your side to go into battle,' her mum had said yesterday.

Norma is probably right on both counts, but Sophie hasn't acknowledged it. During her long stay, she's discovered her mother is right most of the time and it doesn't make for good fellowship. But on the quiet, despite Antonia's assurance, if things work out, she's decided to confess everything to Sami. To say sorry and come clean about the miscarried baby, the infection, the infertility and the lies. In a strange way, she'll then have good on her side.

Sami is upstairs making the bed with worrying precision when the doorbell rings.

'Jemima, the champagne. Of course,' he panics. He should've left it outside. 'Shit, shit, shit.'

He walks slowly down the stairs, his heart thumping. Fucking hell, he'll have to have a word with Charlie about a restraining order at this rate. It's a bloody nightmare.

He opens the door and she's there.

'Avon calling!' she says with a smile. 'Got your apology.'

For a moment he's frozen, dumbstruck. 'That was quick. I only sent it five minutes ago.'

She puts her feet together and bends her knees, air hostess style. 'I think you'll find we run an exceptional service.'

314

He stares at her face, her beautiful face. She's smiling. The hugest of smiles. Thank you, God, thank you. He grins and he grins, standing there on his doorstep, like a laughing idiot.

'Aren't you going to ask me in, dear husband?'

He scoops her up and carries her into the house, then puts her down in the lounge, holding on to her tightly.

'I was a lot thinner the last time you did that,' Sophie says into his chest.

Sami pulls her away and holds her by the shoulders. He looks at her face, imperfect but beautiful. 'I love you just the way you are, Sophie.'

'Are you pleased to see me, Sami?' she asks, her voice a husky croak.

He holds her again. 'You can't begin to know how much. Don't you ever go away again, Sophie Richards. Do you hear me?'

Sophie's eyes are closed. She's cupped by Sami's body, sweaty and warm in their bed. His arms are around her waist and every so often he lifts a hand to play with strands of her hair.

She practised her lines in the car. 'There's something I have to confess.' It's going to be difficult, she knows. He'll be very, very angry. 'I wasn't ever pregnant.' He'll shout and pace. She'll need an excuse. 'You should have asked me to marry you sooner. Then I wouldn't have lied, Sami.'

But of course it started earlier than that, when she met his family, his sisters, all those bloody children. Not a lie as such, but an omission.

'Your sisters have so many kids, Sami.'

'Yeah, bet we will too, one day. Won't that be great?'

'One of each?'

'No, a houseful! You'll be a fantastic mum.'

315

But did she know then, really know and understand? 'The infection is severe, Sophie. It might well affect your fertility in later life.' The consultant's words might have been said long ago, but which eighteen- or nineteen-year-old listens, let alone cares?

The confirmation, the one she actually listened to and took in, was a shock, like a hard, unexpected blow to her chest. 'The sperm count is fine, Sophie. But the pelvic examination. I've re-read the forms. You've answered "no" to the questions about previous fertility issues, STDs. But it seems fairly clear that the problem is with you.'

Perhaps she could have told Sami then and dressed it up not to sound so base, but she'd already told the pregnancy-be-fore-marriage-and-miscarriage-after lie. Sami wasn't there at the appointment, he was away on business, and so she had time to think.

'What should I do? What the fuck should I do?' she had asked Antonia, there at the clinic, waiting to drive her home.

Antonia's face was serious, her eyes huge. 'Sometimes you have to lie,' she'd replied.

'You're quiet, everything OK?' Sami asks, interrupting Sophie's rumination. He kisses the top of her head and pulls the duvet back over them.

Sophie turns towards him, her breasts touching his chest, heart to heart. 'Actually, Sami, I have something to confess.'

Sami moves away, props his head on his arm with an enquiring look on his face. 'Go on, fire away.'

She stares at him, the man she will always love, whether she wants to or not. 'Good on your side. You only end up cheating yourself,' she repeats in her mind.

Taking a breath, she opens her mouth to speak and then closes it again. The expensive lip gloss had been placed carefully

316

beneath the mirror in the downstairs loo, like a malicious wink. She couldn't have missed seeing it if she'd tried. She binned it immediately, but still it nags. The champagne she's kept, perhaps he's bought it for her, it's possible. But he hasn't shaved. Sami always shaves.

'I've been to the doctor. He's prescribed happy pills.'

He looks at her, clearly shocked. 'What? You mean anti-depressants? That can't be—'

'I haven't been well, Sami. Not for a long time. Things have got me down and I've tried to hide it.'

Sophie gazes at Sami's face, his beautiful face.

You're struck dumb and I've told you virtually nothing, she thinks, as she watches him search for the words.

'Oh. I didn't realise.'

She sees his eyes flicker. Embarrassment? Self-reproach? It's difficult to tell.

'You can be poorly mentally as well as physically, you know. I need to get better. So now isn't the time for trying for a baby.'

'Yeah, of course. Absolutely. Poor you.'

He still looks stunned, but there's something else in his face that she can't quite decipher. Guilt? Relief, even? She leans into him. Perhaps she is 'cheating herself' but she doesn't much care. What Sami doesn't know won't hurt him.

She thinks of the lip gloss one more time before deciding to hide it in her mental box with all the other hurt and pain. She'll never let him go. And she's home now. Back for good. Things will be fine. There's no more to confess . . .

CHAPTER THIRTY-NINE

Antonia presses The Ridings front door intercom. 'Sunday, it's Sunday,' she wants to point out to a passing nurse. Not that she'll visit any other day again, but the implied criticism still rankles.

Signing in as usual, she feels a tap on her shoulder. 'They're putting up the decorations in the lounge. Candy's in her bedroom today, love,' the carer with the long grey plait says. 'Shall I let you through?'

Antonia hesitates for a moment, her eyes taking in a Christmas raffle prize covered in cellophane with a huge purple bow. It's displayed on a table next to a plate of mince pies with a note saying, 'Please help yourself'. A few weeks to Christmas, she thinks. The first without David.

She turns back to the carer. 'Is Mrs Jones in her office for a quick word first?'

'Oh, I haven't seen her. I'm not sure if she's in today. Maybe try later?'

Antonia nods, feeling a flip of disappointment. She's grown to like Mrs Jones. 'Laura, please call me Laura.' She wants to show Laura what she's unearthed from her day-long investigation at the Manchester central library. She could have cut corners and saved time by telephoning Zara Singh, she supposes, but that would've been cheating, she feels. Besides, the thought of talking about her dad to a journalist, of all people, still makes her heart flash and her neck prickle. Looking back it seems silly to have been so fearful of the woman's calls, of her interest. She was researching local young heroes of boxing. That's all. The postcard still remains on the kitchen island untouched. Antonia hasn't yet thrown it away, but she will. She has what she wants. From her own efforts too.

She looks towards the empty office door. She wants to say thank you to Laura. Thanks for caring, thanks for sharing, for pointing her in the right direction. But there's another question she'd like to ask about her mum and religion. She's been dwelling on it, more of the 'detail' which nags her before sleep at night.

Towards the end, when Antonia had left school at sixteen and spent more time at Sophie's than at her own home, Candy went from faith to fervour, spending an inordinate amount of time at their local Catholic church. In fairness Antonia has never asked, but neither has the information been offered by Laura or any of the staff at The Ridings. Has Candy ever gone to church either from The Ridings or, in the early days, from prison? Has she asked to? Is religion ever mentioned at all?

Shifting her focus back to the carer, she follows her to a locked door. Her heart racing, she watches the woman punch numbers into a keypad, then follows again down a white-washed corridor until they reach Candy's room.

The door is ajar, but still Antonia knocks, before pushing it back. Entering the bedroom, she smiles. 'Hello Mum! You're in here today,' she says in a bright voice.

Candy is sitting in an armchair, staring fixedly at a small television in the corner. It's a cold early December day outside, but the sun is insistent, shining brightly through the large window. With the heat of the radiator, it feels like summer.

Antonia perches on the bed, ready to wait patiently. 'They like their routine,' she remembers. It's Sunday today, so that's fine, but it's different because she and Candy aren't in the lounge, so she wants to tread carefully.

Letting out her breath, Antonia looks around. She hasn't been in Candy's bedroom since her mum first moved into The Ridings and she was so blinded with apprehension that day she took nothing in. She's always assumed she's guided each Sunday to the lounge because the carers and the nurses are hiding something beyond the locked doors. Restraining straps, a dirty bedroom, no toilet seat or bars on the windows. Perhaps even worse if she allows her imagination to dwell. But the room is lovely. It's an en-suite bedroom, the walls are clean and white, the floral bedding matches the curtains.

There are several greetings cards on the window ledge, all slightly curved from the heat of the radiator. She stands and bends down to peep without touching. There are the cards she's written that year. Valentine's Day, Mother's Day, birthday. And Easter, bloody Easter. 'All my love, Chinue xxx.' But there are other cards too. Birthday and Easter greetings from 'The Staff at The Ridings' and others from individual members of staff, Rose, Emma and Joe. Then she sees a card with a photograph of two chubby black babies attached with a paper clip.

'Is it all right if I look?' Antonia asks her mum.

'They're your second cousins. Twins,' Candy replies, her eyes still on the television screen.

Antonia picks up the card and reads. 'Dearest Candy. I thought you would like to see your brand new great-nephews. Twins, as you can see. I wonder if they will be as mischievous as we were! Love always from Thandi. PS We often think of Chinue and hope she is well.'

Antonia sits down again, still holding the photograph, feeling winded. Thandi, her mother's twin. She married a Nigerian. The last time Antonia saw Thandi, she told her to fuck off.

Mike thumps awake. The complexity of the dream always escapes the moment he opens his eyes, but he knows that he's bleeding, bleeding to death from stab wounds to his chest. He looks over to Olivia and touches her shoulder gently, as though to forgive the Olivia he knows was in the dream.

'Bad dreams, guilty conscience,' his grandmother's always said with a sour face, her arms folded over a huge bosom.

'Then I must be having a grand old time. Shame I'm too ancient to remember,' his grandpa would reply, his eyes twinkling.

'It's only a dream, Mikey. Don't worry, I'm here.' They were his mother's words. Soft and loving words. Mikey was always secure in her warm arms, knowing that she'd never hurt him or his sister, though protect them she would, to the ends of the earth.

Mike tries not to think of Antonia, but he does. Especially in those moments after waking from the dream, his heart hammering with relief. She was a young teenager, not so very much older than Rachel. A teenager who was awoken in the small hours to find her father bleeding to death, her crazed mother holding a blade and the dog howling. It sounded like a dream or a nightmare, a film even, but it wasn't. She called an ambulance and her mother was arrested. The mother pleaded guilty at the trial and was sentenced to life imprisonment. Then later she was sectioned and remanded to a secure hospital. Such a horrendous trauma for someone so young and so vulnerable. Then being left all alone to fend for herself. Like now, just like now.

Mike releases his breath and turns, remembering her troubled expression that night as she told him. Her face was so close to his that they almost touched and she whispered the words, her eyes far away, her hands trembling in his.

He hasn't seen her for weeks, simply dropping Rachel at the end of the White Gables driveway and collecting her from the same spot at the allotted time. 'How's Antonia?' he asks Rachel lightly in the car on the way home, hoping to glean just a little something of how she's faring. He knows she'll meet a man soon enough. The thought is almost unbearable.

'What was that, love?' he asks, turning his head towards Olivia on the other pillow. Olivia has mumbled something he didn't catch.

'I said that you called me Antonia.'

'Did I? I had a bizarre dream. Sorry, I'm only just waking up.'

Olivia turns in the bed and gives Mike a playful thump. 'Rule number one, Mike, never call your wife by the wrong name, especially when she feels like a beached whale.' She strokes her large bump and looks thoughtful. 'Have you seen her lately? Do you pop round any more?'

'No,' Mike replies. 'Never. Too busy at work to get away. Then when I take Rachel, she insists I drop her at the gates so she can saunter down the driveway like a proper grown-up. I think she's representing the family's concern pretty well, don't you?'

Olivia laughs easily. She seems so content now and Mike's grateful for that. 'Yes,' she says. 'I'm almost starting to get the hump. As well as the bump. My eldest child appears to have a higher regard for Antonia than me. But then when it comes to looks and fashion, I really can't blame her. But I must get round to visiting Antonia. She's nice.'

She leans over and kisses Mike on his stubbly cheek. 'I feel so much better now that I'm not puking twenty-four seven. I know I've been grumpy. Thanks for hanging in there, Mike. What on earth would I do without you?'

As Antonia was nearly seventeen and had a job, Barry and Norma had managed to negotiate a stay out of care until a council flat became available for her. In the meantime she'd continued to live at her home in Northern Moor. The two adults promised to keep an eye on her, but in practice it was Sophie who held everything together, from feeding the dog to fending off journalists.

'Doesn't it give you the creeps, still living there? Where it happened?'

It was the question people asked all the time, particularly at the hairdressers. Both the customers and staff. Everyone knew what had happened, everyone talked, not bothering to hold back their blatant curiosity. It was as though Antonia was public property, like a soap or a porn star who had no right to privacy or tact.

'I don't have much choice,' was her stock reply as she washed and brushed and straightened. Not the 'It's none of your bloody business' she wanted to scream.

She stayed with Sophie and her family in Northenden mostly, but she was at home on the day of the trial. When her mum was first arrested a couple of journalists had tracked her down at Barry and Norma's and hovered for hours outside their house. So as the trial approached she felt it wasn't fair to stay longer. They'd been very kind and the boys were still young. But Sophie was with her. She skipped a day off sixth-form college and arrived early at Antonia's house with a Subway sandwich meal deal and cider, so she wouldn't be alone.

The raps at the door were so frequent that she and Sophie became used to the dog's constant barking and hardly heard it. But eventually, when the knocking didn't abate but developed into hammering, Sophie gave in with, 'Don't worry. I'll get it and tell them to piss off.'

Sophie came back into the sitting room and shrugged. 'It must be one of your relatives,' she said, then Auntie Thandi appeared behind her, looking dishevelled and anxious. Her mother's twin, but not identical. Her skin was much darker.

'Chinue! You're not answering the telephone. I've come in a taxi from court. Why are you still here?'

Antonia stayed hunched on the floor, the dog close beside her. 'Mum asked me not to go.'

'Well, of course you have to come. You'll have to give evidence.'

'I'm not giving evidence. Mum doesn't want me to. She doesn't want anyone to.'

'Forget what your mum says. It's for her own benefit. You have to come and tell them what he was like. The judge and the jury, whoever. Explain why she finally snapped. For God's sake, Chinue, please come. The taxi's waiting outside. Come on, love. Just put on your coat and let's go.'

Thandi stepped towards her and held out her hand but Antonia shook her head, her arms tight around her knees. 'No. It's her penance. That's what she said. She made me promise.'

The rant started then, the anger and desperation etched on her aunt's face. Question after question, accusations and insults. Didn't Chinue care? What the hell was she thinking? Candy would get life for murder. Didn't she get that? Was she completely stupid? What kind of daughter was she? She'd live with the guilt for the rest of her life. She was as bad as her father, a stupid, stupid, selfish bitch.

Antonia covered her ears, pummelled the floor with her bare feet and screamed. 'Fuck off. Fuck off. Fuck off. Fuck off.'

'I think you should go now,' Sophie eventually said.

CHAPTER FORTY

'Hello, Olivia! You look chirpy!'

The voice comes from the mum of a boy in Hannah's class and it makes Olivia jump.

'Sorry, Liz. I was miles away,' she replies, her cheeks flushed. 'Oh, thanks. Chirpy but getting huger by the hour! Still, I guess it's better than being miserable and fat.'

Olivia laughs, feeling slightly abashed at how chirpy she feels. It's so very middle-class mother-hen-from-Chorlton of her. To make it worse she's clutching an armful of organic veg covered in soil. 'I think you'll find they sprinkle on the soil in the shop, the way one does with icing sugar on cakes that have burned,' she mocked to her sister not so long ago. Yet here she is in Unicorn, store to the virtuous vegans, buying pulses and veg and actually humming. God knows what she'll make with it, but she promised Mike something nice for dinner because he's been mega busy at work, stuck at his desk again today with deadlines to meet.

'I'm in the third trimester, can you believe. I had a scan yesterday and all is well,' she adds, by way of explanation for the chirpiness, if not the humming.

'Wow, that went quickly. Do you know what you're having?'

'A baby!' Mike would undoubtedly reply, quoting from *Only Fools and Horses*. But Mike doesn't want to know the sex of the baby, he wants a surprise. Her heart lurched just a little when he said it, the 'forgiven but not forgotten' accusations about the miscarriage still hanging around her like an aura. Along, of course, with the ghost of Sami. It's still there, but nebulous and vague, as a phantom should be. It feels a little silly now, but she whipped herself up into such a state of panic at one time she wondered if one could tell colour or ethnicity from a scan. She pictured the sonographer looking accusingly at Mike and saying, 'What the hell are you doing here, you're not the father!' But Mike is the father. Thank God. She finds herself thanking God a lot, which is pretty ironic coming from her doubting lips.

Olivia scrapes off the newly formed layer of ice on the windscreen of her car with a credit card. Climbing into the car, she puts her hand on the mound of her stomach and smiles as she feels the baby squirm. She was so tightly bound with anxiety about Sami and Mike that she forgot to worry about a miscarriage.

Sable cloud's silver lining, she thinks, as she turns on the ignition.

She's now nearly seven months gone, the baby moves regularly and everything looked good on the scan, nose, fingers and toes and a firmly beating heart. Besides, somehow she knows this one is a fighter. She doesn't want to tempt fate with her happiness, but she can't help it. Despite her initial negativity, she feels quite light-headed and giddy with optimism. Then yesterday at the scan, as she gazed at her baby on the screen, she saw what looked like a little willy. She glanced up at the sonographer and knew from her small smile and the slight nod of her head that the baby is a boy. It was all she could do not to point it out to Mike there and then. She knows he'll be so pleased with her, so thrilled when a son is born.

Other than sheer relief, Olivia can't explain the transformation from the woman who didn't want another baby to this, but she feels intensely grateful as she drives. To the hospital for the scan, to Mike for hanging in there and to Hannah for not kicking off about the baby. To her sister for not saying 'I told you so' after the fifth time. To Rachel for putting up with such a crap mum.

Peering through the windscreen, she smiles, thinking of her in-laws and their need to pray aloud. 'If you are up there, Mr Almighty, thank you too. I'll even let you off for the stretch marks.'

Not quite yet eleven, Antonia is early. It's drizzling, of course. David said it always rained in Withington. But he called it 'happy rain'. She should've asked him, 'Why happy?' but she didn't. Seeing the sparkle in his eyes was enough.

Today's another journey to the past, the more immediate past this time. She'd always assumed the gleam was nostalgic, from David's days as a student, and if not that, humorous thoughts of his Friday night banter with Sami and Mike at the pub. But she'd been wrong; her discovery about Misty at the funeral was deeply hurtful and shocking. But now time has passed, she finds it puzzling too; David had loved her, really loved her. Hadn't he?

Pushing the door open, the yeasty dank smell of beer hits her. It's mixed with cleaning products too, but she knows it's a smell that doesn't disappear. Once it's spilled, it stays, greedily absorbed by the floorboards like a drunk.

She heads to the bar, surprised to see two men at separate

tables already clutching pints. One of them catches her eye and nods soulfully. Dark beer, almost black, she knows that it's Guinness.

The lady at the counter turns. 'What can I get you?' Middle-aged and not unfriendly, she chats for a few moments as she pours the orange juice, but she doesn't have red hair, she isn't Misty.

Heading for the empty space beyond the bar, Antonia sits, wondering if this is where David sat on a Friday. He invited her, of course. 'Come to the pub. I want to show you off.' Just like he invited her everywhere. 'Come and watch me play football on Sunday. You need to see my left foot in action. You'll be so impressed.'

She sips her drink slowly, her eyes catching the morose man staring back. He has a fresh pint. What time did he start drinking? Why does he need to so early? What's he escaping? There's always a reason. She tries to reach for understanding or empathy, but the split of emotions is still there.

'It's Antonia, isn't it?'

The sound of the voice makes her start and look up. Misty, it's Misty. It's what she's here for, isn't it? And yet she wants to bolt, to deny who she is and escape.

But Misty is already pulling out a stool. 'Is it OK if I sit down?' she asks.

Antonia nods and Misty sits, smiling hesitantly. She places her wrinkled hands on the table. Huge glistening rings adorn her fingers and they're shaking badly. 'I'm glad you've come,' she says with a catch to her voice. 'I tried to speak to you at the funeral but of course you were busy. I wanted to speak to you in person, maybe visit or something, but I didn't know if you'd want me to.'

Antonia breathes. She thought she might shout when this

moment came. Scream and shake the evil bitch. But the woman's a wreck. Her grey roots are showing through the red, her eye make-up is haphazard and smudged, she looks desperately sad. 'Because I might know about the affair?' she asks quietly instead.

Misty frowns. 'What affair?'

'Between you and David.'

Misty leans forward, her cleavage exposed and creased. 'Oh, love, no! I mean who wouldn't want to with such a lovely handsome man, but no.' She reaches out her hand to take Antonia's and it's surprisingly steady and firm. 'No, Antonia. We had a . . . relationship, a friendship, but it was nothing like that.'

Antonia pulls back her hand. 'But at the wake, people were talking. I heard them. About you and David.' She thinks back to her conversation with Mike after the funeral. That kiss, that intimacy. It feels like years ago. 'People assumed—'

Shaking her head, Misty sighs. 'Yes, assumptions. That's running a pub for you. People make up all sorts of stories. They see what they want to see. Rumours get around. It caused problems for me and Seamus from time to time. He'd start to believe them too, get jealous and, well . . .' She takes a deep breath and smiles a wry smile. 'No affair, love. Very flattering, but stupid. Look at you. Why would he have any interest in me? He loved you, he adored you. You must know that.'

It isn't what Antonia expected. She lifts her hands, confused. 'Then why didn't he tell me? Why didn't he introduce you like he did with his other friends? Why were you a . . . a secret, I suppose?'

The smile from Misty's face falls, tears fill her eyes. 'He had a great big hole here,' she says, putting a hand to her breast. 'His mum. He still desperately missed her. I'm no psychologist, love, but I think he needed someone to talk to—'

'And it should have been me,' Antonia blurts, her words choked. 'But I wouldn't talk to him. I let him down—'

Grasping Antonia's hand again, Misty shakes her head. 'No, love, don't go there. I run a pub. There are things men tell me they wouldn't tell another soul and especially not a wife.' She gazes for a moment, her eyes luminous, as though seeing Antonia's insides. 'We're all human; there's always something we're not proud of, or a side of us we want to hide. He loved you faithfully, Antonia. He wanted nothing but the best for you, your happiness came first.'

Wiping her face with a tissue, Antonia finds herself whispering, the words emerging unexpectedly, honest and raw. 'His adoration was difficult at times. He put me on a pedestal. Thought I was someone I wasn't.'

Sitting back, Misty smiles. 'I know you won't believe it, but I was like you once. I was beautiful too.' She turns towards the bar and lifts a hand to wave to Seamus. 'It's not always easy being perfect. Which, of course, we're not. But imagine how difficult it is for them.'

Mike returns to the office from lunch to find Judith looking comfortable in his chair. He's been to Sam's Chop House for a pint with Sami even though he didn't really have the time. He only had the one pint, but lunchtime drinking isn't a good idea, it does the opposite of what alcohol is supposed to do. He feels drowsy and introspective. Still, Sami was on great form, the best he's seen him for weeks.

'Sophie's home,' Sami said in the pub. 'Thank God. My chances of gastroenteritis have tripled, the house looks as though it's been dusted for prints and I have to put up with Ronan Keating again, but I feel like a newly-wed. Bloody ridiculous, isn't it?'

'So, the baby thing . . .'

'A close shave, Mike. Thank God she's gone off the idea for now. Hopefully it'll be permanent. If I'm honest I'd prefer just to stay as we are. I can't see me with a kid.'

Mike laughed with surprise. He thought he knew Sami so well. 'As long as you're happy, mate, cheers to that!'

Judith is picking up papers from his desk, scrutinising them quickly and putting them in piles. She's reorganising his disorder and he knows better than to stop her. He watches for a while, pleased to see her, relieved she'll be coming back after her maternity leave to organise his working life and to brighten his day. He misses their shared humour; he misses their chats.

'Mislaid your baby already, Jude?' he says with a grin as he removes a stripy scarf knitted by Rachel. 'In Marks and Spencer food hall? Or maybe try Debenhams' changing rooms.'

'Ha, ha. I see from the state of your desk that you've been missing me. A lot.' She lifts her head, looks at Mike and smiles. 'So, fill me in with all the gossip.'

'You're asking the wrong man. No one tells me anything.'

'That's because you don't tell anyone anything.' She gazes at him thoughtfully, her pencil tapping on the desk. 'You seem quiet. How's the merry widow?'

Mike laughs, hoping the laugh will reach his eyes. 'Fine, I believe. Rachel's still going round.' Bloody Gypsy Rose, he thinks with a pang. Antonia was all he thought of at lunch with Sami, desperately wanting the conversation to move on to her. How she really was coping. Whether she had a new man.

Their heads both turn to the door as they hear the shrill squeal of a distressed baby approaching. Judith raises her eyebrows. 'That's what happens when you play "Who's the Daddy?" I wonder who they've come up with this time.'

She takes the baby from an apologetic-looking secretary and

rocks her gently until the crying stops. 'It'll be your turn again soon,' she says with a small frown. 'She's hungry. I'd better go.' She steps to the door but turns before leaving. 'You know what I'm thinking, Mike? Rose-tinted glasses; the grass is greener; absence makes the heart grow fonder. I could add more if my brain hadn't shrunk.' She picks up the woolly scarf from the back of a chair and hangs it on a hook. 'You have a great life, Mike. A lovely family. Remember what you've got.' She watches his face for a moment. 'Just saying . . .' she adds before closing his office door.

CHAPTER FORTY-ONE

Olivia stands in her hallway and looks at her watch. Rachel has netball after school and Hannah's going to a friend's house for tea, so she has time to either attend an aqua-natal class at Chorlton swimming baths or to assuage her conscience by visiting Antonia. She prefers the idea of the former. It's a life saver to make friends with other pregnant mums, not only for the pre-birth gripes and fears, but particularly for after the birth. The support and camaraderie of someone else with stinging stitches and leaky nipples is invaluable. But she most definitely feels guilty about her failure to visit Antonia properly since the funeral. She's been so sweet to Rachel too, taking her bowling or to the cinema and then to Nando's. It's the sort of thing Olivia would do had there not been such a large age gap between Rachel and Hannah. 'Though, would I?' she asks herself, as she studies the clutter of trainers and fairy wings, music stands and jigsaws under the stairs. It's difficult to really know the answers to all the 'if' questions. She's told herself firmly to stop beating herself up, to concentrate on 'scot-free', whatever that actually means, but sometimes it's much easier said than done.

'Antonia. Decision made,' she says out loud. 'After the veg.'

She runs the kitchen tap, dislodging the soil from the vegetables with her fingertips as random thoughts flow through her mind. A dead body. What would you do? How do you know it was dead, even? Arranging a funeral, a wake. Where do you begin? Money, death certificates, probate. Loss of your husband, the person you love. Loneliness, grief, guilt. Living in the same house. Using the bathroom, the bath? It must be overwhelming.

Perhaps she'll find out the answers from Antonia this afternoon. Not that she'll ask, naturally. But maybe the information will be offered. The conversation had flowed all those weeks ago when Antonia stayed for lunch. It'll do so again, she's sure. They're friends after all.

The veg duly prepared and covered in cold water, Olivia picks up her padded jacket and heads for the front door. She's about to close it as the telephone rings.

'Oh, hi Siân. Yes, aqua's on today as far as I know. Chorlton baths this week, Withington next.' She pauses, listens, umms and aahs. 'I was in two minds actually, but if you're going, I'll definitely come too. We haven't caught up for ages.'

Forgetting the guilt, she pulls the door to. It'll make no difference if she visits Antonia tomorrow.

'Shattered Dreams!' the *South Manchester Reporter* headline from the mid-seventies declares from the photocopy in Antonia's hand. Since returning from Withington she's studied the black-and-white photograph endlessly. David never betrayed her, thank God. There's relief and joy mixed with the sadness, but the visit has unsettled her too. Not just the tragedy of a man living with a hidden hole in his heart, or the way Misty seemed to see inside her head, but the memory of the guy in the pub, drinking his life away.

Although it's stuck to his head with sweat, the thickset young boxer in the snap has light hair, maybe ginger, she thinks. The boxing gloves are at the fore of the photograph, partly covering the face which is slightly blurred and distorted by the gum shield. It's difficult to tell if it's truly her dad.

'That's Jimmy!' Candy immediately declared on Sunday in her bedroom, delight brightening her face and diverting her from the television screen.

Despite her desire to cut to the chase as she showed Candy the newspaper article, Antonia bided her time. She let her mum chat and reminisce about old times. But her memories emerged like patchwork. Candy talked of people and places and events which didn't appear to be connected and meant nothing to Antonia.

A middle-aged woman with ruddy cheeks tapped at the open door. She was carrying a mop made of strips of blue cloth and a bucket. 'Sorry to interrupt, love. Do you mind if I do your loo now, Candy?'

'Rose, look it's Jimmy!'

Rose put down her carry box of rags and disinfectants and leaned over. 'Good looker, eh Candy! You said he was a boxer.' Her eyes scanned the article. 'What a terrible shame. I remember you saying. His legs got broke and the rest. Worse than in the ring. Still, it didn't stop you and Jimmy having this smashing lass here.'

Antonia listened to the exchange and smiled. The polite fixed smile of a daughter who didn't know as much about her mother as the care home cleaner. Because she never asked, because she never really listened. Like David, like David.

She turned to her mother and picked up her chubby hand. 'Why did it happen, Mum? Why did they beat him up?'

But Candy leaned forward and balled up her body. She wept

335

and rocked and keened and it took some time for Antonia to hear her words and to understand what she was saying.

'It was my fault. I shouldn't have told him. It was only name calling. I should have been used to it. But he was so angry when I told him. He wanted to shut up their dirty racist mouths. He did it for me. Because he loved me, he adored me. It was all my fault.'

Antonia props the photocopy against a framed photograph of her and David from their wedding day and sighs. As much as she's tried, she can't reconcile the young boxing champion in the picture with the father she remembers. She and Sophie burned the photographs, not just of Jimmy, but of the whole family, on her seventeenth birthday.

'Life begins now. Don't ever look back,' Sophie said, her eyes glinting from the flames of their bonfire like emeralds. 'Now, think of a new name, but make sure it's one you like. You'll have it for a long, long time.'

The 'For Sale' sign on the country road feels ominous as Mike approaches in his car. He's shocked to see that Antonia is selling White Gables. Rachel hasn't mentioned it and why should she? But still, it feels like a reprimand, an illustration of the distance between them.

He indicates right and waits for the traffic to clear. He can see Antonia's frost-covered car parked in its usual space at the front of the house. His heart thuds in his chest. The words 'rose-tinted glasses' are still repeating in his head. Despite the pile of reports on his desk, he's left the office without saying anything to anyone. He's driven fifteen miles to White Gables, the impulse to know whether Judith is right inexorable.

Mike knocks at the door and then waits. He rings the door-bell and then waits again, feeling foolish. Antonia has already made it clear how she feels. Why would she answer the door to someone she's politely but firmly pushed away? He sighs, vaguely wondering if she's watching him from an upstairs window. The humiliation is probably for the best as he's no idea what he would say. Turning up at this time unannounced is ludicrous. He's in cuckoo land. He has to get a grip and move on.

He turns back towards the car, lifts his keys to unlock it and there she is.

Antonia is strolling down the driveway towards him. Her wavy hair is shining and bouncing in the breeze. She's wearing a cream belted jacket with a fur-lined hood and her beautiful smile. 'Hello stranger,' she says when she reaches him and he finds himself smiling too. An inane grin, much like Sami's at lunch.

Antonia feels as though she's gabbling, filling in the lost weeks as though time is in short supply. She tells Mike comical tales about the salon girls and their customers, her Withington visit that morning, her meetings with Charlie and the decisions made about finances and the future. Her happy reunion with Sophie too.

She shows Mike the *Reporter* newspaper cutting about Jimmy, the sales particulars for the house and her tip jar half full of pound coins. Then she asks him if he wouldn't mind unscrewing the U-bend under the sink as it's stuck and changing a light bulb in the hall before he goes. Or, if he prefers, holding the ladders for her while he's here.

'I'm going on, aren't I?' she says, still smiling, still inordinately pleased to see him.

'No, not at all. It's lovely to listen. It's no problem to do the chores. I've always fancied being Oddjob. Though sadly I don't have the hat.'

He gazes with a frown for a minute, then looks down to the sales particulars he's still holding. 'This is your home. It's where you've felt safe . . .'

She's thought about this a lot. Like the crutch of Sophie, there's a fine line between safety and claustrophobia. 'I know, and it's a strange thing to say, but it's also been my prison,' she says, knowing she wouldn't admit it to anyone but him. Then she laughs to ease the sudden tension, lifting her arms to the room. 'A very nice prison, I have to admit.'

Mike nods thoughtfully but says nothing. She's aware he hasn't taken his eyes off her since they sat down at each end of the sofa in the kitchen, but he's quiet. He's gone from very smiley to serious. Or so it seems. He's saying so little that it's difficult to judge.

'Why have you come, Mike?' she eventually asks breathlessly, looking down at her china cup, wondering if perhaps she's done something wrong.

He closes his eyes for a moment and then smiles with a small shrug. 'I'm not really sure. I can't stay long.' Then, looking at her again, so intently, 'I've thought about you so much, wondered how you were.'

He clears his throat and leans towards her. His eyes search her face. Then he asks a question, as though it's popped out. 'Why did your mum—' he starts. 'Why then? Why the final straw that particular night? I know it's none of my business, but . . .' His eyes are still on hers, his face clouded. 'I wish I'd been there to protect you. I wish I could protect you now.'

'But you can't,' she whispers.

'I know. That's the problem.'

Olivia winds down the car window to let in some fresh air or at least let out the hot. Cold winter has started to set in, the afternoons dimming into early evening. But Olivia is having a 'hot pregnancy', as she puts it. She's already pulled her car into a lay-by to take off her thick jacket and fling it on the back seat next to her swimsuit and towel. She's now going through the repetitious cycle of putting on the blower to clear the condensation from the window screen, then opening the window because she's boiling and then closing it because there's a chilly wind, which causes the window to steam up yet again.

Cycles and circles, she muses, thinking how most things come right in the end.

She feels the heat rise yet again. 'Hm, seems you're my very own hot water bottle,' she says aloud to her bump. Perhaps she should've gone swimming after all, but she got caught behind a funeral cortege on the way to the baths. When she overtook the first hearse, the widow turned her head. Her face was so composed, yet vulnerable and sad, and for a moment she thought the woman was Antonia. So she immediately turned the car, the pangs of conscience about not having visited her overcoming her desire to hang out with friends.

She notices the road sign for the sharp bend ahead and drives on carefully, never quite sure when to indicate right. Waiting for the traffic to pass, she catches her glowing face in the car mirror. It's definitely fat. A fat face for a boy! Olivia Turner, who's never had a fat face in her life, has one now.

She smiles wryly at the thought of all the insulation she'll have to lose once the baby is born but the smile dissolves as she focuses on the drive of White Gables. The hesitant dusk is lit by the open front door where Antonia stands, waving. And there is Mike, Mike her husband who's so busy at work he barely has time for lunch. He's striding towards his car, his jacket over his shoulder and he's wearing no tie.

Her indicator winks, but she doesn't move. She stares,

transfixed, as Mike opens the back door of his car and throws in his jacket. He climbs in and swings it round without difficulty as though he does it every day. Then he indicates left and drives straight past Olivia. Blind to the car, blind to her, at ten to four in the afternoon.

CHAPTER FORTY-TWO

Helen has taken to wafting her colleague, Ted Edwards, away with a 'Maybe catch up with you later' type of waft. She's noticed that he always appears in the staff refectory moments after her with an unconvincing, 'Oh, fancy you being here, Helen! I'll keep you company, shall I?'

He's become rather too tactile as well. 'These chairs are very heavy, don't you think, Helen?' he says regularly. She doesn't appreciate being manhandled, even if it is with the pretence of pulling out the chair and pushing her back in.

Helen has always been a person to call a spade a spade, a saying she doesn't particularly get, but she understands the gist. But she's aware that Ted is, to some extent, her benefactor vis-à-vis NY (as he calls it), so she has to try for diplomacy. Unfortunately diplomacy is not her strong point, as Charlie often points out.

'Forty-three days until blast off!' Ted declared only that morning as they passed each other in the foyer.

'I thought we were travelling by aeroplane, not by rocket,' Helen replied.

As she sits down at the refectory table, she muses that it was a witty riposte. She would normally telephone Charlie for a chuckle, but Charlie and Rupert have formed a father and son club she clearly isn't invited to and she finds it rather rankles. But with Ted, the problem isn't so much his day-counting (which is a little odd), but his hand which he places too regularly around her shoulder. Not just his hand, but his thumb too, which he moves in a circular motion on her upper arm.

He's here again today, appearing at her table just as she's about to take a bite of camembert with cranberry on rye, her absolute favourite.

Tact, she reminds herself as her heart sinks. Remember, diplomacy and tact. She might even try some 'grey', as Charlie says.

'Hello, Ted,' she says. 'I was just ruminating on how much I'm going to miss Charles, my dearest husband Charles, when we're away in NY.'

Ted pushes his spectacles up his nose and then settles himself opposite Helen with his All-Bran. 'A snack for the bowels,' he explained yesterday.

'Oh, but of course,' he replies now, smiling. 'Which is precisely why I'll personally see to it that you don't get too lonely, my dear.'

She's never noticed the abundance of hair which protrudes from his nostrils before now. Indeed, in all the years they've worked together she's never really examined his face or any other part of his anatomy. He's a work colleague, a married work colleague, why would she?

She looks at Ted now and sees a grey face and matching hair. But alarmingly, she also sees a self-satisfied look. 'Nudge, nudge, wink, wink,' the look says. She knows what that expression means. She first heard it in a comedy sketch as a young girl

342

and, on one summer's day at a picnic, when David was acting it out with much laughter, he was kind enough to explain it to her.

Helen puts down her sandwich with a sigh. Calling a spade a spade is clearly the only option after all. 'Why did you nominate me for the secondment, Ted?' she asks.

'Well we've always had a rapport, don't you think? And I've always considered you to be an extremely handsome woman.'

Said just like that, in the staff refectory, of all places. It's so absurd that Helen wants to laugh. But beauty is only skin deep, she thinks. Which, of course, it is. How many times has she said that? It's something she's uttered with scorn about Antonia many a time. Yet it's insulting, she now discovers. It's insulting to be judged on something physical and God-given, rather than something earned. Very much so.

Oh, Charlie, I've missed the grey again, she thinks. I'd like to join your club.

Helen scrapes back the chair (a struggle without Ted's assistance). 'How perfectly insulting,' she declares. 'NY can do without me, thank you. You can blast off on your own!'

She stomps out as noisily as she can, the camembert and cranberry on rye left sadly behind. It's all a little thespian, which to her surprise, Helen finds she enjoys.

CHAPTER FORTY-THREE

It's five o'clock, Mike is back at his office desk and signing the post, no wiser about how he really feels about anything in his life than he was three hours previously.

A purple Post-it note is protruding from his diary. *Don't panic,* Judith has scrawled. *Only a hundred and seventy-three days until I'm back! Seriously, though, call me if you need to talk. Remember what's important. Appreciate what you have, xxx*

He rakes his hands through his hair, tempted to call Jude there and then. He's confused. He doesn't know what's important any more. He doesn't love Olivia or his girls any less but at that moment he wants Antonia more. The need is constant and excruciating. He has to stop the wanting and the desire, but he has no idea how to begin.

He reaches for the telephone to call Judith but an incoming call from reception beats him to it. 'Mike, two police officers are in reception for you. Shall I send them up?'

*

Mike hears voices, sees lights. The flashing lights of the police car. The Christmas lights twinkling on the way. The strip lights above the hospital bed.

'Sorry, sir, we did try to contact you at the scene, but your mobile was off and your office people weren't sure where you were,' a police officer says.

Olivia is on a hospital bed, warm just for him, but dead. Her face is pale and empty. Her hair is hidden by bandages. Her chest moves in time with a machine, but her spirit, her essence has gone.

'The trauma team did all they could. We'd like to call someone you're close to, to be here with you. Mike? Can you give us a name and a number, Mike?'

He sits by the bed and numb time passes. Should he touch, should he talk? Like someone in a coma?

He turns to the door. Macclesfield hospital. Why have they brought her here? Turns his head back to Olivia and stares. Can it really be her?

The police come in and out of the room. A man and a woman. Good cop and bad. They give him information he doesn't want. Ask him questions he can't answer.

Olivia wasn't wearing her seat belt, they tell him. The head injuries were inevitable. The lorry driver is traumatised, there was nothing he could do to avoid it, his brakes hopeless on the ice. It was confirmed by several witnesses, they say. She seemed to drive straight at him as though he wasn't there.

The woman officer stares, cocks her head on one side. 'The witnesses say Olivia was visibly distressed,' she says. 'Were there any problems? Any reasons why she might be so upset? Do you know where she was going? There were flowers in the car.'

He doesn't know how to answer, he can't focus, can't think.

But there's a voice behind him. It's shaky. 'No. There were no problems,' it says. 'People with problems don't buy flowers, for God's sake.'

Mike turns to the voice. Then he's standing and sobbing, Sami holding him steady with firm and strong arms.

After a few moments he pulls away. Above the rush of noise in his ears, there's an unmistakable sound, the distant cry of a baby. Someone has given birth, the start of new life. But why would he care? His Olivia is dead.

A new person comes in, wearing a white coat. A doctor, he supposes. 'A terrible accident,' she says. She has kind pale eyes, like his Olivia's. 'I'm so very sorry, Mr Turner. But you'll need to contact your wife's family. So they can come to say goodbye before we . . .' Her words trail off. The baby still cries.

Realisation hits like a slap. His girls, his girls. Little Hannah and Rachel. Oh God, oh God. How will he tell them?

Taking a step to the door, he speaks to the male officer. 'My daughters. I need to go. I need to collect my girls. Can you take me?'

'The girls are fine, mate. They're with Sophie,' Sami replies. His eyes are huge and tears spill on to his navy-blue suit. 'I'll take you home in a while but . . .' He gestures to the doctor. 'They think you should see the baby.'

'What baby?' Mike asks. 'Olivia is dead.'

'They saved the baby, for now. Very small. In an incubator. A boy.'

Ah, that baby, Mike thinks.

'You go. I'll wait here and . . .' Sami starts, his voice choked with emotion. He clears his throat, wipes his face and tries again. 'I'll wait here and look after Olivia until you come back. Go on, mate. She'll be safe here with me, I promise.'

'This way,' the white-coated woman says, gesturing with her arm. 'I'll come with you. Show you the way.'

Still frozen, Mike nods and he follows. A baby, my baby. Puts one foot in front of another and walks. Down a long corridor, past rooms and blank faces. A baby, my baby, he thinks. The one Olivia gave me; the boy that I wanted so much. But there's a voice in his head. 'Be careful what you wish for,' it says.

CHAPTER FORTY-FOUR

Antonia sits at the bottom of the stairs still clutching her mobile. It's dark. The limestone floor is unforgiving. She can hear the muffled cheerful radio chatter from behind the closed kitchen door. Like the chatter she had with Mike only a few hours previously, sealed in that room forever, like a phantom.

She clutches her knees with her head down, trying to breathe slowly and deeply, the way she was taught by Barry when the panic attacks were constant.

'What have I done? What have I done?' beats with the thud of her heart.

But her head replies, 'It's not your fault. Not this time.'

There was hammering at the door at four o'clock. Antonia thought it was Mike as he'd only just left, but there was something urgent and insistent about the noise. She walked cautiously down the limestone stairs, a similar frenetic hammering at a door still crisp in her mind despite the passing years. She looked through the peep hole. It was Olivia, pregnant Olivia. Olivia, Mike's wife.

Olivia swept in with the cold. Then she turned towards Antonia, her hands on hips and her face livid. 'What the hell was Mike doing here?' she demanded. 'I just saw him leave. What the fuck are you playing at?'

Taken aback, she replied, 'It was just a visit, he popped in to see if I was OK. Mike's so thoughtful. I'm really grateful.'

'Thoughtful, like fuck. In the middle of the day when he's meant to be so bloody busy at work? You don't take off your jacket and tie to be *thoughtful*,' Olivia retorted. 'You're a fucking liar!'

'You're as good as the next man. Be proud. Turn the other cheek,' Candy always said. Why should she explain about a blocked sink? In her own home too. So Antonia turned away.

'I think you should leave, Olivia.'

'I'm not leaving until you tell me what's going on.'

Olivia put her hand on Antonia's shoulder and dragged her round. 'Look at me. Tell me. Why was Mike here? What were you doing?' Spit sprayed from her mouth. Her eyes looked electric.

'There's nothing to tell, Olivia. Please leave my house.' Tense but calm; thinking of Candy's words, taking the higher ground.

But Olivia's voice was insistent and shrill. 'What sort of person are you anyway?' Her mouth moved and bile spilled. It was as though she couldn't stop. 'Your husband kills himself so you decide to take mine.' Olivia laughed, a deep laugh that seemed to belong to someone else. 'We're all wondering why. It's what everyone wants to know. It must be her, they say. She's weird. She must have driven him to it. Well, keep away from Mike. Leave us alone. I'm having his child in six weeks, for God's sake.'

That was the final straw. The hypocrisy of the woman.

'*His* child?' Antonia asked with icy calm. 'Are you sure? Not Sami's?' Then slowly, digging in the knife. 'I know about you

349

and Sami. I saw you, I heard you at David's wake.'

Olivia's face lost its colour. 'No. No, Sami is—'

'Infertile? The sperm count story was a lie. Sophie's lie, to suit Sophie. Sami isn't infertile. When the baby is born and Mike finds out, what then, Olivia? What sort of person does that make you?'

Antonia lifts her head, breathes deeply and stares at her shaking hands.

It's not your fault, her mind repeats. They were only words. They were truthful words. Words can't kill. It's the deed which counts and her hands are clean.

PART THREE

CHAPTER FORTY-FIVE

It's her mother's hands Antonia dreams of, her mother's hands pressed on to her father's chest and then lifting them, dripping with blood, to her face.

Sunday mornings were always bad at Chinue's home in Northern Moor because Candy was absent. She was at church. At church before the morning Mass to dust, to carefully put out the prayer books, to lovingly arrange the flowers and then to attend the service with a proud smile. Afterwards she'd stay to scrub away the footprints of her fellows until the next service, happy to do it all again with joy. She'd pop home when she could, her eyes shining with fervour and purpose and fuss over Jimmy. 'I was up at six to bake you a cake, love. Lunch is in the oven. Here's your newspaper. I'll make you a cuppa before I go. I won't be long.'

But this day was a Holy Day and not just any Holy Day, but Easter Sunday. There were Masses at church all morning and then again at night. Chinue had been to the early service, then she'd slipped in the house, lingering in her bedroom and browsing through old hair magazines borrowed from the salon, wishing she could have escaped to Sophie's. But even if she had been invited, she would've said no. The Easter Bunny visited Sophie's house, the boys hunted for chocolate eggs in the garden and ate them for breakfast and lunch. Then family visited, aunties, uncles and cousins. They ate roast turkey with all the trimmings for dinner and then played games. She'd have been in the way.

Chinue turned over a page and studied a photograph of Twiggy's bob from the sixties. If only, she thought, but her hair would curl, the blow-drying impossible.

Her mind flitted to Sophie. She wondered if her brothers had found the Mini Eggs she'd left under their pillows, if they felt sick yet. The Farrells didn't have family round, not even at Christmas. Jimmy had fallen out with his brother, over the drinking, probably. Auntie Thandi wasn't welcome, not since she married.

Chinue was hungry, her stomach rumbling. She knew there was Irish stew in the oven on a low heat. 'Eat it when you want, love. It likes to be cooked,' Mum had said at church. But she was reluctant to go downstairs. She didn't know what sort of temper her dad would be in. She'd spent so much time out of the house since starting work at the hairdressers that she'd lost track of his moods. Sometimes he was fine, he went for walks with the dog and told a few jokes at tea. But his mood could change 'on a sixpence', as her mum put it. Something on the television or in the newspaper he'd found comical only yesterday would enrage him today. That's when he'd reach for the Guinness.

Hunger overwhelming, Chinue sighed and headed quietly down the stairs.

'Wondered when you'd appear. Sacha needs a walk,' her dad

said as she entered the kitchen. He was sitting at the table with the newspaper. The ashtray was full but there was no sign of beer cans.

'It's raining,' she replied.

'The dog still needs a walk.'

'Why don't you take her?'

Chinue had become braver since starting work. The pay wasn't good but it was money. Money she was squirrelling away.

'I would if I wasn't in fucking pain. Just do as I tell you and don't argue.'

Chinue took the lead from the hook on the door and slipped on her mum's cagoule, nearly too small now. She'd pushed it with her dad as far as she could for today, but she was close, very close to walking out for ever.

'I'm in fucking pain.' That's all her dad ever said. He took pills and crushed them in his rotten teeth but there was no pain as far as she could see, just excuses.

Other people's dads didn't stay in the house all day smoking roll-ups and feeling sorry for themselves, ranting endlessly about politics or a football transfer or the price of beer. Other people's dads didn't start on the Guinness after breakfast and progress to whisky by tea-time. The rest of it too. It was the rest of it she didn't want to think about. If she left, her mum would be on her own. With him.

Chinue enjoyed walking once she was away from the housing estate and used to the cold and the rain. If anyone asked, she'd say she hated Sacha, the dog. But that wasn't true. She was a good old girl, a sweet-natured dog. It wasn't Sacha's fault she was Jimmy's. It wasn't Sacha's fault that Jimmy would scream at her mum when he was pissed, that he would raise his fist to his wife but not to a dog.

The rain had relaxed into drizzle by the time she and Sacha arrived at the gardens. Wythenshawe Park always gave her a buzz, the haunted mansion at its centre drawing her in. She had picnics and pear cider there with Sophie. They'd stroll around the farm, coo at the small piglets, christen the ugly adult pigs with the names of old teachers, stare at the well-hung bull. Or go to the swings, hang out with lads, sometimes kicking a ball, sometimes snogging the bolder boys in bushes. She did sports there too, was part of a club. Chinue was good at athletics, sprinting and hurdles in particular.

'Well, you don't get the sporting gene from me, that's for sure,' her mum would laugh, clapping proudly when Chinue won yet another race by a head.

But of course Jimmy never came to watch. 'Not interested in sport,' he'd say.

'Come on Sacha,' Chinue said on that Sunday, smoothing the damp fur from the dog's eager eyes and removing the lead. 'Never mind the drizzle. Let's run!'

'You were a long time. Your dinner's cold,' Jimmy stated when she returned from the park.

Taking off the wet cagoule, Chinue glanced at the table. The stew was on a plate, its greasy yellow edges beginning to solidify.

'Why didn't you leave it in the oven? It looks disgusting.'

'Don't be so ungrateful. Mum put it there.'

Chinue frowned. 'Did she?'

'She's been and gone back. So, you'll eat it.'

Avoiding eye contact with her dad, she sat down. She could tell from the tone of his voice he was annoyed with her mum for being at church too much.

'Where've you been all this time anyway? Slagging with some boy?'

'No. Walking Sacha, obviously.'

His voice was just a touch slurry at the other end of the table. No one else would have noticed. She didn't need to look for the empty cans. She wondered how many were gone.

'Eat your food.'

Breathing deeply, she stared at the congealing food, the fury slowly rising from her feet to her chest. It looked disgusting. He'd left it out on purpose, just to pick a fight. He was so, so pathetic.

'Eat your fucking food,' her dad said, his voice deliberate and quiet.

Pathetic, pathetic, you're so pathetic, she thought, still staring at her plate.

Her dad abruptly leaned forward. 'What have you done with your hair?' he asked, his sour breath smacking her face.

Chinue touched her head and tensed. 'Pathetic, pathetic,' she chanted inside.

'Nothing,' she replied. 'I was running; it was raining. It just curls a bit when it rains.'

'Black hair. Fucking black hair. Are you black, then?'

'No. I was running. It fell out of its bobble. That's all.'

But the fire was still rising inside her. Anger, hatred and loathing, bubbling up to her mouth. 'Pathetic, pathetic', still chanting. She lifted her head and stared.

'You are so pathetic, Dad.'

The words blistered out.

'Just look at you sitting there. Spiteful, pathetic and drunk. Feeling sorry for yourself all the time. Drinking the money Mum brings home because poor you, you only get benefits. Look at you with your bad teeth and dribble. You stink, you disgust me. Change your clothes, brush your teeth, get a job. Get a life like everyone else has to.'

357

There was silence for a moment. She could hear the tap dripping.

'Have you finished?' he asked, his voice steely and calm.

He turned and opened the cutlery drawer behind him. The tap was still dripping. Then he slowly rotated back. His eyes were bloodshot. There were scissors in his hand.

'You've had your say about me. Let's look at you now, shall we?'

Lurching before she could move away, he trapped her against the table with the weight of his body. Then he gathered her hair in his hand, dragging her off the chair and into the living room, her long mane still tight in his fist. Hauling her towards the mirror above the fireplace, he breathed heavily, grunting. Then he lifted the scissors and chopped, pulling and hacking, the blunt kitchen scissors tugging painfully at her roots. Furious and indiscriminate, he continued to cut, the long wads of wavy hair floating to the floor.

When he'd finally finished, he held her chin to the mirror, forcing her to look, his leering sunken face touching hers. 'See, you are black.'

The anger erupted then, taking over the fear. Her teeth gritted and her hands clenched into tight balls. The desire to bite, to kick and to pummel for all those years screamed to break out. She pulled back her arm and with all the force she could muster she swung at his face. Her fist connected solidly with his mouth, but he was too quick for her second go. Grabbing both her wrists with one hand, he punched her hard in the stomach with the other.

As she lay there, doubled up and struggling to breathe, the pain was unbearable. Yet she almost wanted to smile. The feel of her knuckles against his teeth had been worth it. But then Jimmy grasped her hand. 'Come with me,' he said.

*

The lights were off, which was a little strange and Sacha wasn't at the front door to greet Candy. It was late, but not that late, so Jimmy must have taken her for a walk. Which was a good thing, Candy thought. Jimmy rarely left the house when he was drunk. It would be nice to have five minutes to wind down, to catch her breath and to chat to Chinue, if she was up, before the demands began. Not that Candy minded. It was her lot.

She'd had such a lovely day. The church was lit yellow with daffodils. She'd greeted the parishioners at the church door, handing them a prayer sheet and chatting. How she loved that feeling of being accepted, of belonging.

Candy took off her shoes at the door and padded up the stairs towards her bedroom to search for her slippers. The door was closed, the house silent. Perhaps Jimmy was asleep after all. She turned the handle cautiously, ready for Sacha to run out and greet her but careful not to wake Jimmy.

Sacha whined in the darkness and Candy turned her head towards the sound. Chinue was sitting on the floor next to the old gas fire, her arms around her knees and her head down. Slants of light from the ill-fitting curtains lit her in blocks. Shaking her head in confusion, Candy glanced at the bed. Jimmy was there, fast asleep; she could see the dark outline of his body.

'Chinue? What are you doing in here?' Then after her eyes became accustomed to the dark. 'What's happened to your hair?'

Chinue lifted her head and silently held out her hand. Candy gazed for a moment. Her mind was sluggish, too sluggish, trying to catch up, trying to work out what she was being offered. But as her eyes finally focused, she saw they were scissors. They were the orange-handled scissors that belonged in the kitchen. The handles were moist and the metal gloopy.

'I'm so sorry, Mum,' Chinue whispered.

*

Candy is quiet today. She's back in the stifling lounge of The Ridings, now decorated in red and gold tinsel for Christmas. Squashed in her chair, she's staring at the television screen, but not, Antonia suspects, seeing anything. Not on the screen anyway.

She lifts her mum's puffy hand and gives it a squeeze, as ever remembering those hands on that night. It's difficult to reconcile the two women. The slim Candy had stared, her mind now sharp and calculating. She stared at Jimmy's body, white and naked, punctured and bloody, and she knew what to do.

'Take off your clothes, love, and give them to me to put on. Trim your hair, make it neat. Then stand in the shower and scrub. Scrub every inch. Your face, your hair and your nails. Wipe down the shower then put on your pyjamas and go to bed until I call.' She thought for a moment. 'Put my clothes in the wash basket. I'll leave them outside the door. Collect up your hair, every last bit and flush it away.'

She gently pulled Chinue to her feet, holding both hands in hers, pointing upwards like a joint prayer. Then her eyes rested on her child's. Deep, potent and strong.

'This is my fault, not yours, Chinue. My fault. I should have been here. Remember that always, love. I did this. Me. We'll never speak of it again.'

There was a last smile of reassurance from her mum. 'Everything will be fine. Go to bed until I call. You start from there, love. That's the story you tell. Forever.'

She did what her mum told her to do. She went to bed and closed her eyes, her head feeling light on the pillow without her long hair, but leaden with fear, confusion and dread. Almost asleep, she was woken by her mother's screams and the howling of the dog.

*

A bright voice shakes Antonia back to today. 'Morning, Antonia!'

Laura Jones looks fresh, her cheeks shiny, like a polished apple. 'I believe you missed me the other Sunday. Did you want a word?'

Antonia shakes her head. 'It was only to say thanks for pointing me in the right direction about Jimmy. You know, to the library.'

'Oh, no problem. Glad to help. It was a lovely idea to have it printed and framed. Isn't your girl clever, Candy? I wouldn't have thought of that.'

She touches Antonia's shoulder, a feather touch of care, which stings behind Antonia's eyes. 'Well, give me a shout if you need me.'

Antonia smiles her frozen polite smile and turns back to the silent television screen. She won't need Mrs Jones. The seeping of the past, the digging and the need for detail has stopped. She was on the verge of telling Mike everything when he visited on the afternoon of Olivia's death, to spilling it out, the truth. To confessing it all and to saying, 'Dad cried and begged me for forgiveness before falling asleep, but still I stabbed him when he slept and couldn't stop.' But something held her back. The anxiety of rejection? The fear of him discovering the ugliness underneath? She doesn't know. Survival, perhaps. Or maybe the secret has become a part of her she doesn't want to let go. But it was the right decision, absolutely. Some things, she knows, are best hidden beneath the skin.

ACKNOWLEDGEMENTS

Many thanks to:

My lovely family – Elizabeth, Charlotte, Emily and Jonathan. And my mum and dad, Ron and Mary, gone but still loved.

My fabulous writing friends and my gin buddies (you all know who you are!)

My wonderful readers and supporters – Liz Ball, Hazel James, Richard and Bo Baker.

People who have helped on the way – Robert Peett, Jeremy Brinton, Jane Butcher, Michael Thorn and Eric Akoto.

My agent Kate Johnson, my editor Phoebe Morgan, and the whole team at Avon.